PE Civil Breadth
Review Manual

Md Rashad Islam, Ph.D., P.E.

Dr. Md Rashad Islam, P.E.
islamunm@gmail.com

ISBN-13: 978-1-957186-05-4

First Edition, September 2022
Reprinting with minor revision, March 2023

Printed in the United States of America

Preface

This PE Civil Breadth review manual book contains the review of appropriate materials such as theory, analysis, equations, etc. required to study for the Computer-Based Testing (CBT) of the PE Civil Breadth (morning) examination by NCEES. ***PE Civil Reference Handbook*** has been used to explain the theory and solve the problems. The exam specification of all disciplines (construction, structural, geotechnical, transportation, water and environmental engineering) have been checked to verify that this book is appropriate for the breadth exam (morning session) of any civil engineering sub-discipline. The following 8 topics are covered which are specified for all disciplines and are primarily covered in the breadth exam (morning session):

- Project Planning (27 solved examples)
- Means and Methods (15 solved examples)
- Soil Mechanics (30 solved examples)
- Structural Mechanics (42 solved examples)
- Hydraulics and Hydrology (35 solved examples)
- Geometrics (20 solved examples)
- Materials (27 solved examples)
- Site Development (11 solved examples)

- Total solved problems: 207

The book has been thoroughly inspected with the help of professional editors to fix typos, editorial issues, and poor sentence structure. Despite this, if there is any issue, please excuse us and report it to the author. The author is also requesting the readers to report any concern about the book. Any suggestion to improve this book, or any issue reported, will be fixed in the next edition with proper acknowledgement. Thanking you.

Dr. Md Rashad Islam, P.E.
Associate Professor
Colorado State University – Pueblo
islamunm@gmail.com
https://www.csupueblo.edu/profile/md-islam/index.html

Allowed Resources

There are some resources which can be used during the exam depending on the depth selection (Structural, Geotechnical, Transportation, Construction or Water and Environmental Engineering). However, only one material is required for the Breadth (morning) exam. This material is the ***PE Civil Reference Handbook*** supplied by the NCEES. This resource can be used both in the Breadth (morning) and Depth (afternoon) sessions.

The resources allowed for depth (afternoon) exam can also be accessed during the breadth (morning) session, but may not be required to use. In addition to the ***PE Civil Reference Handbook,*** one additional resource can be opened at a time.

The following books may be studied for the breadth (morning) examination but cannot be used during the exam:

- Garber and Hoel, *Traffic and Highway Engineering*, Cengage. [*Good for traffic analysis*]
- Islam et al. *Engineering Statics*, CRC Press. [*Good for statics*]
- Liu and Evett, *Soils and Foundations*, Pearson. [*Good for soil mechanics and foundation*]
- Nunnaly, S.W. *Construction Methods & Management*, Prentice Hall. [*Good for construction methods and site preparation*]
- Mott and Untener, *Applied Fluid Mechanics*, Pearson. [*Good for fluid mechanics*]
- Islam, M. *Civil Engineering Materials – Introduction and Laboratory Testing*, CRC Press [*Good for materials and mix designs*]
- Mubarak, S. Construction Project Scheduling and Control, Wiley. [Good for project scheduling]

Table of Content

Chapter 5. Hydraulics and Hydrology

A. Open-channel flow
B. Stormwater collection and drainage (e.g., culvert, stormwater inlets, gutter flow, street flow, storm sewer pipes)
C. Storm characteristics (e.g., storm frequency, rainfall measurement and distribution)
D. Runoff analysis (e.g., Rational and SCS/NRCS methods, hydrographic application, runoff time of concentration)
E. Detention/retention ponds
F. Pressure conduit (e.g., single pipe, force mains, Hazen-Williams, Darcy-Weisbach, major and minor losses)
G. Energy and/or continuity equation (e.g., Bernoulli)

Chapter 6. Geometrics

A. Basic circular curve elements (e.g., middle ordinate, length, chord, radius)
B. Basic vertical curve elements
C. Traffic volume (e.g., vehicle mix, flow, and speed)

Chapter 7. Materials

A. Soil classification and boring log interpretation
B. Soil properties (e.g., strength, permeability, compressibility, phase relationships)
C. Concrete (e.g., nonreinforced, reinforced)
D. Structural steel
E. Material test methods and specification conformance
F. Compaction

Chapter 8. Site Development

A. Excavation and embankment (e.g., cut and fill)
B. Construction site layout and control
C. Temporary and permanent soil erosion and sediment control (e.g., construction erosion control and permits, sediment transport, channel/outlet protection)
D. Impact of construction on adjacent facilities
E. Safety (e.g., construction, roadside, work zone)

How to Prepare for PE Civil Exam

There is not a single way to prepare for the PE Civil Exam – not every method works for all. Select your depth area of civil engineering (Structural, Geotechnical, Transportation, Construction or Water and Environmental Engineering). The Breadth (morning) Exam specification is same for all depth areas of civil engineering. However, the breadth (morning) questions may vary depending on your selected depth (afternoon) area.

The author recommends the following steps.

Step 1. Manage the PE Civil exam specifications and the ***PE Civil Reference Handbook*** supplied by the NCEES.
Step 2. Manage any two Review manuals from different authors for the Breadth (morning) session.
Step 3. Study chapter by chapter with the easier chapter first; work on practice examples on parallel.
Step 4. Study your depth section on parallel; work on practice examples on parallel.
Step 5. At the end, take 2-3 full sample exams both on breadth and depth sections.

Remember you do not need to pass individually both Breadth (morning) and Depth (afternoon) exams. The results is the combined effect of both exams. Therefore, study your comfortable areas more.

Some Useful Tips

- Always update yourself on the exam policy from the https://ncees.org/ website and from your friends who took the exam recently. The NCEES exam policy updates very frequently and many of the practical information are not available at the website.
- PE Civil Ref Handbook will be always open in one side of the computer screen. You can open one additional reference at a time.
- Try to memorize which equation is available at which reference.
- No calculation may be required for about 50% of the questions.
- The number of questions in the morning is not fixed to be 40. It may be slightly less or more. If you spend less time in morning, you will get the remaining time back in the afternoon. More specifically, if you stop at 3 hr 30 min in the morning, your afternoon time will start from 3 hr 30 min.
- You may be able to access your Afternoon (Depth) reference manuals in morning as well.
- Practicing the problems at home may take longer time as the home environment is not so comfortable.
- Learn to navigate to a particular topic using the Ctrl + F button of the computer keyboard.
- While practicing, use any NCEES recommended calculators. Carry 2 on the exam day.
- Don't forget to carry the photo ID on the exam day.
- If you fail the exam, you will lose the exam fees only - nothing else! Don't panic!
- Whenever you see a problem, first try to eliminate some options before start solving.
- Whenever you see a problem difficult, skip it by flagging and move forward. Come back to the problem later. This strategy is very helpful to whip on the time.
- Some questions are long, however, the solutions are mostly short for long questions.
- You don't need to score 100% to pass the exam. About 70% score is believed to be good.
- Breadth (Morning) exam may not the same for everybody in the exam room.
- If you flag/skip a question you can get a chance to review them just before the final submission. You can go back to previous question at any time but cannot see the preview of all flagged/skipped questions until you go to the end of exam.
- Save some time to get used to the computer based testing format.
- It is very difficult to concentrate on the last hour especially in the afternoon session. Carry some chocolate or Tylenol to keep your brain calm on the exam day.
- Do not forget to contact the author (islamunm@gmail.com) whenever you feel so.

Chapter 1
Project Planning

Due to many requests, the author has released this manual in a very short amount of time. The author will keep on improving the book. The author is also requesting the readers to report any concern about the book at islamunm@gmail.com

At the very beginning let us clarify a few items. The exam specification for the PE Civil Breadth (Morning) section is same for all civil engineering disciples. However, different candidates will get different questions in the Breadth Exam. Even two candidates of same specialty (say, structural engineering) may not see the same questions. The PE Civil Ref. Handbook is a great help. However, make sure you are familiar with the meaning of symbols; know equation is available and where it is available; know the basic theories of common topics, and so on. CTL+F does not work for all equations. You do not need to do any calculation in about 50% of the questions. If you save some time in the morning; you can use that time in the afternoon.

1.1 Quantity Take Off Methods

Quantity take off problems are relatively easy to figure out. You just need to know a little bit about geometry and use a little bit of engineering common sense. The most likely questions that you will see during the exam are quantity take off for:

- Soil (excavation, hauling, compacting)
- Formwork for concrete
- Masonry work, and
- Steel (structural beams, steel in concrete)

The following examples will give you sufficient knowledge on these topics.

Example 1.1

Find the quantity of standard size bricks (8 in. x 3.75 in. x 2.25 in.) you should have delivered to your project if the following conditions are given:

- Wall is 8 ft high, 14 ft wide
- Two opening: one 48 in. x 72 in., one 32 in. x 48 in.
- Mortar joints are 0.5 in. thick
- 2 rows are required
- Allow for 3% brick waste

Solution:

Net surface area of the wall = Gross surface Area – openings surface area
= (8 ft x 14 ft) – [(48 in. x 72 in.) ÷ 144] – [(32 in. x 48 in.) ÷ 144]
= 77.33 ft^2
Surface area of a brick as positioned (with mortar) = (8 in. + 0.5 in.) (2.25 in. + 0.5 in.)
= 0.1623 ft^2
Number of bricks = Divide Net wall area by surface area = 77.33 ft^2 / 0.1623 ft^2 = 476.5
Total number of bricks for 2 rows = (476.5)(2 rows) = 953 bricks
Total number of bricks considering 3% waste = (953 bricks)(1.03) = <u>982 bricks</u>

Example 1.2

A project uses standard size bricks (8 in. x 3.75 in. x 2.25 in.) with the following conditions are given:

- Wall is 8 ft high, 14 ft wide
- Two opening: one 48 in. x 72 in., one 32 in. x 48 in.
- Mortar joints are 0.5 in. thick
- 2 rows of bricks are required
- Allow for 3% brick waste
- Total number of bricks considering 3% waste = 982 bricks

Assume 25% waste of mortar. The required mortar (ft^3) is most nearly:

Solution:

Vol. of a brick = 8 in. x 3.75 in. x 2.25 in. = 67.5 $in.^3$
Vol. of a brick with mortar = (8 in. + 0.5 in.) x (3.75 in. + 0.25 in.) x (2.25 in. + 0.50 in.)
= 93.5 $in.^3$
Vol. of mortar per brick = 93.5 – 67.5 = 26 in.3 = 0.015 ft^3
Total mortar = 982 x 0.015 ft^3 = 14.73 ft^3
Considering 25% waste = 1.25 x 14.73 ft^3 = <u>18.4 ft^3</u>

Example 1.3

Board Feet is a measurement of lumber volume. A board foot is equal to 144 cubic inch of wood. The board feet for one 2x4 lumber that is 10 feet long is most nearly:

Solution:

1 x (2 in. x 4 in.) (12 x 10 in.) = 960 $in.^3$ = <u>6.67 board feet</u>

Example 1.4
You are building a 60 ft x 7.5ft concrete wall. The design is the diagram below with 9 in. spacing of vertical rebar.

- 3/4 in. clear cover both sides of the wall.
- 1.5 in. off the ground and 0.75 in. on top of wall.

The total weight (lb) of the rebars is most nearly:

Solution:

When calculating the number of bars required find the total length Divided by the spacing of the bars and add 1.

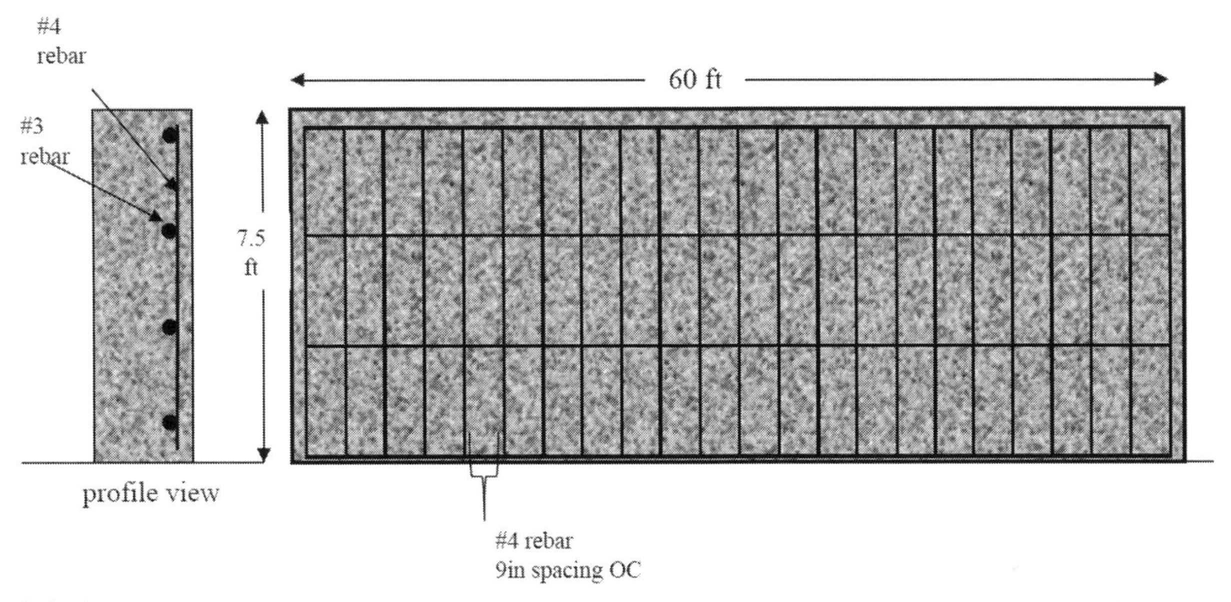

Solution:

Steel in the horizontal direction.

Length of #3 rebar = 60 ft – (2 ends)(3/4 in. clear) / 12) = 59.875 ft
A #3 rebar weighs 0.375 lb/ft.
4#3 rebar weighs = 4 x 0.375 lb/ft x 59.875 ft = 89.8 lb

Steel in the vertical direction.

1.5 in. off the ground and 0.7 5in. on top of wall.
Total length of a #4 rebar = 7.5 ft – 1.5/12 ft – 0.75/12 ft = 7.31 ft
No of bar required = (60 ft x 12 in.) / 9 in.) + 1 = 80 + 1 = 81
A #4 bar weighs = 0.668 lb/ft
Weight of #4 rebar = 81 (7.31 ft)(0.668 lb/ft) = 396 lb

Total Weight of rebar = 90 lb + 396 lb = 486 lb

Example 1.5

Find the weight of the steel rebar in concrete filled drilled shaft which is 35 ft deep. The design calls for 8 vertical #10 rebars, and the ties every 5 ft are #4 rebar. The diameter of the cylinder is 2 ft. Disregard any concrete cover offset for steel length.

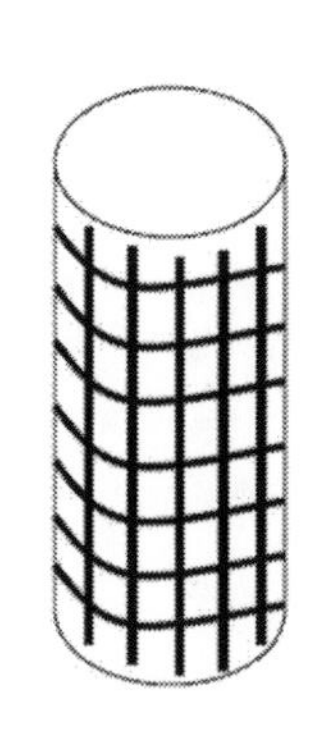

Solution:

Steel in the vertical direction:

No of vertical bars = 8

Total length of vertical bars = 35ft/bars x 8 bars = 280 ft

Weight of #10 = 4.303 lb/ft

Total weight of the vertical direction = (4.303 lb/ft)(280 ft) = 1,205 lb

Steel in the horizontal direction:

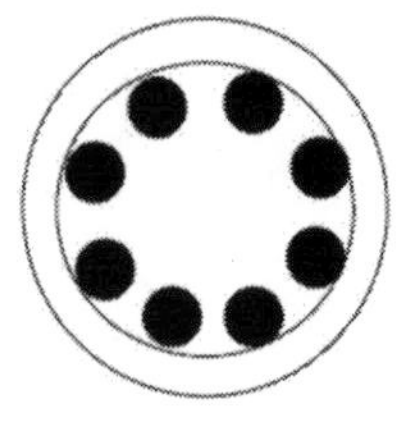

Number of ties, using trick of trade #3 = 35 ft / 5 +1 = 8 ties

Length of ties = circumference of the circle = $\pi D = \pi(2\text{ft})$ = 6.283 ft

Total length of ties = (6.283 ft)(8) = 50.3 ft

Weight of #4 rebar = 0.668 lb/ft

Total Weight of #4 rebar = (0.668 lb/ft)(50.3 ft) = 33.6 lb

Total weight of Rebar = 1205 lb + 33.6 lb = 1238.6 lb

Example 1.6

Find the Roofs area if the roof has a 1/5 rise over run angle with a 3 ft overhang. The length of the house is 75 ft. The width of the house is 50 ft.

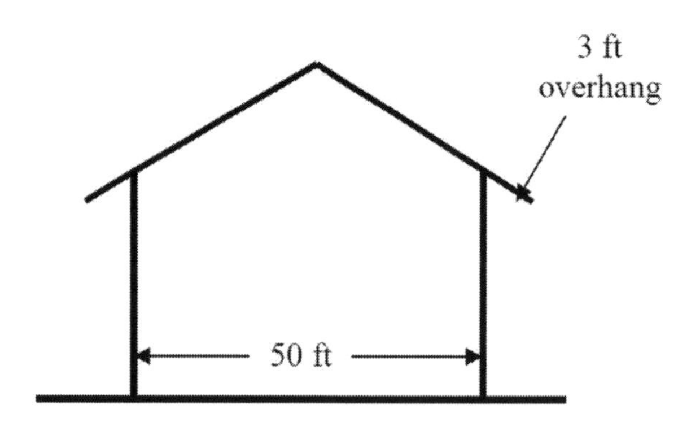

(Ref: EngineeringDesignResources)

Solution:

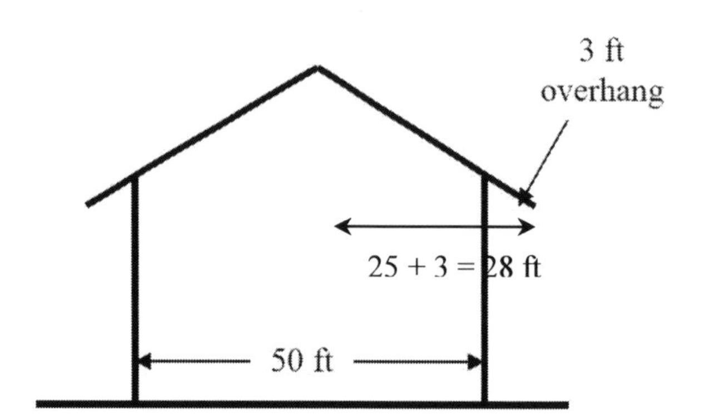

Horizontal half-length = 28 ft
Vertical height = 28 ft / 5 = 5.6 ft

Inclined length (rafter length) = $\sqrt{(28\,\text{ft})^2 + (5.6\,\text{ft})^2} = 28.55\,\text{ft}$

Area of the Roof = 2 sides x rafter length x building length
= 2 x 28.55 ft x 75 ft = 4,283 ft^2

Example 1.7
Find the weight of steel in the plan view of the building below.

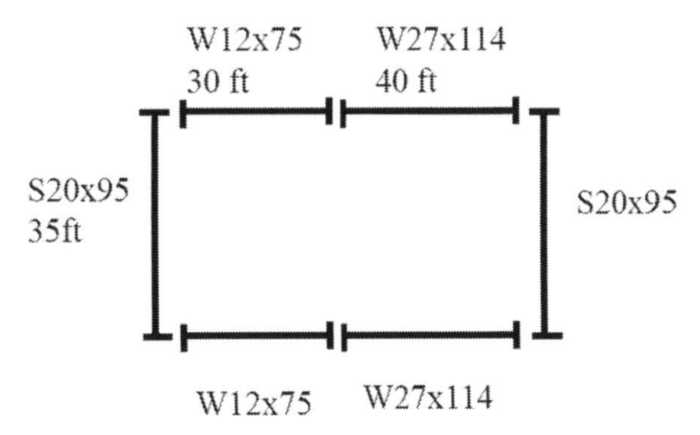

(Ref: EngineeringDesignResources)

Solution:

Weight of each beam:

- S20x95 (35ft) = 95 lb/ft x 35 ft= 3,325 lb
- W12x75 (30ft) = 75 lb/ft x 30 ft= 2,250 lb
- W27x114 (40ft) = 114 lb/ft x 40 ft= 4,560 lb

Because the other three beams are the same size you can add the three beams and multiply by 2 to get the total weight of steel.
Total weight of the beams = (3,325 + 2,250 + 4,560) x 2 = 20,270 lb

1.2 Cost Estimating

The steps involved in cost estimating are;

a) Materials Estimates: This is the quantity take off step that was already discussed in an earlier section
b) Calculate Material Costs: So here you just need to multiply the quantity by the cost per unit.
c) Equipment Estimates: To figure out this section you might have to understand equipment production rates to calculate the amount of time you will need the equipment. These estimates are in a different study section that I will later show you. So for now let assume they will give you the equipment production rate to do the jobs and the cost of the equipment. You may have to multiply an efficiency factor to increase or decrease the production rate if it is given.
d) Calculate Equipment Costs: Multiple the equipment cost/day by the number of days required.
e) Personnel Estimates: The exam question will give you crew size, the cost/hr for each crew member, and the production rate of the crew or members.
f) Calculate Personnel Costs: Using the above information multiple number of hours to do the job by the cost per hour to do the job.
g) Sum up all the costs
h) Multiply the overhead and Profit to the total cost
i) Congratulations…You have the total project cost now.

j) The easiest way to explain cost estimates is just to do practice problems which are the same difficulty as the exam. There are some examples below.

Example 1.8

A contractor is required to excavate and transport 2500 yd^3 soil to the construction site. The contractor team includes the following:

- An excavator with a production rate of 12.5 yd^3/hr
- A loader with a production rate of 200 yd^3/day
- Two dump truck with a production rate of 100 yd^3/day per truck
- 8 hours work-day
- Excavation and transportation may continue parallel (simultaneously)

The number of days required to finish the job is most nearly:

Solution:

$$\text{Excavation period} = \frac{5{,}000\,yd^3}{12.5\,\frac{yd^3}{hr}} = 400\,hr = \frac{400\,hr}{8\,\frac{yr}{day}} = 50\,days$$

$$\text{Loader period} = \frac{5{,}000\,yd^3}{200\,\frac{yd^3}{day}} = 25\,days$$

$$\text{Truck period} = \frac{5{,}000\,yd^3}{200\,\frac{yd^3}{day}} = 25\,days$$

The job can be completed in 50 days. While excavating, loading and trucking can be executed.

Example 1.9

Consider a crew of one-foreman, three-laborers. The foreman gets paid $60 per hr and the laborer get paid $30 per hr. The crew is able to concrete 30 yd^3 per day. A work day is 8 hours per day. If the crew has to place concrete for 3,078 cubic feet. Calculate the total cost of the personnel involved in concreting.

Solution:

Total concrete volume = 3,078 ft^3 = 3,078 / 27 yd^3 = 114 yd^3
Cost of the crew per hour = (1 x 60) + (3 x 30) = $150
Number of hours required for the crew = 114/30 = 3.8 day = 3.8 days x 8 hr/days
= 30.4 hr $\approx$ 31 hr
Total cost for the personnel = 31 hour x $150 / hour = $4,650

Example 1.10

A contractor need to backfill and compact a trench that has the dimensions that are 150 x 50 x 1.5 ft. The contractor is going to use a dump truck that can carry 12 CY, and travels at an average speed of 40 mph. The borrow pit is located 45 miles from the construction site. The truck driver makes $50 per hr and works 8 hours per day. Loading time for the truck is 30 minutes and unloading time is 5 minutes. The contractor has to rent the truck at $500 per day. The cost of soil is $20 per CY bank volume basis. The soil has a swell factor of 18% and shrinkage factor of 15%. Calculate the cost of backfilling the trench.

Solution:

1. Materials Estimates:

Volume to be fill = 150 ft x 50 ft x 1.5 ft = 11,250 CF = 416.67 CCY

BCY = 416.67 CCY / (1 - 0.15) = 490 BCY

LCY = 490 BCY x 1.18 = 578 LCY

2. Calculate Material Costs: \$20 per BCY x 490 BCY = \$9,800

3. Equipment Estimates: You know the cost of one truck is \$500/day. So to calculate the equipment costs you need to figure out how long you need the truck.

-578 LCY need to be transported, the truck can carry 12 CY.

-578 LCY/12 CY = 48.16 Trips ≈ 49 Trips

Time for one trip = Loading time + unloading time + Travel Time (to and from)

-Travel time = Distance/Velocity = 45 mile / 40 miles/hr = 1.125 hr

-Travel time = 1.125 + 1.125 + 30/60 + 5/60 = 2.83 hr

-Total time required = 2.83 hr x 49 trips = 138.8 hr ≈ 139 hr

-Total days = 139 hr / 8 per day = 17.3 ≈ 18 days

4. Equipment Costs = 18 days x \$500 per day = \$9,000

5. Personnel Costs: \$50 per hr x 139hr = \$6,950

Total costs = \$6950 + \$9000 + 9,800 = <u>\$25,750</u>

The problem didn't call for overhead and profit so don't worry about it.

Example 1.11

Of these 4 approaches to estimating construction projects, which one is the most accurate?

A. Project Comparison Estimating or Parametric Cost Estimating
B. Area & Volume Estimating
C. Assembly & System Estimating
D. Unit Price & Schedule Estimating

Solution: Project Comparison Estimating or Parametric Cost Estimating uses information from previous similar projects and scales the cost data up or down to more closely match the current project. This method is mostly used in the preliminary stages of planning to arrive at an estimated budget price. Area & Volume Estimating takes in to account the projects square footage or cubic footage and applies multipliers to arrive at an estimated cost of construction. Assembly & System estimating breaks the project down into assemblies or systems (i.e. HVAC system, plumbing system, structural system) and then applies multipliers to arrive at an estimated cost of construction. And, Unit Price & Schedule Estimating breaks the project down into the smallest possible pieces (i.e. bricks, doors, air handling units) and then applies a unit price to each. The sum of these unit price calculations is the cost estimate. The correct answer is D.

1.3 Project Schedules

1.3.1 Arrow Networks

Arrow networks are also called the arrow diagramming method (ADM), activity on arrow (AOA) network, or the I-J method (because activities are defined by the from node, I, and to node, J). In arrow diagram, the arrow represents the activity and the node represents the connection between two activities. The following example will clarify the concept.

Example 1.12
Draw the arrow network for the project given below.

Activity	Immediately Preceding Activity
A	–
B	A
C	A
D	B
E	C, D

Solution:

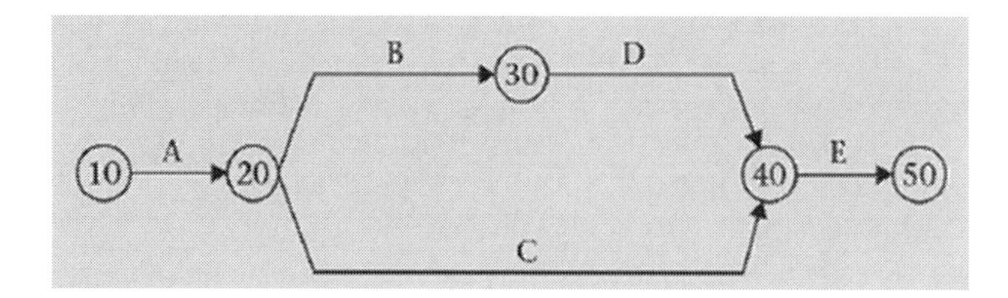

In this example, the project has only five activities, each represented by an arrow, as shown. Each arrow connects two nodes (depicted by circles with numbers in them): the from-node and the to-node. These nodes represent events: an event is a point in time when an activity starts or ends. In computer software, events with significance can be created as milestones, and they are either start milestones, such as Notice to Proceed, or finish milestones, such as Substantial Completion.

In this example, activity A starts the project. Activities B and C follow, but independently. In reality, depending on the availability of resources and other factors, activities B and C may occur concurrently, overlap, or occur consecutively. However, both B and C cannot start until A is complete. Activity D must wait until activity B is complete. Once both C and D are complete, activity E can start. The end of activity E means the project is completed. Activity A is considered a predecessor activity to activities B and C. Similarly, activity B is a predecessor to activity D. Conversely, we can say that activities B and C are successor activities to activity A, activity D is a successor to activity B, and so on. Activity A has successors but no predecessors. Activity E has predecessors but no successors. All other activities have both successors and predecessors.

A node in an arrow network represents an event or a point in time. This event is the starting or ending point of an activity (or activities). Node 10 represents the start of activity A (and hence the start of the project). Node 20 represents the end of activity A and the start of activities B and C. Node 30 represents the end of activity B and the start of activity D. Node 40 represents the end of activities C and D, and the start of activity E. Node 50 represents the end of activity E and the project.

Example 1.13
Draw the arrow network for the project given below.

Activity	Immediately Preceding Activity
A	–
B	A
C	A
D	B, C

Solution - A

The main problem in this case, as shown in Figure below, is that both activities B and C start from node 20 and finish at node 30. Hence, both are identified as 20–30.

This situation will create an identity problem. To solve this problem, we introduce a fictitious activity and an additional node. This fictitious activity is called a dummy activity, d. It is treated in the critical path method (CPM) calculations and in computer programs as a real activity even though it is not.

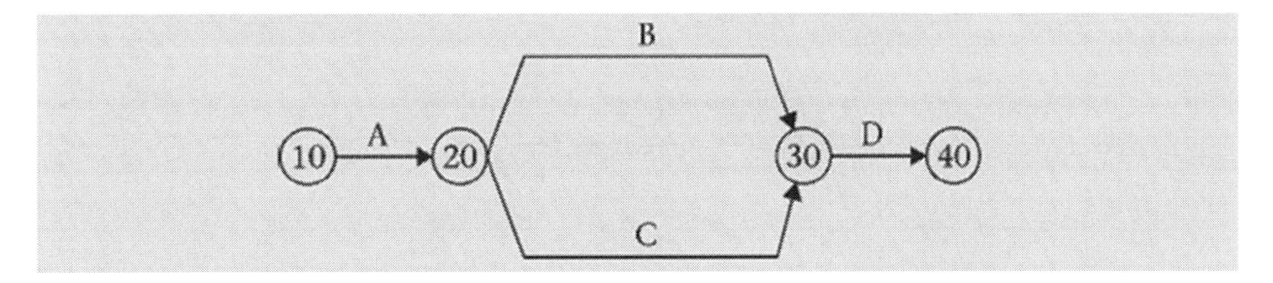

Solution - B

In this case, activity B is identified as 20–30, whereas activity C is 20–40, as shown in Figure 3.3. Note that the dummy can be inserted in different positions, as shown next. They all serve the same purpose.

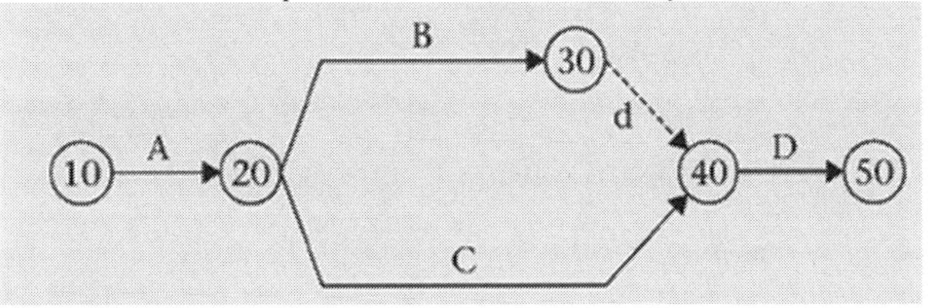

Other Solutions

The position of the dummy is not unique in this example, it can be inserted in different positions, as shown

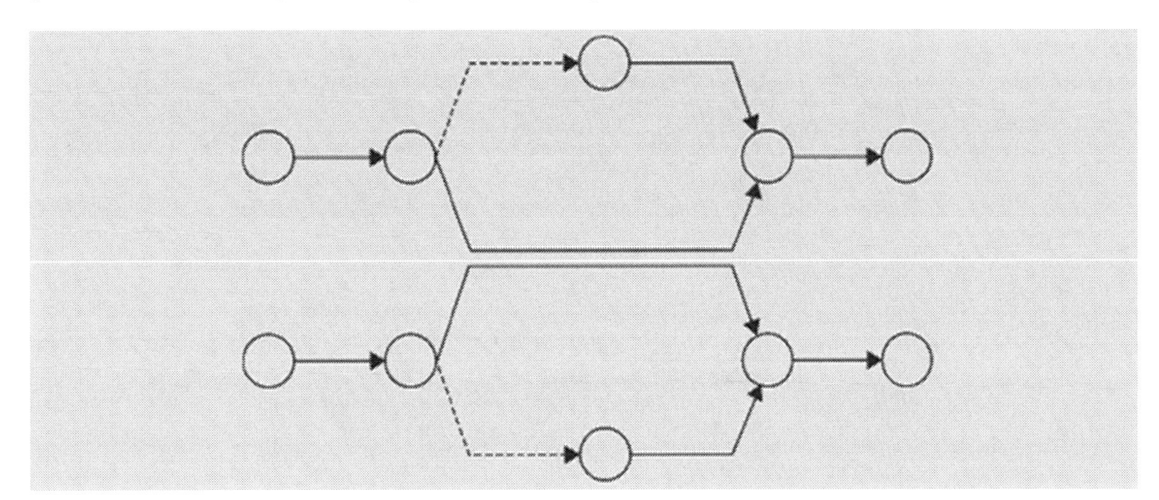

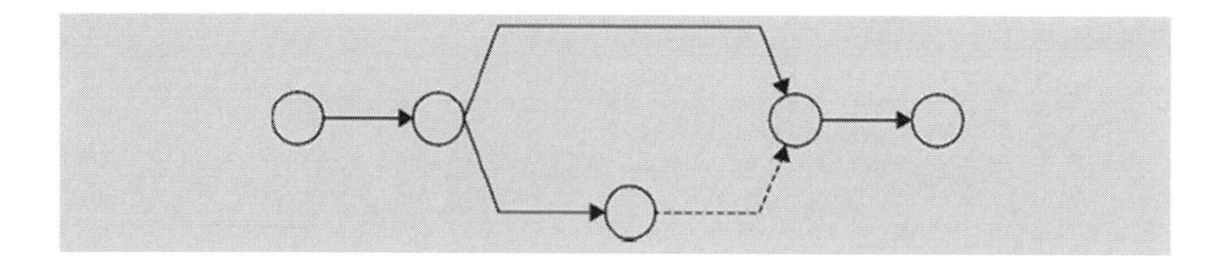

Example 1.14

Draw the arrow network for the project given below.

Activity	Immediately Preceding Activity
A	–
B	A
C	A
D	B
E	B, C
F	C

Solution:

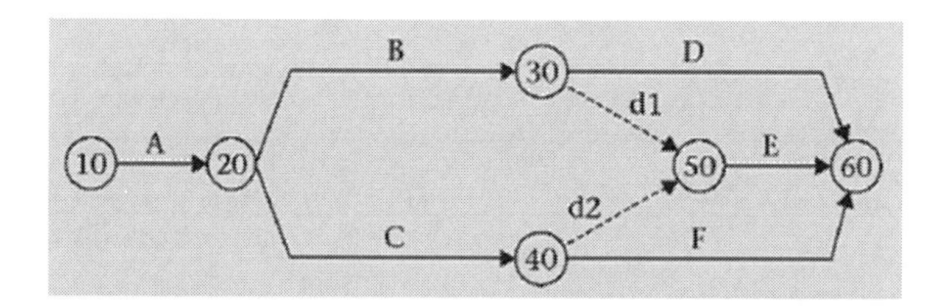

We can define a dummy activity as a fictitious activity inserted in an arrow network to maintain proper logic or to distinguish the activities' identities. Two more examples demonstrate the need for dummy activities to straighten up the logic.

Example 1.15

Draw the arrow network for the project given below.

Activity	Immediately Preceding Activity
A	–
B	–
C	–
D	A, B
E	B, C

Solution:

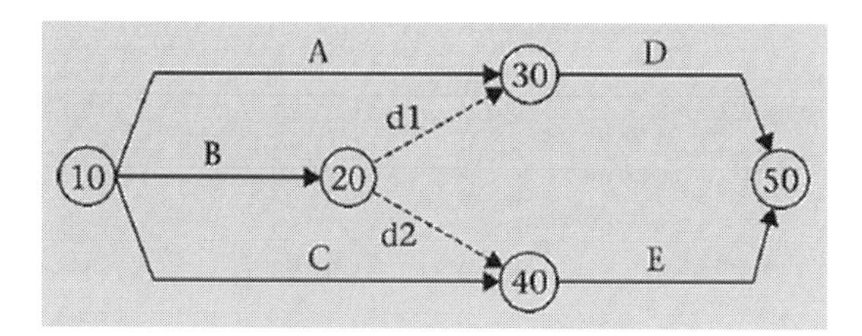

1.3.2 Node Networks

Node networks are also called activity on node (AON) networks. In node networks, a node represents an activity. Nodes (activities) are connected with arrows (or lines) that represent logical relationships. There is no need in the node diagram for dummy activities. A scheduling novice can draw a node diagram much easier than an arrow diagram. We like to start any network with one node (whether this node represents an event or an activity) and end it with one node. Doing so may require one or two fictitious activities in node diagrams that start or end with more than one activity. We call these activities PS (project start) and PF (project finish), displayed as diamond-shaped nodes.

Example 1.16
Draw the node network for the project given below.

Activity	Immediately Preceding Activity
A	–
B	A
C	A
D	B, C

Solution:

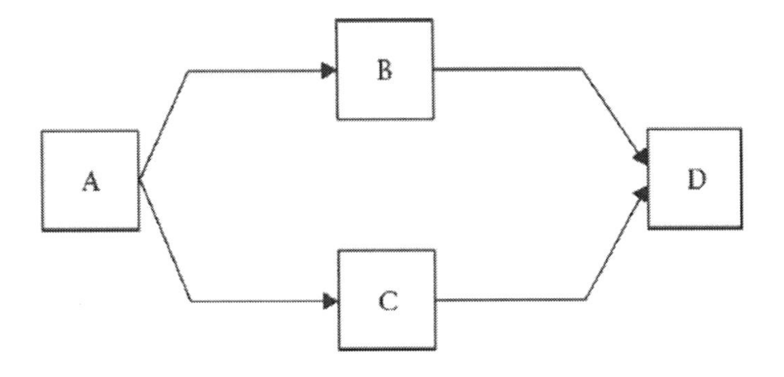

Example 1.17
Draw the node network for the project given below.

Activity	Immediately Preceding Activity
A	–
B	A
C	A
D	B
E	B, C

Solution:

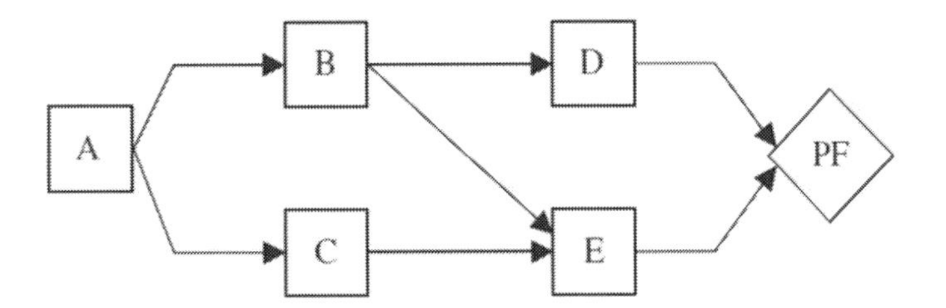

Example 1.18

Draw the node network for the project given below.

Activity	Immediately Preceding Activity
A	–
B	A
C	A
D	B
E	B, C
F	C

Solution:

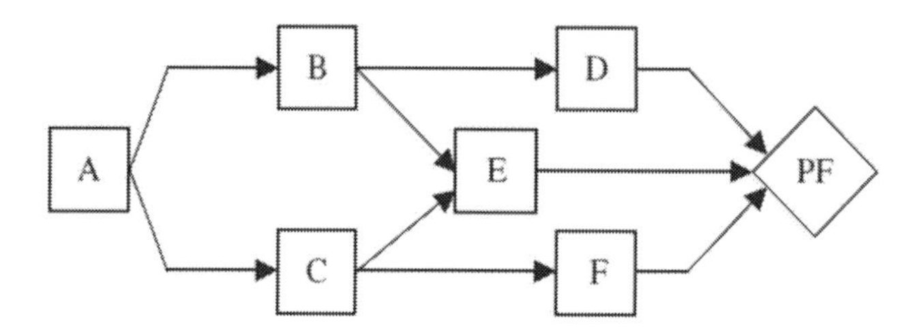

1.3.3 Recommendations for Proper Node Diagram Drawing

Some recommendations for proper node diagram drawing are listed below. Note that in most of the preceding points, the word improper may not mean incorrect.

1. Since nodes in arrow diagrams (events) are always drawn as circles, we like to draw nodes in node diagrams (activities) as squares (rectangles). Doing so not only eliminates confusion between an arrow network and a node network but also, more importantly, defines the "start side" and the "end side" of an activity. This distinction is important in precedence networks. Milestones are usually drawn as diamonds to emphasize the fact that they have no duration; thus, nodes have no sides. See Figure below.

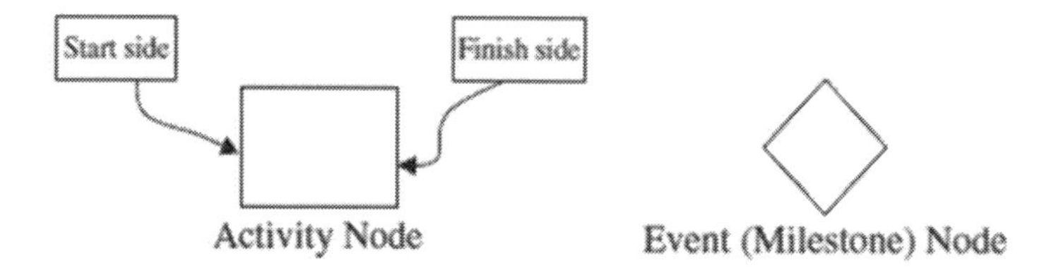

2. Do not connect nodes (in node diagrams) from the top or bottom (see Figure below). Connect only the sides. The left side represents the start side, and the right side represents the end (finish) side.

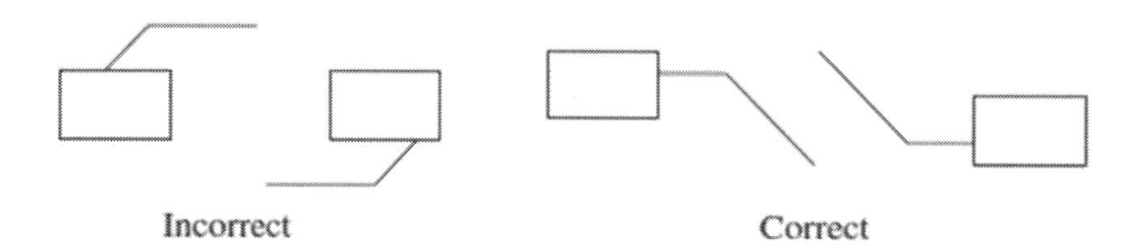

3. Although networks are not time-scaled, in general, they should be designed from left to right in an almost chronological order. Relationship lines (arrows) can be horizontal, inclined, or broken; however, they should be positioned, in general, from left to right. Try to avoid the situation shown in Figure below.

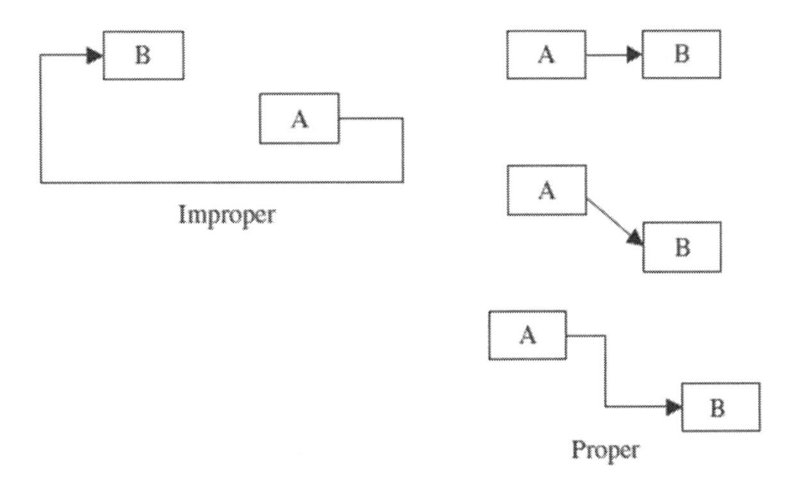

4. Do not combine relationship lines (see Figure below). These relationships are independent from their start to their end. Besides, one of them may carry a lag while the other one may not (or may carry a different lag).

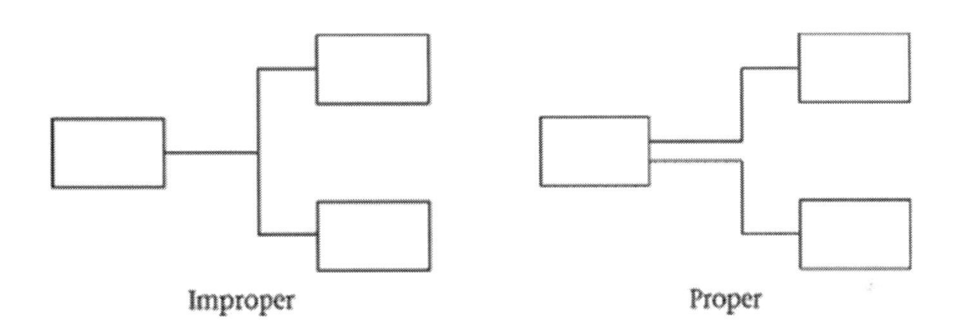

5. Try to minimize line crossings (see Figure below). When two lines (relationships) must intersect, make a "jump" on one of them to indicate that they do not intersect or meet.

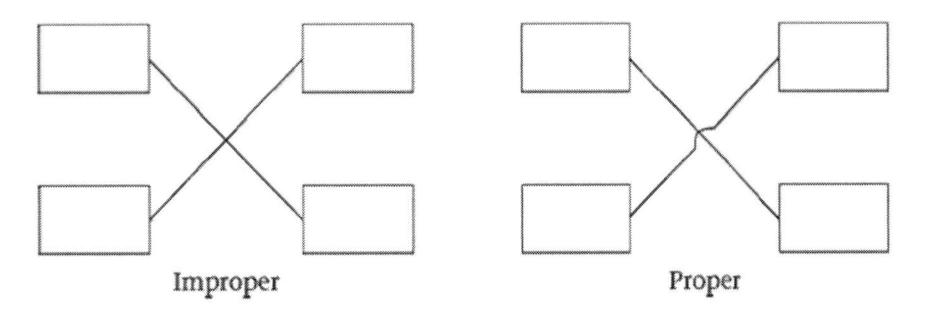

6. Start the network with one node and finish it with one node. If the network starts with only one activity, then there is no need for an additional node. If it does not start with only one activity, then insert a PS (Project Start) milestone node at the start and tie it to those activities that start the network, as shown in Figure below. The same concept applies to the end of the network: if it ends with one activity, then there is

no need for an additional node. If not, then insert a PF (Project Finish) milestone node at the end and tie those activities that end the network to it as shown in Figure below.

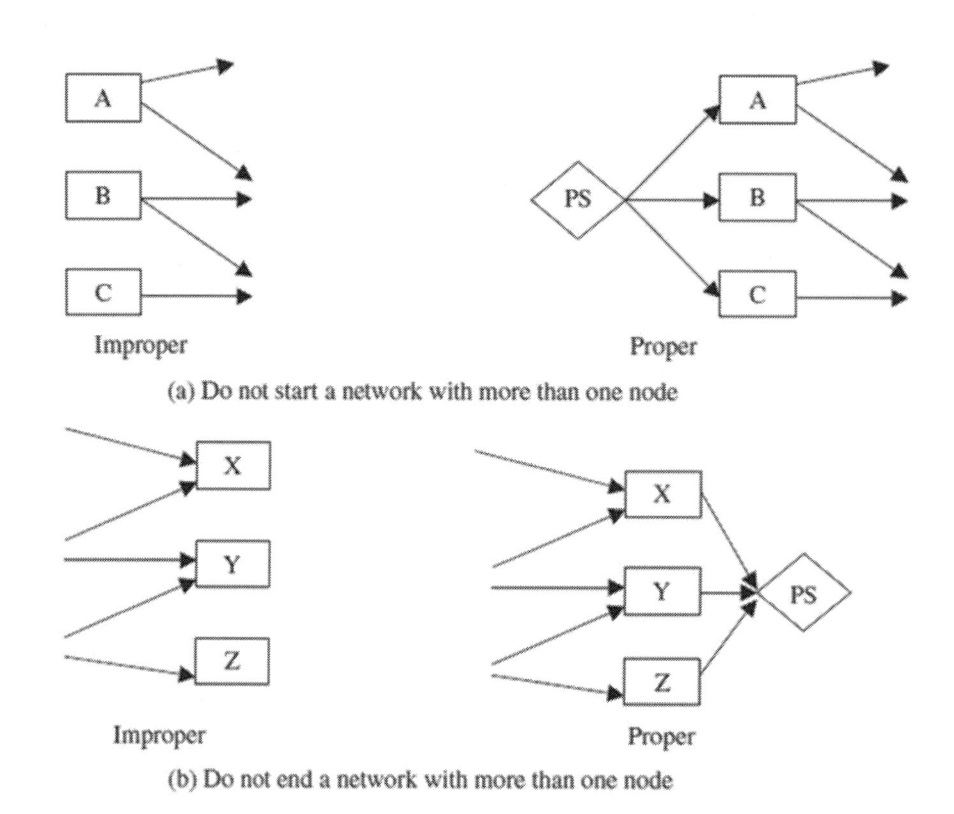

(a) Do not start a network with more than one node

(b) Do not end a network with more than one node

7. In many cases of hand drawing, you will need to redraw the network after your first attempt. Although your first attempt may be logically correct, it may look awkward and confusing. Redraw it to minimize lines crossing and relocate activities to be as near as possible to their predecessors and successors.

1.3.4 Critical Path Methods

Some definitions used in critical path method (CPM) are listed below.

Activity, or task: A basic unit of work as part of the total project that is easily measured and controlled. It is time- and resource-consuming.
Backward pass: The process of navigating through a network from end to start and calculating the late dates for each activity. The late dates, along with the early dates, determine the critical activities, the critical path, and the amount of float that each activity has.
Critical activity: An activity on the critical path. Any delay in the timely completion of a critical activity will result in a delay in the entire project.
Critical path: The longest continuous path in a network from start to finish. It represents the summation of the durations of activities and lags along that path, taking into consideration calendars, constraints, resources, and other impacting factors.
Driving relationship: A relationship from a predecessor activity that controls the start or finish of a successor activity. For any activity with predecessors, there must be at least one driving relationship.
Early dates: The early start date and early finish date of an activity.
Early finish (EF): The earliest date on which an activity can finish within project constraints.
Early start (ES): The earliest date on which an activity can start within project constraints.

Event: A point in time marking the start or end of an activity. In contrast to an activity, an event does not consume time or resources. In computer software, events with significance can be created as milestones, and they are either start milestones, such as Notice to Proceed, or finish milestones, such as Substantial Completion.
Forward pass: The process of navigating through a network from start to end and calculating the completion date for the project and the early dates for each activity.
Late dates: The late start date and late finish date of an activity.
Late finish (LF): The latest date on which an activity can finish without extending the project's duration.
Late start (LS): The latest date on which an activity can start without extending the project's duration.
Total float (TF): The maximum amount of time an activity can be delayed from its early start without delaying the entire project or violating a schedule constraint.

Example 1.19
Draw the logic network and perform the CPM calculations for the schedule shown next.

Activity	Immediately Preceding Activity	Duration (days)
A	–	5
B	A	8
C	A	6
D	B	9
E	B, C	6
F	C	3
G	D, E, F	1

Solution:

The Forward Pass
The project starts with activity A, which starts at the beginning of day 1 (end of day 0). It takes 5 days to finish activity A; it finishes on day 5 (end of the day).

At this point, activities B and C can start. Activity B takes 8 days; it can start on day 5 (directly after activity A finishes), so it can finish as early as day 13. Similarly, activity C can finish on day 11 (5 + 6). Activity D follows activity B. It can start on day 13 (end of B) and end on day 22. Activity E must wait until both activities B and C are finished. Activity C finishes on day 11, but activity B does not finish until day 13. Thus, activity E cannot start until day 13. With 6 days' duration, activity E can then finish on day 19. Activity F depends on activity C only. Thus, it can start on day 11 and finish on day 14. The last activity, G, cannot start until activities D, E, and F are finished. Through simple observation, we can see that activity G cannot start until day 22 (when the last activity of D, E, and F finishes). Activity G takes 1 day, so it can finish on day 23. Figure below shows the completed logic network. For this example, we have calculated two types of dates:

1. The expected completion date of the project: day 23
2. The earliest date when each activity can start and finish

These dates are called the early start (ES) and the early finish (EF) dates for each activity. As you will soon learn, an activity cannot start earlier than its ES date and cannot finish earlier than its EF date, but it may start or finish later than these dates.
In mathematical terms, the ES time for activity j (ES_j) is as follows:

$$ES_j = \max(EF_i)$$

where (EF_i) represents the EF times for all immediately preceding activities.

Likewise, the EF time for activity j (EF_j) is as follows:

$$EF_j = ES_j + Dur_j$$

where Dur_j is the duration of activity j.

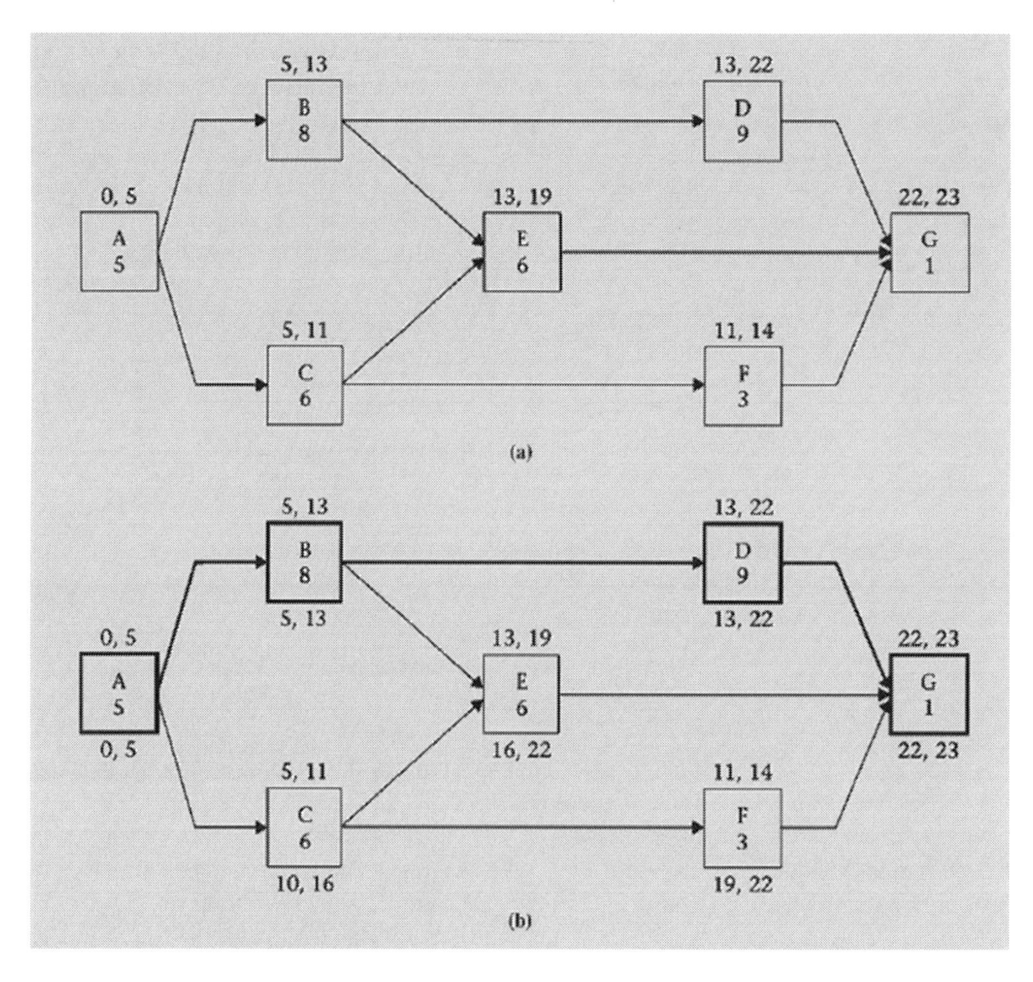

The forward pass is defined as the process of navigating through a network from start to finish and calculating the early dates for each activity and the completion date of the project.

The Backward Pass

Now let us start from the end of the project and work our way back to the start. We already know the end-of-project date5: day 23. Activity G must finish by day 23. Its duration is only 1 day, so it must start no later than day 22 (23 − 1) so that it does not delay the project. Similarly, activities D, E, and F must finish no later than day 22 so that they will not delay activity G. Through simple computations, we can find their late start dates: activity F: 22 − 3 = 19; activity E: 22 − 6 = 16; and activity D: 22 − 9 = 13. Activity C must finish before activities E and F can start. Their late start dates are 16 and 19, respectively. Clearly, activity C must finish by the earlier of the two dates, day 16, so that it will not delay the start of activity E. Thus, its late start date is day 10 (16 − 6). Similarly, activity B must finish by the earlier of its successors' late start dates: day 13 for D and day 16 for E. Therefore, the late finish date for activity B is day 13, and its late start date is day 5 (13 − 8). The last activity (from the start) is A: It must finish by the earlier of the late start dates for activities B and C, which are day 5 for B and day 10 for C. Consequently, the late finish date for activity A is day 5, and its late start date is day 0 (5 − 5).

In mathematical terms, the late finish (LF) time for activity j (LF_j) is as follows:

$$LF_j = \min(LS_k)$$

where (LS_k) represents the late start times for all succeeding activities.

Likewise, the late start (LS) time for activity j (LS_j) is as follows:

$$LS_j = LF_j - Dur_j$$

The backward pass is defined as the process of navigating through a network from finish to start and calculating the late dates for all activities. This pass, along with the forward-pass calculations, helps identify the critical path and the float for all activities.

If you refer to Figure-b, you can see that for some activities (light lines), the late dates (shown under the boxes) are later than their early dates (shown above the boxes). For other activities (thick lines), late and early dates are the same. For the second group, we can tell that these activities have strict start and finish dates. Any delay in them will result in a delay in the entire project. We call these activities critical activities. We call the continuous chain of critical activities from the start to the end of the project the critical path. Other activities have some leeway. For example, activity C can start on day 5, 6, 7, 8, 9, or 10 without delaying the entire project. As mentioned previously, we call this leeway float.

There are several types of float. The simplest and most important type of float is total float (TF):

$TF = LS - ES$ *or* $TF = LF - EF$ *or* $TF = LF - Dur - ES$

We tabulate the results in the following table (boldface activities are critical):

Activity	Duration (days)	ES	EF	LS	LF	TF
A	5	0	5	0	5	0
B	8	5	13	5	13	0
C	6	5	11	10	16	5
D	9	13	22	13	22	0
E	6	13	19	16	22	3
F	3	11	14	19	22	8
G	1	22	23	22	23	0

With the completion of the backward pass, we have calculated the late dates for all activities. With both passes completed, the critical path is now defined and the amount of float for each activity is calculated.

The Critical Path

If we think about the situation in the project we have just scheduled, we will notice that activities A, B, D, and G are "driving" the schedule. These activities are critical because any delay in their start or finish will delay the entire project. For example, if activity B takes 9 days instead of 8 days, it will finish on day 14. Activity D can then start and will finish on day 23. Finally, activity G can start on day 23 and will finish on day 24, which is 1 day past the originally scheduled date. This delay in the project completion date may not occur with a delay (within certain limits) in other activities, such as C, E, or F. Project managers usually focus on the critical path because of its criticality and direct impact on the project finish date. Knowing not only which activities are critical and which are not but also the impact of the delay of one activity on other activities and on the entire project is the crux of understanding scheduling.

Following are five observations about the critical path:

- In every network, there must exist at least one critical path.
- More than one critical path may exist. Multiple paths may share some activities.
- Any critical path must be continuous from the start of the project until its end. There is one exception: when a constraint is imposed (which is discussed later), a path may become critical as a result of the constraint, from the start until the constrained activity, or from the constrained activity until the end. In general, the entire path must be either critical or noncritical.
- If all paths in a network must go through one particular activity, this activity must be critical.
- Some people like to define *critical path* as the path with zero float. This definition is correct only if no imposed finish date is used in the backward-pass calculations (again, this point is discussed later). However, our definition-the longest path in a network, from start to finish-is more appropriate because it is always true. We can also say that the critical path is the path with least float.

Example 1.20

Draw the logic network and perform the CPM calculations for the schedule shown next.

Activity	Immediately Preceding Activity	Duration (days)
A	–	5
B	A	8
C	A	6
D	B	9
E	B, C	6
F	C	3
G	D, E, F	1

Solution:

Performing forward and backward passes yields the solution shown below. The critical path is A, C, F, H, I. Activities B, D, E, and G have total floats equal to 2, 13, 2, and 7, respectively.

Let us examine the impact that one activity may have on other activities when it consumes its total float or part of it. In example 4.2, if activity B is delayed by only 1 day and starts on day 3 (which is well within its available float), it will finish on day 9.

Remember: We always mean the end of the day. Activity E, then, cannot start on its early start date (i.e., day 8). The earliest date E can start is day 9. If we delay activity B by 2 days, activity E cannot start until day 10 and, thus, becomes critical. This 1- or 2-day delay in the start of activity B will not affect the project completion date. However, if we delay activity B by more than 2 days, it will finish past day 10, which will affect the start of the critical activity H and, thus, delay the entire project. This discussion illustrates the concept of total float, which was defined previously as the maximum amount of time an activity can be delayed without delaying the entire project. Note, though, that this delay, within the total float, may (and did in this case) or may not delay the early start of the following (succeeding) activities.

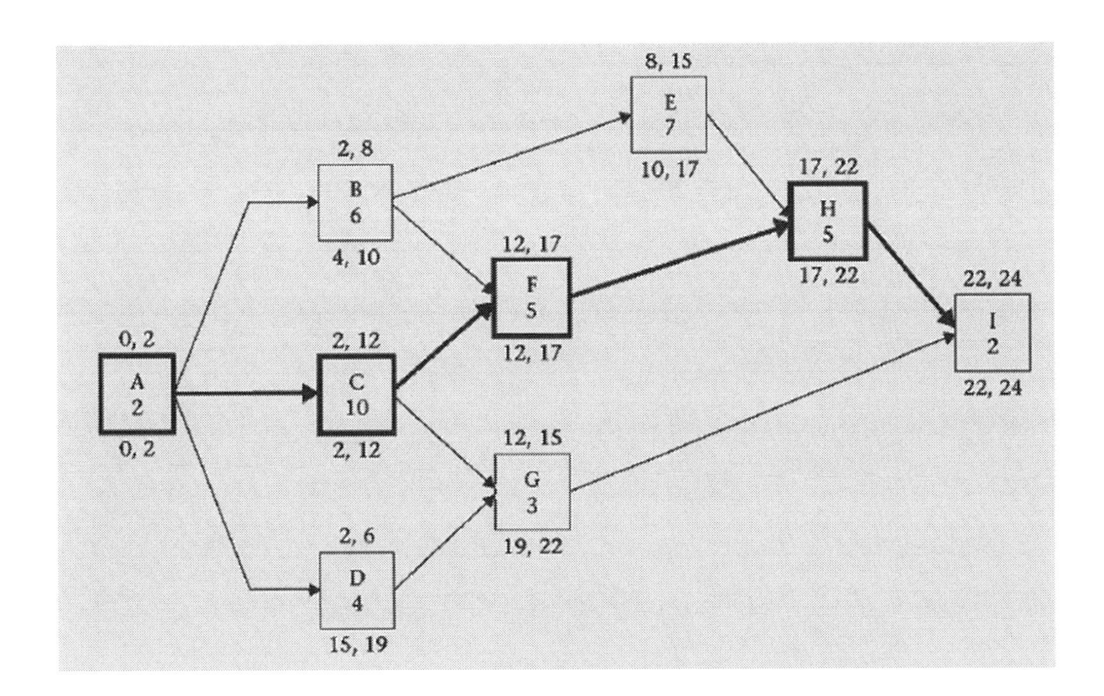

Now let us apply the same discussion to activity G. It has 7 days of total float. Delaying it by as many as 7 days will not impact the succeeding activity, I. The same argument applies to activity E, only with 2 days of total float.

Next, we discuss yet another case of total float. Consider activity D, which has 13 days of total float. When we delay it by 1 or 2 days, for example, we notice that this delay does not impact the early start of the following activity, G, since G is waiting for the completion of activity C as well. However, when the delay of activity D exceeds 6 days, the situation changes. If we consider delaying activity D by 7 days, it finishes on day 13. Activity G, then, cannot start until day 13. It should finish on day 16, which will not delay activity I or the entire project. This 7-day delay in activity D delays the early start of its successor (activity G), yet it does not delay the entire project. We can increase this delay to 13 days (which is the total float for activity D) without affecting the completion date of the entire project, but it does impact the succeeding activity, G.

We can divide activity D's 13-day total float into two portions: the first 6 days will not delay its successor. This is called free float (FF). The other 7 days will cause a delay to its successor even though they will not delay the entire project. This is called interfering float (Int. F). We can look at the situation this way: activities D and G share the 7-day interfering float. If the first activity uses it, it will be taken away from the next activity. Similarly, we can determine that activity B has no free float (total float is all interfering float). The free float of activity G equals its total float (no interfering float). To calculate free float for an activity, we need to compare its early finish date with its successor's early start date. When there is only one successor activity (Figure-a below), the calculation is simple:

Activity G's free float, $FF = 22 - 15 = 7$ days. When the activity has more than one successor (Figure-b below), you must pick the earliest early start date among the successors: activity B's free float, $FF = \min(12, 8) - 8 = 0$ days. In general, free float is calculated by using the following equation:

$$FF_i = \min(ES_{i+1}) - EF$$

where $\min(ES_{i+1})$ means the least (i.e., earliest) of the early start dates of succeeding activities.

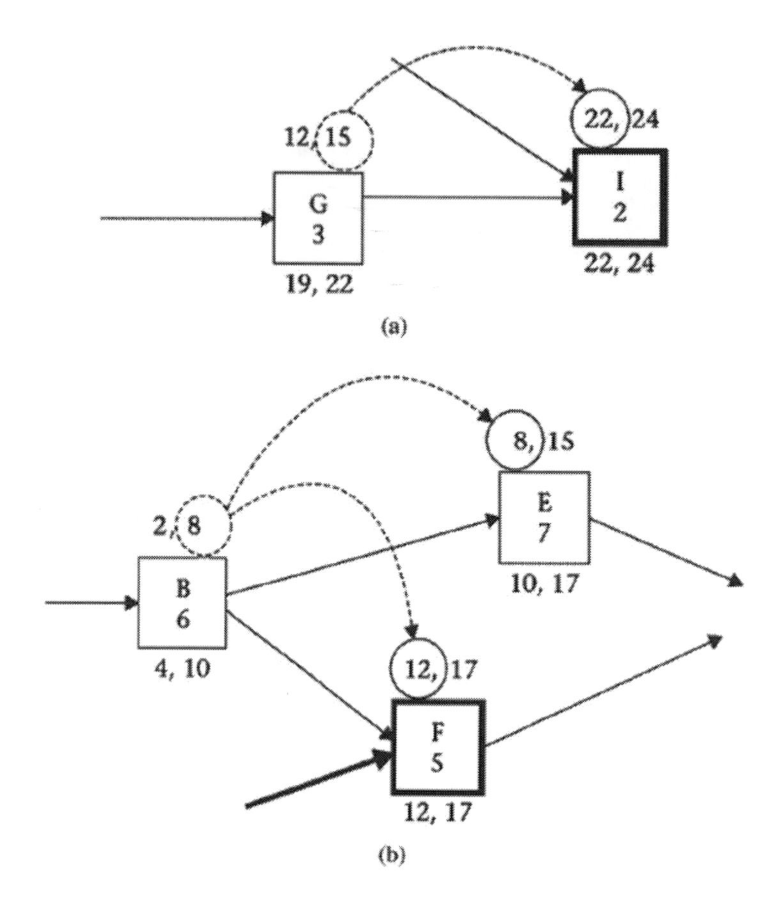

1.3.5 Lags and Leads

In some situations, an activity cannot start until a certain time after the end of its predecessor. A typical example is concrete operations. Let us imagine this sequence:

1. Form the concrete column.
2. Install the steel reinforcement (commonly known as *rebar*).
3. Place the concrete.
4. Wait for the concrete to set (attain sufficient strength).
5. Strip the forms.

Note that the fourth step is not a real activity to which we must allocate resources and a budget. It is merely a waiting period, commonly known as a lag. A node network can accommodate such a lag if we simply put the lag on the relationship line between Place Concrete and Strip Forms, as shown in Figure-a below. This 3-day lag means a minimum waiting period of 3 days. Waiting less than 3 days violates the preceding logic, whereas waiting more than 3 days does not violate the logic. In some networks, the lag number is put inside a little box for better visibility. Thus, a lag is defined as a minimum waiting period between the finish (or start) of an activity and the start (or finish) of its successor. Arrow networks cannot accommodate lags. The only solution in such networks is to treat it as a real activity with a real duration, no resources, and a $0 budget (Figure-b below).

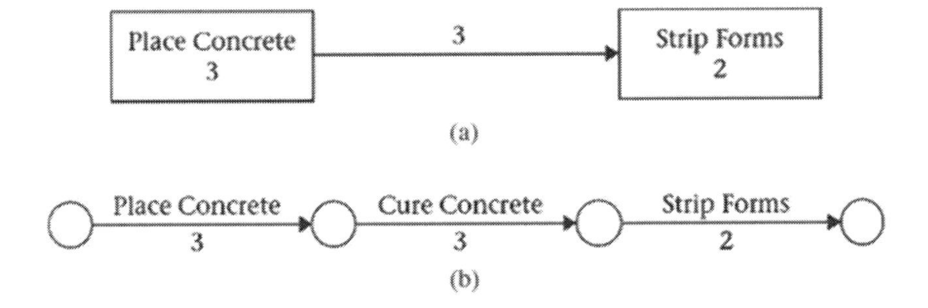

Example 1.21
For the following schedule, draw the node network, perform the CPM calculations, mark the critical path, and complete the table.

Activity	Immediately Preceding Activity	Duration (days)	Lag
A	–	5	
B	A	6	
C	A	4	3
D	A	5	
E	B	3	
F	C, B	2	

Solution:

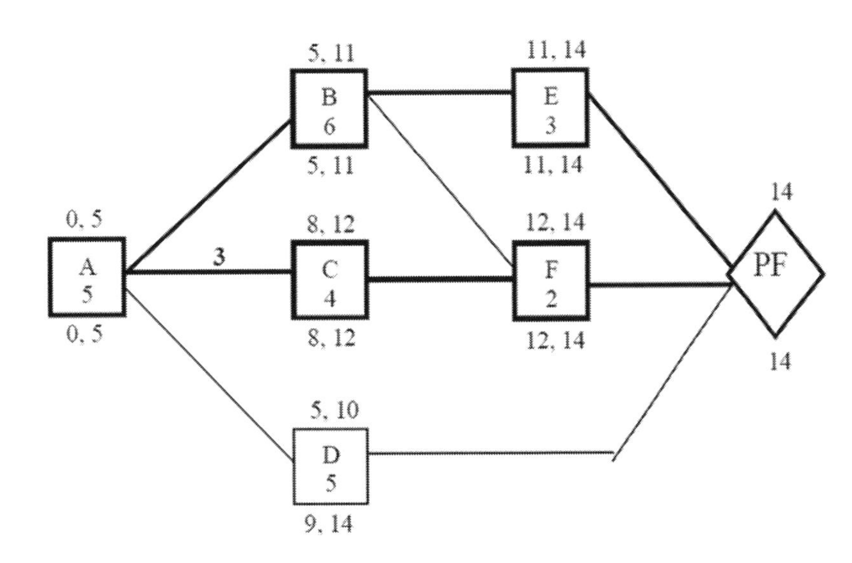

Activity	Duration (days)	Immediately Preceding Activity	Lag	ES	EF	LS	LF	TF	FF
A	5	–		0	5	0	5	0	0
B	6	A		5	11	5	11	0	0
C	4	A	3	8	12	8	12	0	0
D	5	A		5	10	9	14	4	4
E	3	B		11	14	11	14	0	0
F	2	C, B		12	14	12	14	0	0

1.3.6 Precedence Networks

Precedence networks are node networks that allow for the use of four types of relationships: finish to start (FS), start to start (SS), finish to finish (FF), and start to finish (SF). Four types of relationships are possible in precedence networks:

1. *Finish-to-start (FS) relationship*: The most common type of relationship is the FS relationship. Many project managers still insist on using only this type. Many examples of this type exist, such as the following:
   - The concrete cannot be placed (poured) until the formwork has been built.
   - The doors cannot be hung until door frames have been installed.

2. *Start-to-start (SS) relationship*: The SS relationship is common and extremely useful. Examples of this type are as follows:
   - Excavation for the foundation cannot start until clearing and grubbing begins (usually with a certain lag; i.e., a certain percentage is completed).
   - Laying felt on the roof cannot start until sheathing has started (also usually with a lag).

3. *Finish-to-finish (FF) relationship*: The FF relationship is also common and useful. Examples of this type are as follows:
   - Landscaping cannot finish until the driveway is finished.
   - Backfilling a trench cannot finish until the pipe in the trench has been laid.

4. *Start-to-finish (SF) relationship*: The SF relationship is uncommon and almost nonexistent in construction projects.

Example 1.22
The following relationship means:

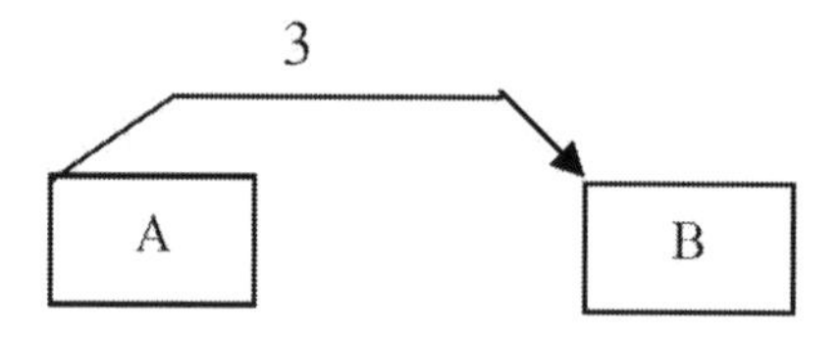

A. Activity B has to start exactly 3 days after the start of A
B. Activity B can start at least 3 days after the start of A
C. Activity B can start at most 3 days after the start of A
D. None of the above

Solution: B

Example 1.23
The following relationship means:

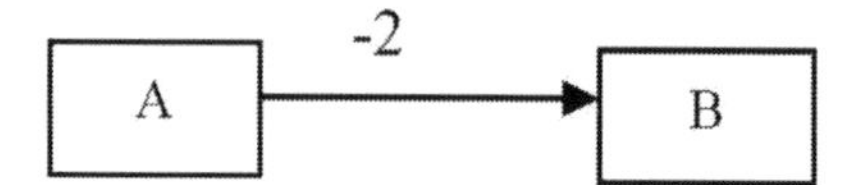

A. Activity A can start 2 days before the start of activity B
B. Activity B can start 2 days after the completion of activity A
C. Activity B can start 2 days before the completion of activity A
D. Activity B has to start at least 2 days before the completion of activity A

Solution: C

Example 1.24
Given the data below, draw the precedence network, perform the CPM calculations, and compute the table entries.

Activity		Duration (days)	Immediately Preceding Activity	Relation Type	Lag	ES	EF	LS	LF	TF	FF
A		4	–			?	?	?	?	?	?
B		3	–			?	?	?	?	?	?
C		8	A	SF		?	?	?	?	?	?
D		7	A, B			?	?	?	?	?	?
E		6	D	SS	3	?	?	?	?	?	?
F		3	D			?	?	?	?	?	?
G		5	F	SS	2	?	?	?	?	?	?
			F	FF		?	?	?	?	?	?

If the relationship is not mentioned, it is finish to start (FS). If not lag is mentioned, it is zero.

Solution:

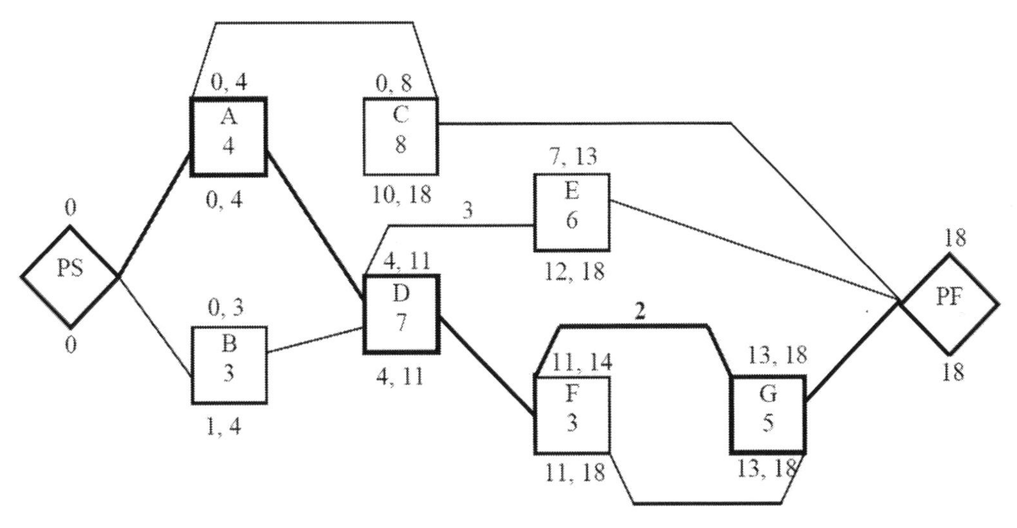

Activity	Duration (days)	Immediately Preceding Activity	Relation Type	Lag	ES	EF	LS	LF	TF	FF
A	4	–			0	4	0	4	0	0
B	3	–			0	3	1	4	1	1
C	8	A	SF		0	8	10	18	10	10
D	7	A, B			4	11	4	11	0	0
E	6	D	SS	3	7	13	12	18	5	5
F	3	D			11	14	11	18	4	0
G	5	F	SS	2	13	18	13	18	0	0
		F	FF							

Note that this example is so big and cannot be solved in 6 minutes. The actual exam will have smaller question. Bigger problem is included here to explain the full concept.

1.3.7 Earned Value Analysis (EVA)

Earned Value Analysis (EVA) allows the project manager to measure the amount of work actually performed on a project beyond the basic review of cost and schedule reports. EVA provides a method that permits the project to be measured by progress achieved. The project manager is then able, using the progress measured, to forecast a project's total cost and date of completion, based on trend analysis. Oftentimes the term earned value is defined as the budgeted cost of worked performed or BCWP.

Planned Value PV, also known as Budget Cost of Work Scheduled (BCWS), describes how far along project work is supposed to be at a given point in the project schedule and cost estimate. Cost and schedule baseline refers to the physical work scheduled and the approved budget to accomplish the scheduled work.

Actual Cost (AC), also called Actual Cost of Work Performed (ACWP), is the cost incurred for executing work on a project. This figure tells you what you have spent and, as with Planned Value, can be looked at in terms of cumulative and current. Cumulative AC is the sum of the actual cost for activities performed to date. Current AC is the actual costs of activities performed during a given period.

Schedule variance. Schedule Variance status does indicate the dollar value difference between work that is ahead or behind the plan and reflects a given measurement method.

$$SV = EV - PV$$
$$SV = BCWP - BCWS$$

If the variance is equal to 0, the project is on schedule. If a negative variance is determined, the project is behind schedule and if the variance is positive the project is ahead of schedule.

Cost Variance. The cost variance is defined as the difference between earned value and actual costs.

$$CV = EV - AC$$
$$CV = BCWP - ACWP$$

If the variance is equal to 0, the project is on budget. If a negative variance is determined, the project is over budget and if the variance is positive the project is under budget.

Schedule Performance Index. The SPI is defined as a measure of schedule efficiency on a project. It is the ratio of earned value (EV) to planned value (PV). The SPI is equal to earned value divided by planned value,

$$SPI = EV/PV = BCWP / BCWS$$

An SPI equal to or greater than one indicates a favorable condition and a value of less than one indicates an unfavorable condition.

Cost Performance Index. The CPI is as a "measure of cost efficiency on a project. It is the ratio of earned value (EV) to actual costs (AC). The CPI is equal to the earned value divided by the actual costs,

$$CPI = EV / AC = BCWP / ACWP$$

A CPI equal to or greater than one indicates a favorable condition and a value of less than one indicates an unfavorable condition.

Question 1.25
A flooring subcontractor has to install three types of flooring to an existing building:

Type	Quantity	Unit Price	Total Price
Carpet	2,600 SF	$2.30 /SF	$ 5,980
Vinyl tile	1,200 SF	$2.95 /SF	$ 3,540
Ceramic tile	3,330 SF	$4.95 /SF	$16,484

The subcontractor was given 10 days to finish the work. Assume he has crews to start all three jobs concurrently. Four days after the start of the work, he found out 800 SF of Vinyl tile has been installed in the Actual Cost of $2,488. The installation of Vinyl tile after this 4-day is most nearly:

A. under budget, and ahead of schedule
B. over budget, and ahead of schedule
C. under budget, and behind the schedule
D. over budget, and behind the schedule

Solution:

Without formal analysis for Vinyl tile:

- Budgeted quantity of carpet installed in 4 days = (1,200/10 SF per day) x 4 day = 480. The subcontractor actually installed 800 SF of carpet. So, ahead of schedule.
- Actual cost in 4 days is $2,488, whereas the budgeted cost of work performed is 800 SF x $2.95 per SF = $2,360. So, over-budget

The correct answer is B.

With formal analysis for Vinyl tile:
ACWP = $2,488
BCWP = 800 SF x $2.95 per SF = $2,360
BCWS = (1,200/10 SF per day) x 4 day x $2.95 = $1,416
CV = *BCWP* – *ACWP* = $2,360 – $2,488 = – $128 (negative, over-budget)
SV = *BCWP* – *BCWS* = $2,360 – $1,416 = $944 (positive, ahead of schedule)

1.4 Activity Identification and Sequencing

Project Planning and Project Schedules is an involved process requiring input from nearly all aspects of the design and construction process. Available resources (material and labor), time, budget, code issues, and governmental/societal constraints must all be taken into consideration during the planning process to ensure the project is completed on time and within budget. Without planning, the master schedule cannot be constructed. And without a master schedule, there is no roadmap to steer the project to completion. A planning and scheduling tool used in the construction industry is the Critical Path Method (CPM). CPM is for projects that are made up of a number of individual activities. If some of the activities require other activities to finish before they can start, then the project becomes a complex web of activities.

CPM can help you figure out:

- how long your complex project will take to complete
- which activities are critical, meaning that they have to be done on time or else the whole project will take longer

In general, the preparation of a CPM schedule includes the following four steps:

1. Break down the project into work activities. Any project, no matter how large or small, must be divided into smaller entities, called activities, or tasks. An activity is a unique, definable element of work. In this step, there is no absolutely correct or incorrect way to break down the project into work activities. In this regard, there are two schools of thought:
    a. Restrict the number of activities for the simplicity of the project schedule
    b. Break the project down into smaller activities. Factors that should be considered in breaking down the project into individual activities for better control are Nature of the work/homogeneity, Location/floor/segment, Size/duration, Timing/chronology, Responsibility/trade, Phase, Contractual restrictions, Level of confidence in the duration:
2. Determine activities' durations
3. Determine logical relationships
4. Draw the logic network, and perform the CPM calculations
5. Review and analyze the schedule
6. Implement the schedule
7. Monitor and control the schedule
8. Revise the database and record feedback
9. Cost/resource allocation (or loading)
10. Resource leveling

Example 1.26
The first step in assembling a CPM project plan is to define the __________ including duration, start date, finish date, predecessors, etc.

A. tasks
B. activities
C. events
D. jobs

Solution:

In CPM project planning, activities are the individual steps or tasks of entire project used to build the schedule or plan. The correct answer is B.

Example 1.27
When assembling a CPM (Critical Path Method) model, which of the following is not a necessary variable?

A. A list of all project activities needed for completion
B. Milestone dates or events to gauge progress
C. Which designer will accomplish a given portion of the design
D. The amount of time required for each of the activities

Solution:

To accurately portray a project schedule in a CPM model, a list of all project activities, milestone dates or events, and the amount to time for each activity are all needed. Additionally, which activities depend on other activities is also required information. Who is actually going to perform each activity is not necessary in putting the CPM model together. The correct answer is C.

References:

- Mubarak, S. *Construction Project Scheduling and Control,* 3/e, Wiley.
- EngineeringDesignResources

Chapter 2
Means and Methods

2.1 Construction Loads

In the PE Civil Breadth (morning) exam, it is expected that the PE Civil Reference Handbook is a good enough resource. The handbook does not specify the details of construction load. Therefore, it can be said that some basic load calculation especially gravity load from a tributary area and basic mechanics (statics) from construction should be good enough. The tributary area is defined as the area of floor or roof (in plan) that causes loading on a particular structural element. The following example will explain the load calculation procedure. Chapter 4 explains the load calculation in more details.

Example 2.1
The plan of a three story building has a roof dead load of 30 psf and a flat roof with negligible slope. The roof live load from ASCE 7 is 20 psf.

- Roof dead load = 30 psf
- Snow load = 0
- Roof live load = 20 psf
- Floor dead load = 40 psf
- Floor live load = 60 psf

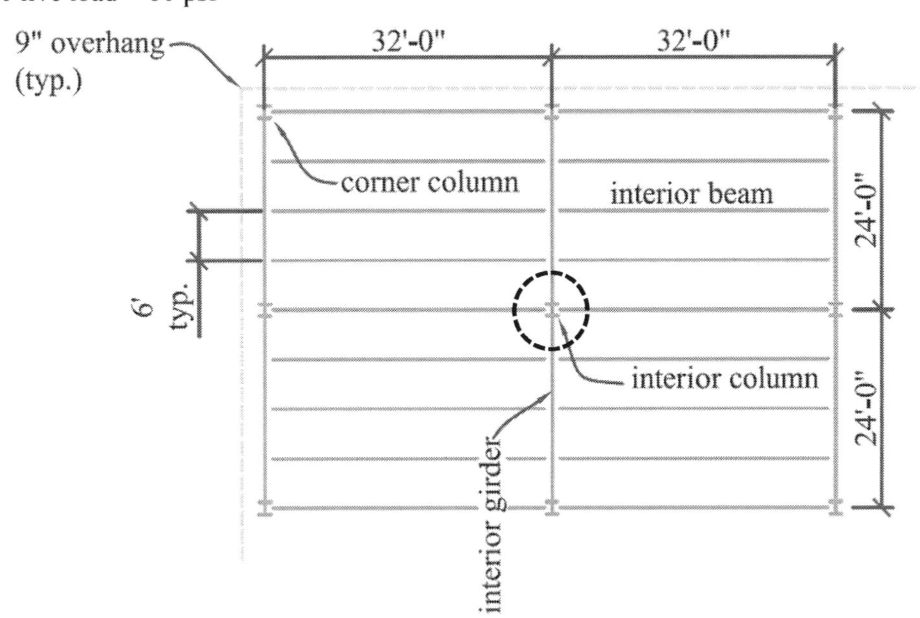

The total service axial load (kip) on interior column (circled below) is most nearly:

[the theory is the column will carry load from 50% of the dimension (up to next column) of each side]

Solution:

Tributary area of interior column = (24 / 2 + 24 / 2) ft x (32 / 2 + 32 / 2) ft
= 768 ft^2

Uniform load = Roof loads + Floors load
= (30 + 20) psf + 2 floors (40 + 60) psf [Three stories: 2 floors, 1 roof]
= 250 psf

Concentrated service axial load = 250 psf x 768 ft^2 = 192,000 lb = 192 kip

Example 2.2

A rectangular beam for a 22-ft simple span if a service dead load of 500 lb/ft (not including the beam weight) and a service live load of 1.0 kip/ft are to be supported. The beam is 27 in. by 14 in. in cross-section. The concrete unit weight is 150 pcf. The total service load (kip/ft) is most nearly:

Solution

Cross-sectional area = 14 x 27 $in.^2$ = 378 $in.^2$ = 378 / 144 ft^2 = 2.625 ft^2
Weight per unit length = 2.625 ft^2 x 150 lb/ft^3 = 394 lb/ft
Total load = 500 lb/ft + 1000 lb/ft + 394 lb/ft = 1,894 lb/ft

Some problems on the equilibrium of particles and rigid body are very often seen in the Breadth exam. From Newton's third law of motion, we know that every action has its own and opposite reaction. This means, if you apply a force to a wall it will react with an equal amount of force on you, if the wall does not move (i.e., rigid). Therefore, every action is equal to its reaction in any direction. This is called the equilibrium condition. If we sum up this action and reactions in a direction it will be zero as these two are numerically equal but the signs are opposite. Thus, we can write the following three equations for two dimensional conditions:

$\sum F_x = 0$ (the summation of forces along the x-direction is zero)
$\sum F_y = 0$ (the summation of forces along the y-direction is zero)
$\sum M = 0$ (the summation of moment at any point about any axis perpendicular to the plane is zero)

Example 2.3

A crane carries five crews with the loading as shown below. The crane arms make an angle of 60° with the deck. The force, F_1 (lb) in the crane arms are nearly:

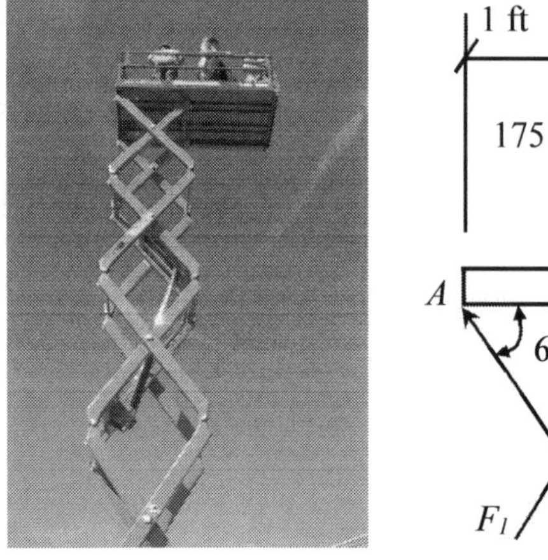

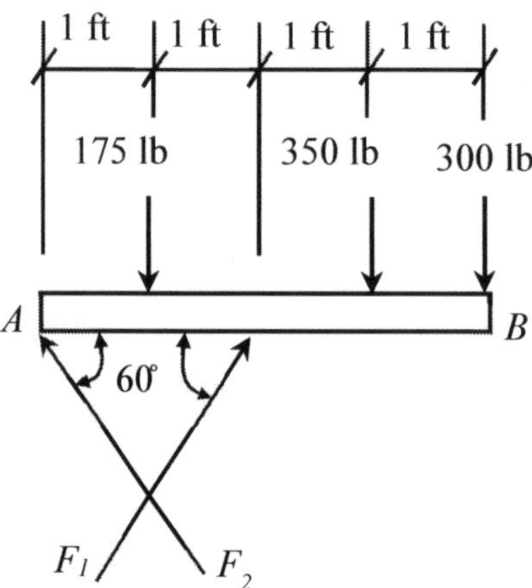

Solution:

To be in equilibrium, the summation of the moment about the point A must be zero.

$\sum M \text{ at } A = 0\ (\downarrow\!\!\lrcorner + ve)$

$$(175\text{ lb})(1.0\text{ ft}) + (350\text{ lb})(3.0\text{ ft}) + (300\text{ lb})(4.0\text{ ft}) - (F_1 \sin 60)(2.0\text{ ft}) = 0$$

175 lb.ft + 1,050 lb.ft + 1,200 lb.ft – 1.732 F_1 ft = 0

2,425 lb.ft – 1.732 F_1 ft = 0

1.732 F_1 ft = 2,425 lb.ft

Therefore, F_1 = 1,400 lb

Note that if the problem asks F_2 also, then you can apply $\sum F_y = 0$. If the problem asks only F_2, then apply $\sum M = 0$ at the F_1 force point.

Example 2.4

A 30-in. diameter wheel is to be rolled over an obstacle of 7-in. in height as shown below. The wheel load is 300 lb. If a pushing force of 200 lb is applied as shown at an angle of 40° with the ground, will the wheel roll over the obstacle? The factor of safety against the overturning of the wheel over the obstacle is most nearly:

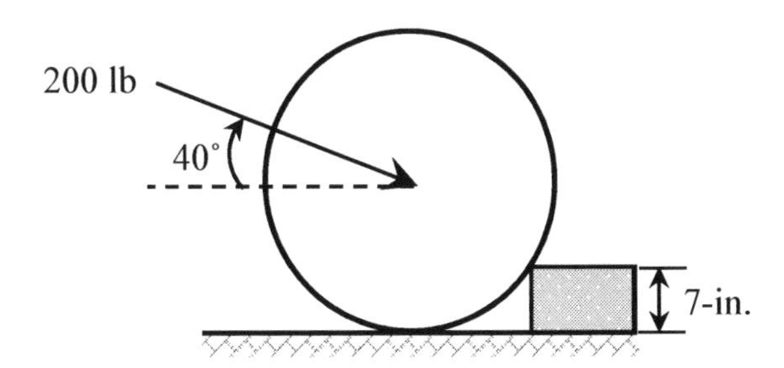

Solution:

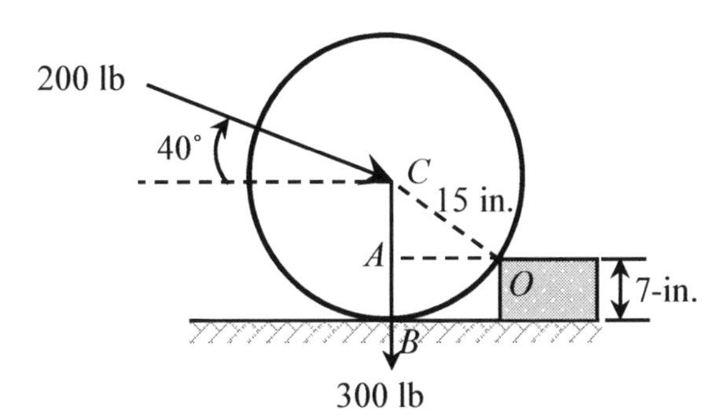

To intend to roll over the obstacle, the overturning moment with respect to the point O must be equal to the resisting moment (or the clockwise and the counter-clockwise moments must be equal).

Radius, OC = 15 in.

$CA = BC - AB$ = 15 in. – 7 in. = 8 in.

$$OA = \sqrt{OC^2 - AC^2} = \sqrt{(15\text{ in.})^2 - (8\text{ in.})^2} = 12.69\text{ in.}$$

Overturning moment about O = 200 lb cos40 (8 in.) = 1,225.7 lb.in.

Resisting moment about O = 200 lb sin40 (12.69 in.) + 300 lb (12.69 in.) = 5,438.4 lb.in.

The resisting moment is much larger than the overturning moment. So, the body will not roll over the obstacle.

$$\text{Factor of Safety} = \frac{\text{Resisting Moment}}{\text{Overturning Moment}} = \frac{5{,}438.4 \text{ lb.in.}}{1{,}225.7 \text{ lb.in.}} = 4.4$$

The body will not roll over, and the factor of safety against overturning is 4.4.

Example 2.5

A concrete wall is being lifted and placed by six cables as shown below. The profile of the cabling system is also shown. The total load to be supported by the cable system is 12 kip and the cable system is symmetric about the vertical centerline.

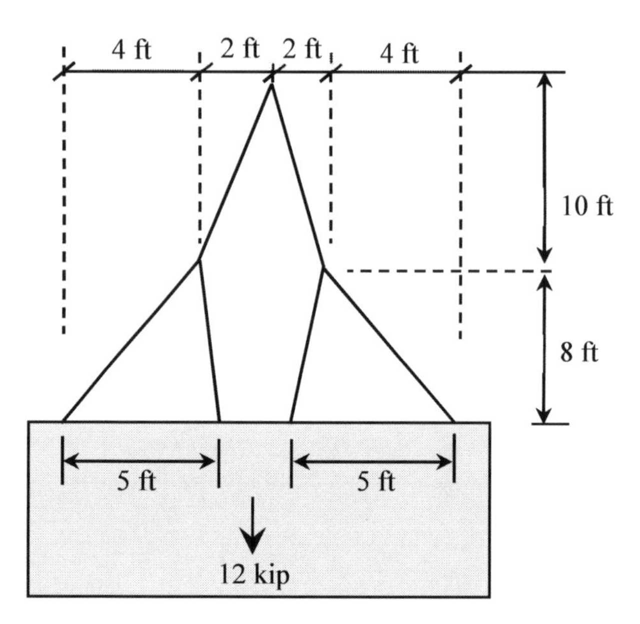

The force (kip) at any of the top two-cable is most nearly:

Solution:

Being symmetric, the force will be distributed equally in both cables.

$$\sum F_y = 0 \left(\uparrow +ve\right)$$

$$2T\left(\frac{5}{\sqrt{26}}\right) - 12\,\text{kip} = 0$$

$T = \underline{6.12 \text{ kip}}$

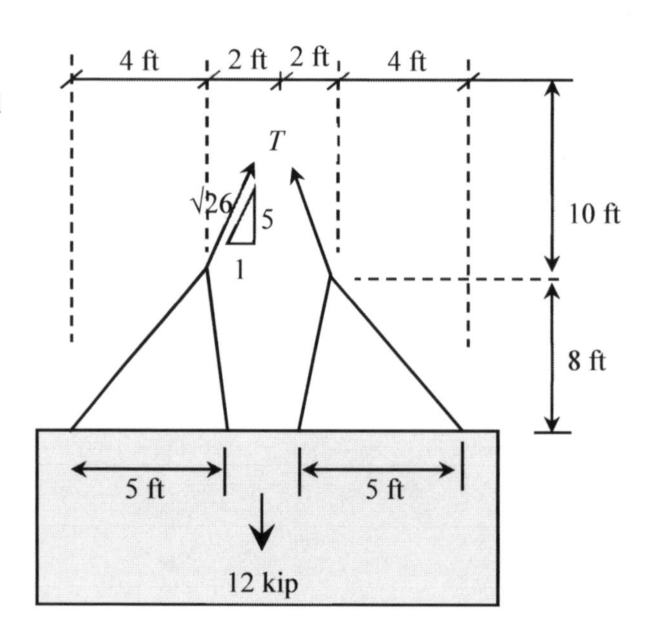

Example 2.6

A 20-kip sphere is supported by two rigid planes as shown below. The plane, *AB* is inclined with the horizon at an angle of 35° and the other plane *AC* is vertical. The joints of *AB* and *AC* are pin connected. If the contact surfaces are frictionless, the forces (kip) exerted by the spherical body on the planes *AB* and *AC* are most nearly:

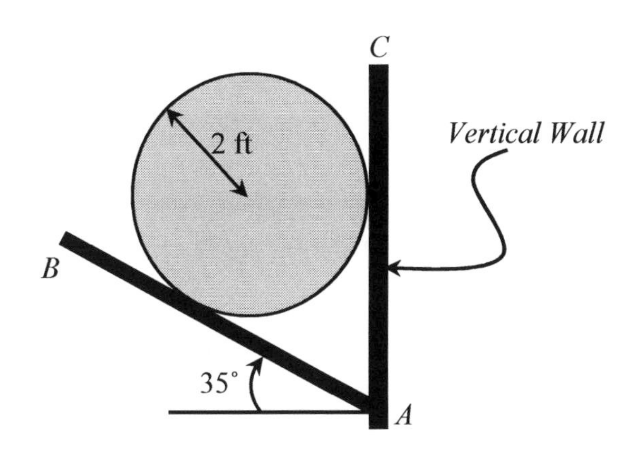

Solution:

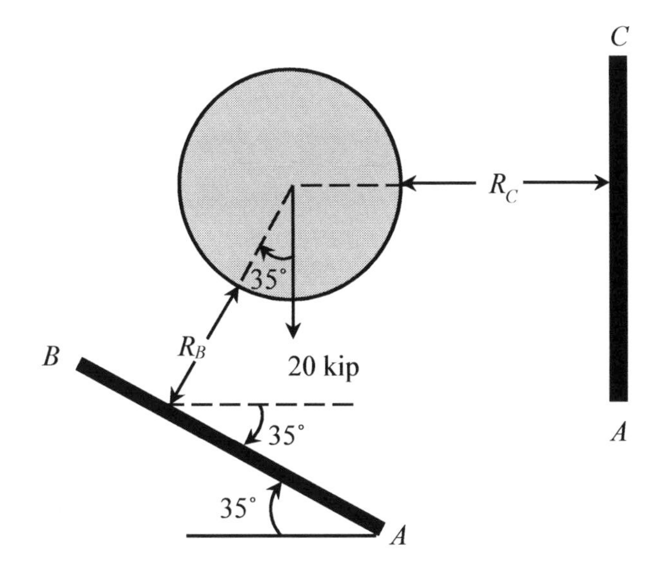

$$\sum F_y = 0 \; (\uparrow +ve)$$

$R_B \cos 35 - 20 \text{ kip} = 0$

$R_B \cos 35 = 20 \text{ kip}$

$R_B = 20 \text{ kip} / \cos 35$

$R_B = \underline{24.4 \text{ kip}}$

$$\sum F_x = 0 \; (\rightarrow +ve)$$

$R_B \sin 35 - R_C = 0$

$R_C = R_B \sin 35$

$R_C = 24.4 \text{ kip} \sin 35$

$R_C = \underline{14 \text{ kip}}$

Example 2.7
A 10-kip tractor is used to lift 1,800-lb of soil as shown below. Each axle is a single-axle single-tire each side. The reactions at the tires (A_y and B_y) per tire in kip are most nearly:

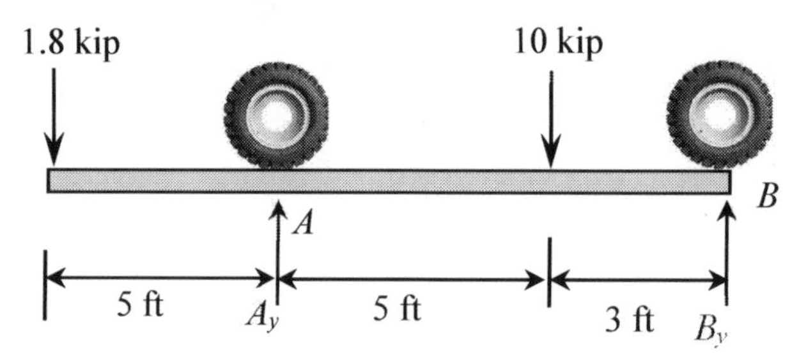

Solution:

$$\sum M \text{ at } A = 0 \; (\circlearrowright + ve)$$

10 kip (5 ft) – 1.8 kip (5 ft) – B_y (8 ft) = 0
50 kip.ft – 9.0 kip.ft – 8B_y ft = 0
41 kip.ft – 8B_y ft = 0
8B_y ft = 41 kip.ft
B_y = 5.125 kip (↑)
B_y = 5.125 kip / 2 tires = 2.56 kip per tire (↑)

$$\sum F_y = 0 \; (\uparrow + ve)$$

A_y + B_y – 1.8 kip – 10 kip =0
A_y + B_y – 11.8 kip = 0
A_y + 5.125 kip – 11.8 kip =0
A_y = 11.8 kip – 5.125 kip
A_y = 6.675 kip (↑)
A_y = 6.675 kip / 2 tires = 3.34 kip per tire (↑)

Example 2.8
A 90-kg man is hanging using two cables as shown below. Cable *BC* is horizontal and cable *AB* makes an angle of 20° with the surface. The tensions (N) at the cables *AB* and *BC* respectively is most nearly:

A. 3581.6, 3426
B. 3581.6, 2426
C. 2581.6, 2426
D. 2581.6, 3426

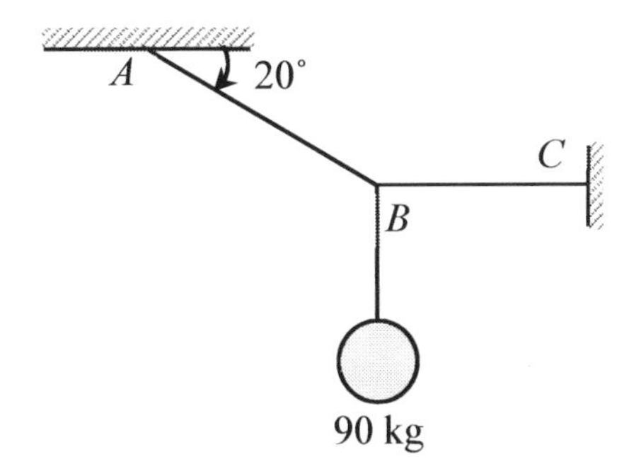

Solution:

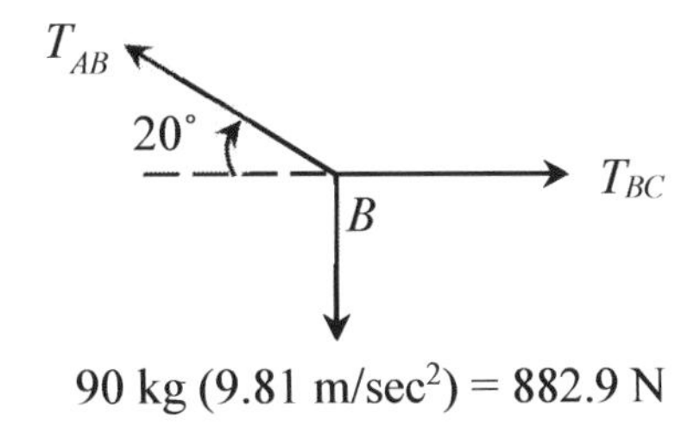

90 kg (9.81 m/sec^2) = 882.9 N

$\sum F_y = 0 \; (\uparrow +ve)$

$T_{AB}(\sin 20) = 882.9\,\text{N}$; Therefore, T_{AB} = 2,581.6 N

Now, $\sum F_x = 0 \; (\rightarrow +ve)$

$T_{BC} - T_{AB}(\cos 20) = 0$

$T_{BC} = 2{,}581.6\,\text{N}(\cos 20)$; Therefore, $T_{BC} = \underline{2{,}426\,\text{N}}$; The correct answer is C.

Example 2.9

While constructing a retaining wall, wood strut is used to support the freshly placed concrete wall as shown in figure below. At this stage, the soil exerts a force of 500 lb/ft at the height of 1.0 ft from the ground. The foundation of the wall can be considered a hinge support to be conservative. The developed force in the wood strut for the equilibrium condition is P = 60 lb/ft. The vertical support reactions at the foundation wall, if the wall weighs 2.5 kip/ft is nearly:

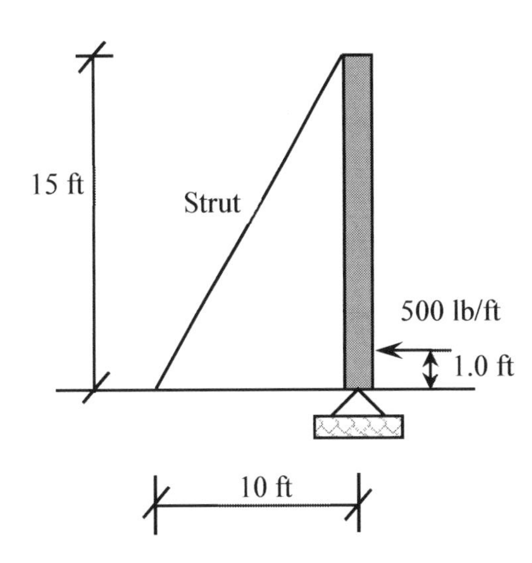

Solution:

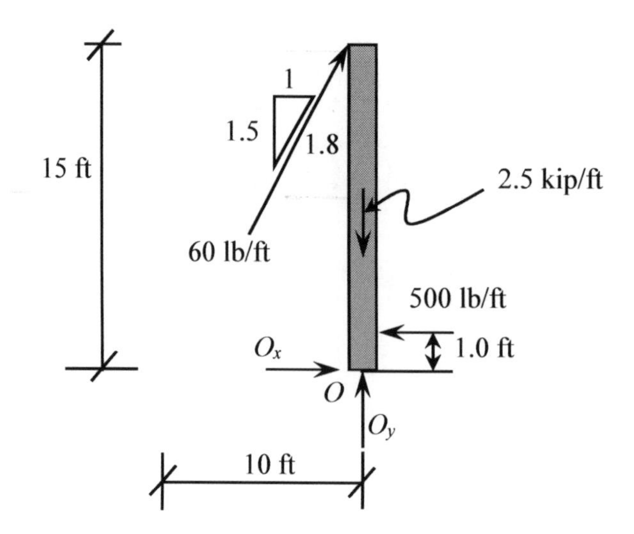

$$\sum F_y = 0 \left(\uparrow +ve\right)$$

$$P\left(\frac{1.5}{1.8}\right) - 2,500\,\text{lb/ft} + O_y = 0$$

O_y = 2,500 lb/ft – P (1.5/1.8) lb/ft
O_y = 2,500 lb/ft – 60 (1.5/1.8) lb/ft
O_y = 2,500 lb/ft – 50 lb/ft
O_y = 2,450 lb/ft (↑)

2.2 Construction Methods

Several construction methods are mentioned below.

- Modular Construction
  - Off-site construction of modular units that are transported to the jobsite and assembled into the finished construction.
  - Units can be basic "shells" up to finished assemblies including interior and exterior finishes and services.
  - Modular construction can be:
    - Timber
    - Light gauge steel
    - Concrete
    - Composites
  - Light gauge exterior finishes may be applied either during unit fabrication or onsite.
  - Masonry exterior finishes generally must be applied onsite.
- Panelized Construction
  - Wall, floor, and/or roof panels are constructed offsite and assembled at the jobsite into the finished construction.
  - Closed Panel Systems
    - Insulation and other materials included within the panel construction are assembled prior to delivery to the jobsite.

        - Panels can be assembled using timber, light gauge steel, or concrete.
        - Panels can include electrical, mechanical, plumbing, windows, doors, and other finishes.
    - Open Panel Systems
        - Insulation and other materials included within the panel construction are not assembled prior to delivery to the jobsite.
        - Insulation and other materials are applied at the jobsite along with exterior and interior finishes, electrical, mechanical, plumbing, windows, and doors.
- Hybrid
    - Combination of Modular and Panelized Construction including:
        - Construction assemblies of closed and open panels, precast concrete foundations, pre-assembled electrical, mechanical, and plumbing services, etc.
    - Construction assemblies utilizing insulated concrete formwork (ICF)

2.3 Temporary Structures and Facilities

Temporary structures support or brace permanent work during construction and include:

- Temporary supporting systems such as earthwork sheeting & shoring
- Temporary bracing
- Soil backfill
- Formwork systems
- Scaffolding
- Underpinning of foundations

Another type of temporary structure includes temporary or emergency shelters, public art projects, lateral earth retaining structures in construction zones, construction access barriers, temporary grandstands and bleachers, sound system and lighting support structures for parades and public events, and indoor and outdoor theatrical stages.

Earthwork Shoring/ Sheeting System. Sheeting & shoring using steel soldier piles, sheet piles, and slurry walls, are used to prevent soil movement and cave-ins during the excavation of earth. These systems help minimize the excavation area and protect nearby buildings or structures.
Spaced sheeting involves inserting spaced timber shores, bracing, trench jacks, piles, or other material to resist the pressure from surrounding earth.
Close sheeting requires continuous solid sheeting along the entire length of excavation.

Temporary Bracing System. Temporary bracing systems are used to keep a structure or other building systems stable before the permanent bracing is installed, or the element becomes self-supporting. It is commonly used in construction of masonry walls, tilt-up precast concrete panels, steel frames, large timber framed walls and wood trusses. During the whole construction of wood frame, temporary cross-bracing adds lateral stability and helps prevent collapse of building structures. During excavation, there are two main types of temporary bracing systems:

a. Internal bracing:

- Resist movement of equipment and materials
- Not used for deep excavation
  One type of internal bracing is rakers which rest on foundation mat or rock to support the wall
  Another type is cross lot bracing which extends from one side of the excavation to the other to retain earth wall

b. Tie backs:

- Most effective in firm ground
- Provide a clear working space within the excavation, yet it is more expensive than internal bracing systems, and it might extend beyond the property lines of the building site
- Underpinning of Foundations

A support to an existing foundation to provide either additional depth or bearing capacity. Mainly used in the following situations:

- construction of a new project with a deeper foundation adjacent to an existing building
- settlement of an existing structure
- change in use of a structure
- addition of a basement below an existing structure

Scaffolding System. Provides a temporary, safe working platform for the erection, maintenance, construction, repair, access or inspection, etc. of structures or other building systems.
Formwork. Formwork is primarily used for standard poured-in-place concrete construction. Various materials can be used for formwork, such as wood, steel, plastic, aluminum, etc.
Falsework. Used to support spanning or arched structures in order to hold the component in place until its construction is sufficiently advanced to support itself.

Temporary support structures also includes for formwork used to mold concrete to form a desired shape, scaffolding to give workers access to the structure being constructed, and shoring which is temporary structural reinforcement used during repairs.

Example 2.10
The temporary structure built to mold concrete to the desired size and shape, and controls its position and alignment is called __________.

A. Fakework
B. Formwork
C. Fieldwork
D. Framework

Solution:

Formwork is the temporary structure built to mold concrete to the desired size and shape, and controls its position and alignment. The correct answer is B.

2.4 Miscellaneous Problems

Example 2.11
An 8-in. x 8-in. post is used temporarily to support a concrete slab weighing 2,500 lb. Ignoring the weight of the post, what is the compression load (psi) transferred to the temporary footing?

Solution:

Stress = Force / Area = 2500 lb ÷ (8 in. x 8 in.) = 39.1 psi.

Example 2.12

The 3rd floor of an office building has an elevation of 28 ft. The floor-to-floor dimension is 14 ft. The structure has a 6-in. concrete slab on 14 in. bar joist. A 10 in. uninsulated duct, 6 in. high recessed fluorescent lights, and 2 – 3 in. water lines are routed in the ceiling plenum in the joist space. Calculate the maximum ceiling height that can be achieved.

Solution:

3rd floor is at 28 ft and the floor-to-floor dimension is 14 ft. This puts the 4th floor elevation at 42 ft. Subtracting the floor slab (6 in.), the bar joists (14 in.), the ductwork (10 in.), and the light fixtures (6 in.), gives a ceiling elevation of 39 ft. The difference in the ceiling elevation and the 3rd floor elevation is the maximum ceiling height. The plumbing pipes can be routed in the joist space and thus is neglected.

Maximum ceiling height, 39 ft – 28 ft = 11 ft

Example 2.13

A reinforced-concrete beam has the following loading. Which of the following is the most appropriate reinforcement pattern?

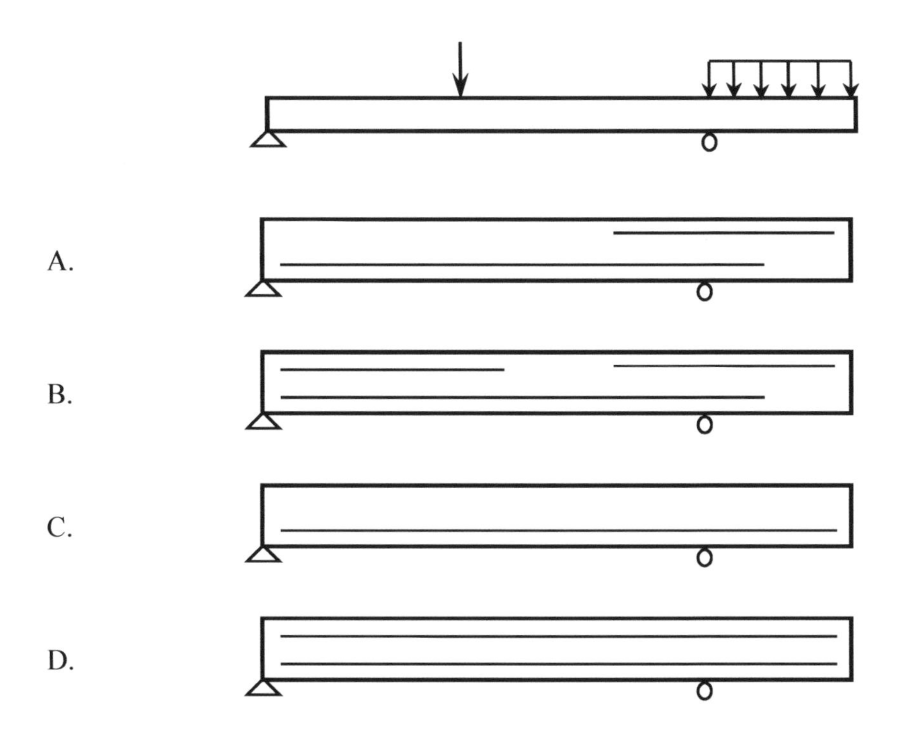

Solution:

For positive moment (or downward deflection) reinforcement is provided at the bottom side and vice versa. In other words, reinforcement is provided at the tension side.

In option B, at the left support the top reinforcement is not required as no negative moment will be developed for being a pin support.

Option C does not provide reinforcement at the top side of the right support. The top reinforcement is required at the top side of the right support as negative moment will be developed for continuous.

Option D provides reinforcement in both sides which is non-engineering and over-design.

The correct answer is A.

Example 2.14

A crane with a 120-ft boom is being used to install a load on the roof of the 65-ft high building as shown below. The load is to be dropped at point, *A*, from where the crew on the top of building will take care. Point, *A* is 5-ft away and 5-ft upper than the top of building. What should be horizontal distance, X (ft) from the edge of the building to the boom foot? The boom foot is located 5-ft from the surface. The crane boom can make a minimum of 45° with the surface, and the load cannot be lifted up with cable.

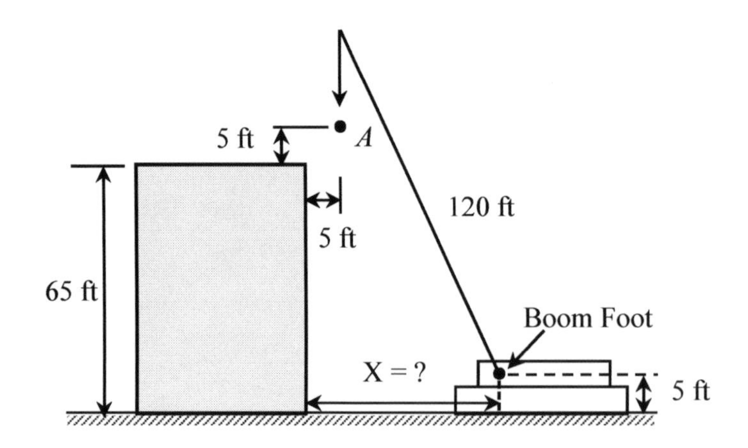

A. 45
B. 55
C. 35
D. The 120-ft crane is not suitable for this operation

Solution:

Imagine a right-angle triangle with corner points of A, and Boom foot.

$$\theta = \sin^{-1}\left(\frac{65}{120}\right) = 33^o \text{ less than } 45^\circ$$

The crane is unable to make this operation.
The correct answer is D.

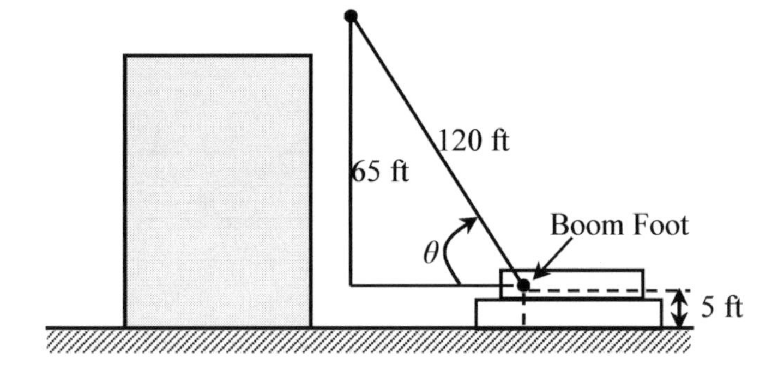

Example 2.15

A bridge is to be jacked up to replace its bearings. The design requires a hydraulic ram with a minimum capacity of 2,000 kN. The hydraulic rams that are available are rated in tons. Note that 1 ton = 2,000 lb. The minimum size (tons) ram to use is most nearly:

Solution: 2,000 kN = 2,000,000 N = 2,000,000 x 0.225 = 450,000 lb = 450,000/2,000 = 225 ton
[1 N = 0.225 lb]

Chapter 3
Soil Mechanics

The topics presented in this chapter are ordered as specified in the NCEES PE Civil Exam specifications. This chapter, i.e., Chapter 3 is also primarily based on Chapter 3 of the PE Civil Handbook.

3.1 Lateral Earth Pressure

This topic is based on Article 3.1 of the PE Civil Handbook. Lateral earth pressure is the horizontal pressure exerted by the soil being held in place by retaining walls, basement walls, tunnels, deep foundations or braced excavations. If the soil is not fully saturated, pore-water pressure does not exist. In moist soil, the soil particles absorb some water by chemical bonding, and the weight of moist soil apply pressure below it. That absorbed water cannot play any active role in applying pressure. If an infinitesimal small element is considered at depth, *z* from the surface. The vertical pressure on top it can be determines as follows:

$$p_o = \gamma z$$

where:

γ = Unit weight of soil, moist or dry
z = depth of the point to be considered

The horizontal pressure on this element can be determined as follows:

$$p_o = K\,\gamma z$$
$$p_H = K_o\,p_o$$

where:

K_o = Lateral earth pressure coefficient

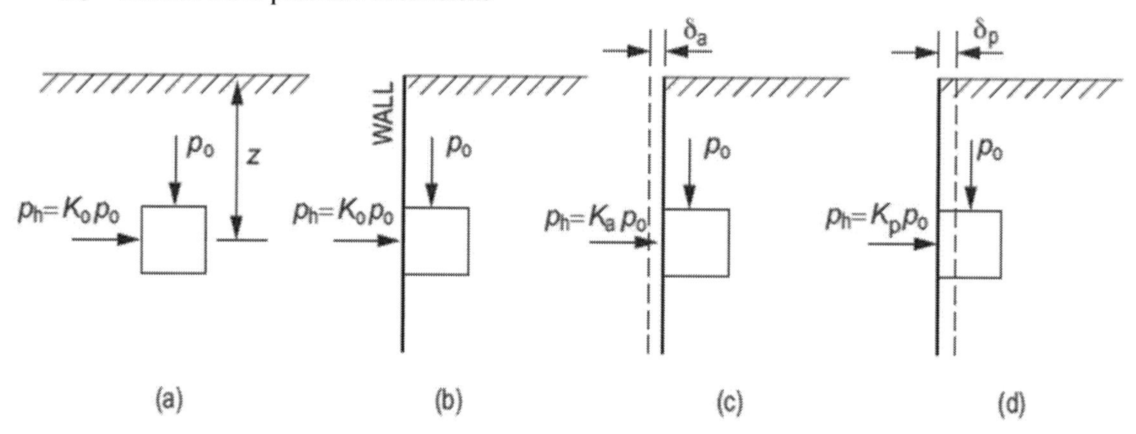

The above figure shows the stress states on a soil element subjected only to body stresses, where:

a) In situ geostatic effective vertical and horizontal stresses
b) Insertion of hypothetical infinitely rigid, thin frictionless wall and removal of soil to left of wall
c) Active condition of wall movement away from retained soil
d) Passive condition of wall movement into retained soil

Earth pressure at rest refers to lateral pressure caused by earth that is prevented from lateral movement by an unyielding wall. In actuality, however, some retaining-wall movement often occurs, resulting in either active or passive earth pressure. If a wall moves away from soil, the earth surface will tend to be lowered, and lateral pressure on the wall will be decreased. If the wall moves far enough away, shear failure of the soil will occur, and a sliding soil wedge will tend to move forward and downward. The earth pressure exerted on the wall at this state of failure is known as *active earth pressure*, and it is at minimum value. If, on the other hand, a wall moves toward soil, the earth surface will tend to be raised, and lateral pressure on the wall will be increased. If the wall moves far enough toward the soil, shear failure of the soil will occur, and a sliding soil wedge will tend to move backward and upward. The earth pressure exerted on the wall at this state of failure is known as *passive earth pressure*, and it is at maximum value.

3.1.1 At-Rest Earth Pressure

Normally Consolidated Soils, $K_o = 1 - \sin\phi'$

Overconsolidated Soils, $K_o = (1 - \sin\phi')OCR^{\Omega}$ where, $\Omega = \sin\phi'$

K_o = at-rest earth pressure coefficient
ϕ' = effective friction angle of soil
OCR^{Ω} = overconsolidation ratio
Ω = OCR factor

3.1.2 Rankine Earth Pressure

The Rankine theory for determining lateral earth pressures is based on several assumptions. The primary one is that there is no adhesion or friction between wall and soil (i.e., the wall is smooth). In addition, lateral pressures computed from Rankine theory are limited to vertical walls. Failure is assumed to occur in the form of a sliding wedge along an assumed failure plane defined as a function of the soil's angle of internal friction. Lateral earth pressure varies linearly with depth, and resultant pressures are assumed to act at a distance up from the base of the wall equal to one-third the vertical distance from the heel at the wall's base to the surface of the backfill. The direction of resultants is parallel to the backfill surface.

3.1.2.1 Rankine Active and Passive Coefficients (Friction Only)

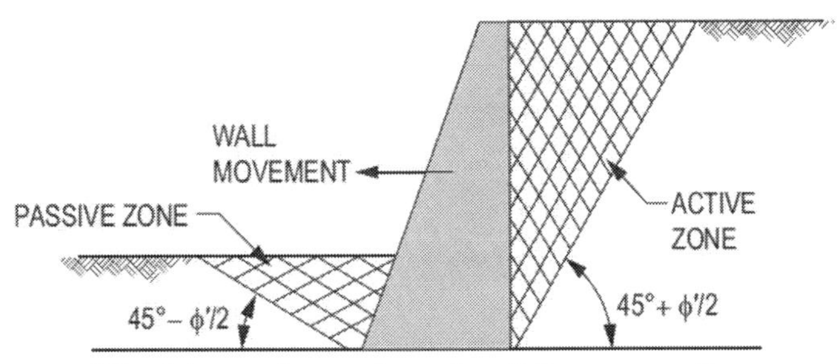

Figure. Development of Rankine active and passive failure zones for a smooth retaining wall

Active earth-pressure coefficient, $K_a = \dfrac{1 - \sin\phi'}{1 + \sin\phi'} = \tan^2\left(45 - \dfrac{\phi'}{2}\right)$

Passive earth-pressure coefficient, $K_p = \dfrac{1 + \sin\phi'}{1 - \sin\phi'} = \tan^2\left(45 + \dfrac{\phi'}{2}\right)$

Active lateral pressure, $p_a = K_a p_o$
Passive lateral pressure, $p_p = K_p p_o$
Overburden pressure, $p_o = \gamma z$

The lateral force can be determined as the triangular area of the pressure diagram, i.e.,

Active lateral force $P_a = \dfrac{1}{2}(K_a p_a)z = \dfrac{1}{2}(K_a \gamma z)z = \dfrac{1}{2}K_a \gamma z^2$

Passive lateral force $P_p = \dfrac{1}{2}(K_p p_p)z = \dfrac{1}{2}(K_p \gamma z)z = \dfrac{1}{2}K_p \gamma z^2$

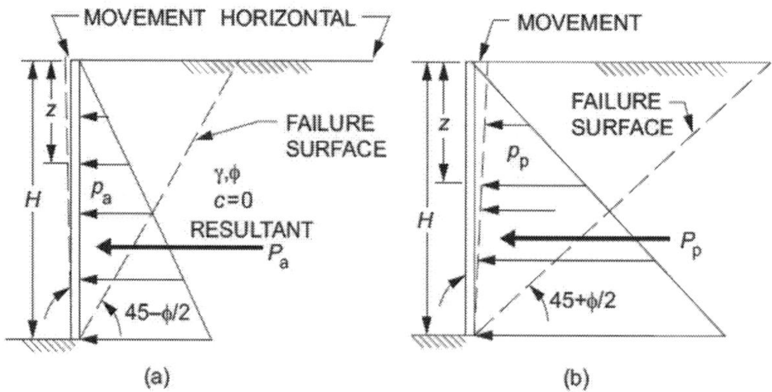

Figure. Failure Surfaces, Pressure Distribution and Forces: (a) Active case, (b) Passive case (the author believes that the angles shown in above figure from the PE Civil Handbook should be opposite. $45+\phi/2$ for active case and $45-\phi/2$ for passive case. See the previous figure for active case)

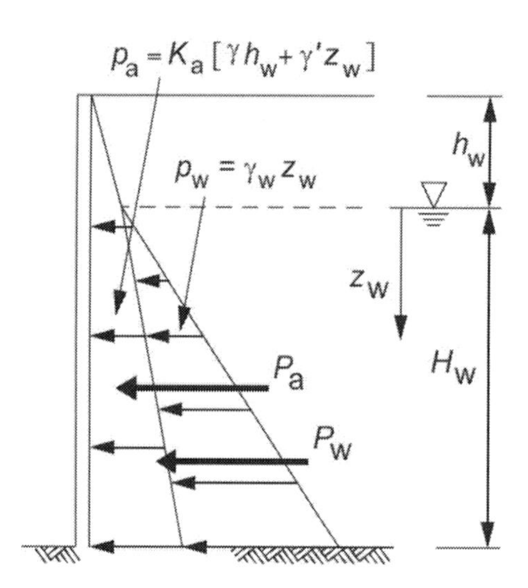

Figure. General Distribution of Combined Active Earth Pressure and Water Pressure

where

h_w = depth to water level from ground surface
z_w = depth below groundwater level
H_w = height of water below base of wall
γ = unit weight of soil
γ' = effective unit weight of soil
p_w = water pressure
P_a = lateral force from active pressure
P_p = lateral force from passive pressure

Example 3.1

Figure below shows a 20-ft-high retaining wall. The wall is at active pressure condition. A building is proposed at X distance from the face of the wall as shown. Determine the minimum distance (X) from the face of the wall to avoid the soil failure.

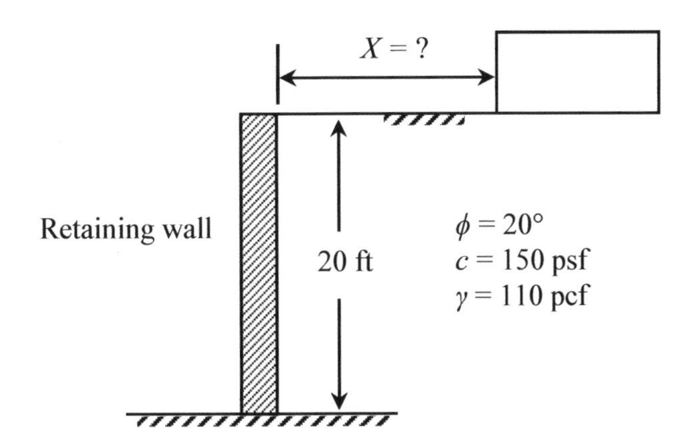

Solution:

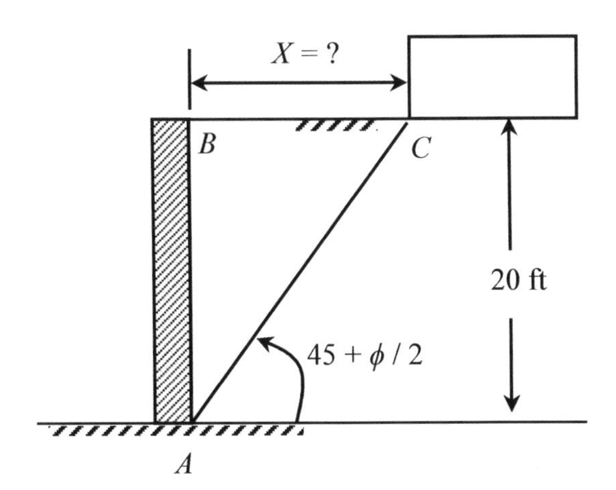

$45 + \phi / 2 = 45° + 20° / 2 = 55°$

From the figure above: <BAC = 90° – 55° = 35°

Now, $\tan 35 = \dfrac{X}{20\text{ ft}}$

Therefore, X = 14.0 ft

Example 3.2

Which one of the following statements regarding lateral earth pressures is correct?

K_o = Coefficient of earth pressure at rest
K_A = Coefficient of active earth pressure
K_P = Coefficient of passive earth pressure

A. $K_o = K_A = K_P$
B. $K_o < K_A < K_P$
C. $K_o > K_A > K_P$
D. $K_o > K_A < K_P$

Solution:

Assume a value of effective friction angle, say, $\phi' = 30$

$K_o = 1 - \sin 30 = 0.50$

$$K_a = \frac{1 - \sin\phi'}{1 + \sin\phi'} = \frac{1 - \sin 30}{1 + \sin 30} = 0.333$$

$$K_p = \frac{1 + \sin\phi'}{1 - \sin\phi'} = \frac{1 + \sin 30}{1 - \sin 30} = 3.0$$

The correct answer is D.

Example 3.3

A 6 m high retaining wall is shown below. Determine:

a. Rankine active force per unit length of the wall and the location of the resultant
b. Rankine passive force per unit length of the wall and the location of the resultant

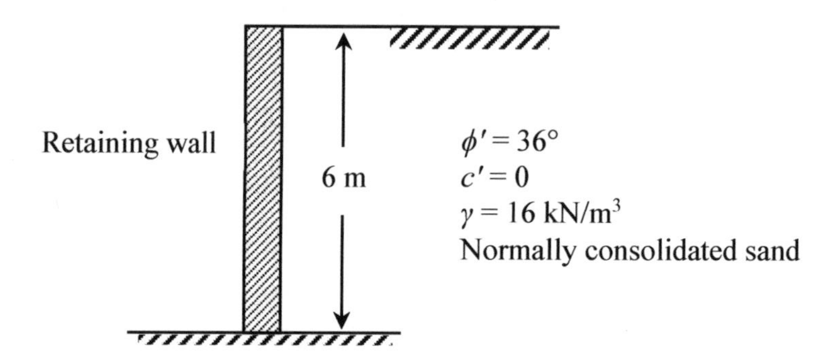

Solution:

Part a.

Rankine's active earth-pressure coefficient, $K_a = \frac{1 - \sin\phi'}{1 + \sin\phi'} = \frac{1 - \sin 36}{1 + \sin 36} = 0.26$

At depth, $z = 0$ (surface), the effective vertical pressure, $p_o' = \gamma' z = 0$

At depth, $z = 6$ m, the effective vertical pressure, $p_o' = \gamma' z = 16$ kN/m^3 (6 m) $= 96$ kN/m^2

Horizontal active pressure at the bottom $= K_a \times p_o' = 0.26 \times 96$ kN/m^2 $= 24.96$ kN/m^2

Active force per unit length of wall $= ½ \times 6$ m $\times 24.96$ kN/m$^2 = 74.88$ kN/m

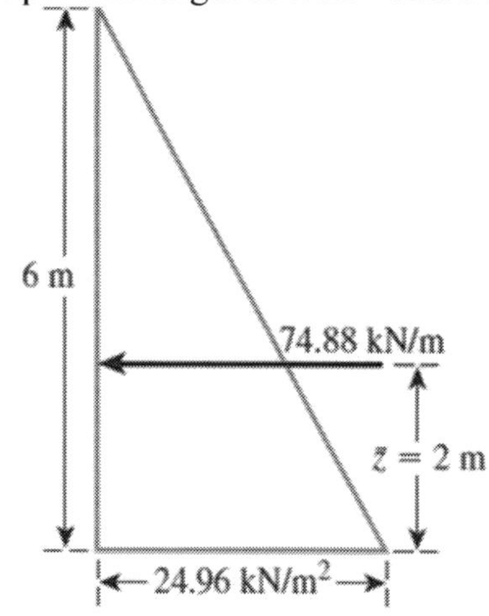

Part b.

Rankine's passive earth-pressure coefficient, $K_p = \dfrac{1+\sin\phi'}{1-\sin\phi'} = \dfrac{1+\sin 36}{1-\sin 36} = 3.85$

At depth, $z = 0$ (surface), the effective vertical pressure, $p_o' = \gamma' z = 0$

At depth, $z = 6$ m, the effective vertical pressure, $p_o' = \gamma' z$
$= 16\ \text{kN/m}^3\ (6\ \text{m}) = 96\ \text{kN/m}^2$

Horizontal passive pressure at the bottom $= K_p \times p_o'$
$= 3.85 \times 96\ \text{kN/m}^2$
$= 369.6\ \text{kN/m}^2$

Passive force per unit length of wall $= ½ \times 6\ \text{m} \times 369.6\ \text{kN/m}^2 = 1{,}108.8\ \text{kN/m}$

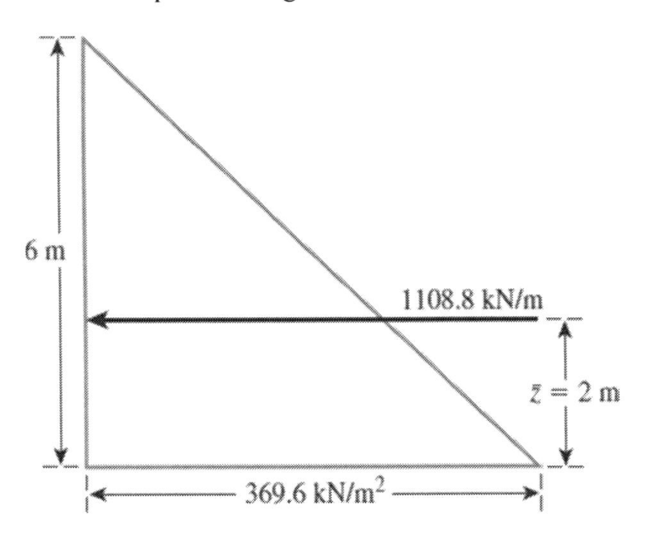

Example 3.4

Figure (a) below shows a 15-ft-high retaining wall. The wall is restrained from yielding. Calculate the lateral force per unit length of the wall. Also, determine the location of the resultant force. Assume that for sand, $OCR = 2$.

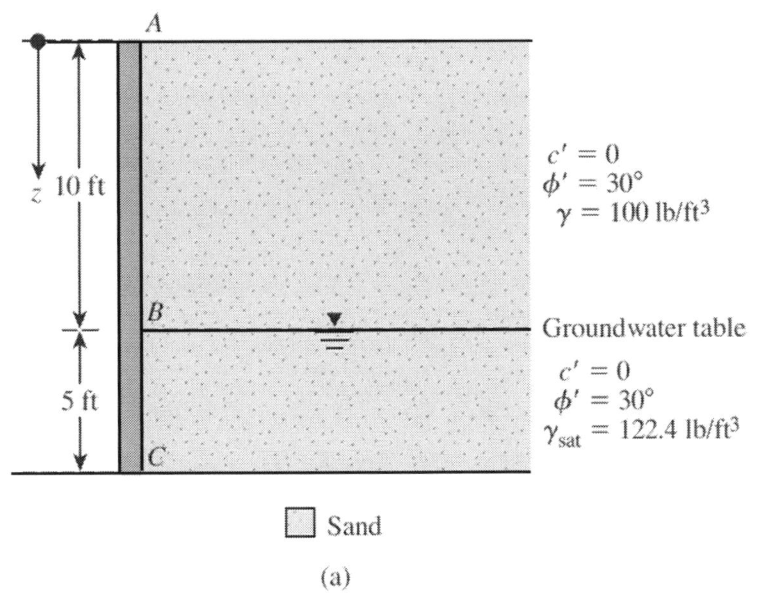

(a)

Ref: Das, B. Principles of Geotechnical Engineering, 7/e, Cengage.

Solution:

$$K_o = (1-\sin\phi')(OCR)^{\sin\phi'} = (1-\sin 30)(2.0)^{\sin 30} = 0.707$$

At depth z = 0, vertical effective pressure p_o' = horizontal pressure p_h' = pore-water pressure, u = 0

At depth z = 10 ft, vertical effective pressure $p_o' = \gamma' z$ = (100 pcf) (10 ft) = 1,000 psf

Horizontal pressure $p_h' = K_o\ p_o'$ = 0.707 x 1,000 psf = 707 psf
Pore-water pressure, u = 0

At depth z = 15 ft, vertical effective pressure $p_o' = \gamma' z$
= (100 pcf) (10 ft) + (122.4 – 62.4 pcf) x (5 ft) = 1,300 psf

Horizontal pressure, $p_h' = K_o\ p_o'$ = 0.707 x 1,300 psf = 919.1 psf
Pore-water pressure, $u = \gamma_w z_w$ = (62.4 pcf) (5 ft) = 312 psf

The effective pressure profile is shown in Figure (b) and the pre-water pressure profile is shown in Figure (c).

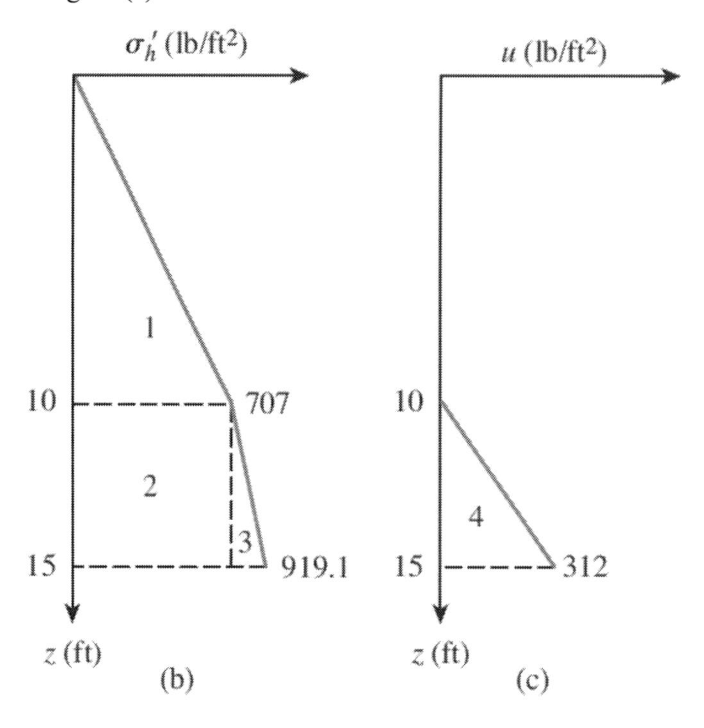

(b) (c)

Total horizontal force = Area 1 + Area 2 + Area 3 + Area 4
= ½ x 10 ft x 707 psf + 5 ft x 707 psf + ½ x 5 ft x (919.1 – 707 psf) + ½ x 5 ft x 312 psf
= 3,535 lb/ft + 3,535 lb/ft + 530.3 lb/ft + 780 lb/ft
= <u>8,380.3 lb/ft</u>

The location of the resultant can be found by taking the moment about the bottom of the wall.

$$z_{from\ bottom} = \frac{3{,}535\left(5+\frac{1}{3}\text{of } 10\,\text{ft}\right)+3{,}535\left(\frac{1}{2}\text{of } 5\,\text{ft}\right)+530.3\left(\frac{1}{3}\text{of } 5\,\text{ft}\right)+780\left(\frac{1}{3}\text{of } 5\,\text{ft}\right)}{8{,}380.3} = \underline{4.83\,\text{ft}}$$

Note: The NCEES exam will not ask to you to solve this type of entire problem. They will ask a part of it. If you understand the entire problem, you should be able to answer whatever they ask you.

Example 3.5

For the retaining wall shown below, determine the force per unit length of the wall for Rankine's active state. Also find the location of the resultant about the bottom of the wall.

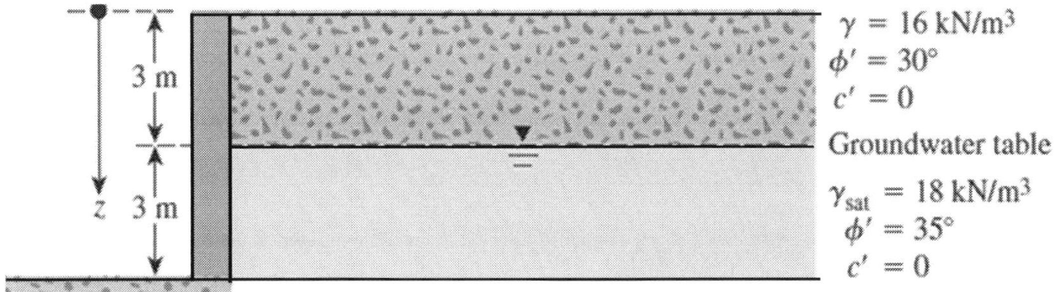

Ref: Das, B. Principles of Geotechnical Engineering, 7/e, Cengage.

Solution:

For the upper layer, $K_a = \dfrac{1-\sin\phi'}{1+\sin\phi'} = \dfrac{1-\sin 30}{1+\sin 30} = 0.333$

For the lower layer, $K_a = \dfrac{1-\sin\phi'}{1+\sin\phi'} = \dfrac{1-\sin 35}{1+\sin 35} = 0.271$

At depth, $z = 0$ (surface), the effective vertical pressure, $p_o' = \gamma' z = 0$

At depth, $z = 3$ m (bottom of upper layer), the effective vertical pressure, $p_o' = \gamma' z$

= 16 kN/m³ (3 m) = 48 kN/m²

Horizontal active pressure at the bottom of upper layer = K_a x p_o'

= 0.333 x 48 kN/m²

= 16 kN/m²

Horizontal active pressure at the top of lower layer ($z = 3$ m) = K_a x p_o'

= 0.271 x 48 kN/m²

= 13 kN/m²

At depth, $z = 6$ m (bottom of lower layer), the effective vertical pressure $p_o' = \gamma' z$

= 16 kN/m³ (3 m) + (18 – 9.81) kN/m³ (3 m)

= 72.57 kN/m²

At depth, $z = 6$ m (bottom of lower layer), horizontal active pressure = K_a p_o'

= 0.271 x 72.57 kN/m²

= 19.67 kN/m²

The water pressure starts from z = 3 m and increases with depth.

At depth, $z = 6$ m (bottom of lower layer), the water pressure = $\gamma_w H_w$

= 9.81 kN/m³ (6 m – 3 m)

= 29.43 kN/m²

At depth, $z = 6$ m (bottom of lower layer), total horizontal active pressure

= 19.67 + 29.43 = 49.1 kN/m²

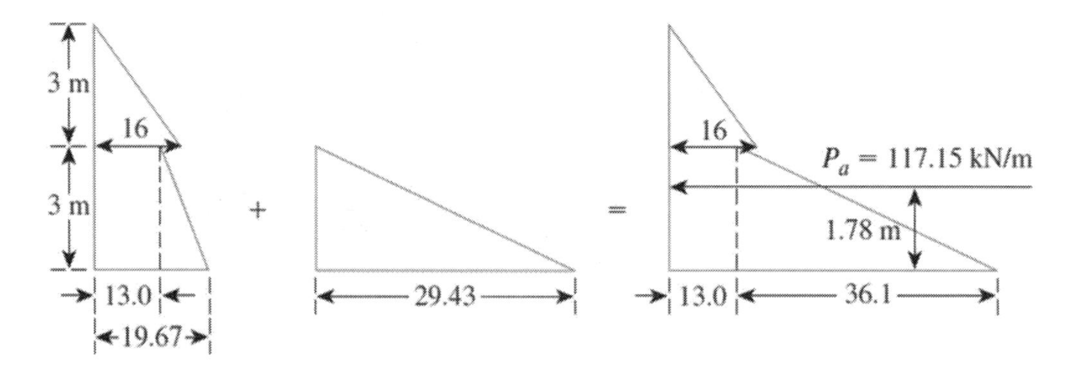

Total force = Area of pressure diagram

= ½ x 3 m x 16 kN/m^2 + 3 m x 13 kN/m^2 + ½ x 3 m x (49.1 – 13) kN/m^2

= 24 + 39 + 54.15

= 117.15 kN/m

The location of resultant can be found by taking moment about the bottom of wall.

$$z_{from\ bottom} = \frac{24\left(3+\frac{1}{3}\text{of } 3.0\,\text{m}\right)+39\left(\frac{1}{2}\text{of } 3.0\,\text{m}\right)+54.15\left(\frac{1}{3}\text{of } 3.0\,\text{m}\right)}{24+39+54.15} = \underline{1.78\,\text{m}}$$

Note: The NCEES exam will not ask to you to solve this type of entire problem. They will ask a part of it. If you understand the entire problem, you should be able to answer whatever NCEES asks you.

3.1.2.2 Rankine Active and Passive Coefficients (Friction and Cohesion)

Figure shows a frictionless retaining wall with a cohesive soil backfill. The active pressure against the wall at any depth below the ground surface can be expressed as:

$$p'_a = K_a(\gamma z - u) - 2c'\sqrt{K_a}$$

The passive pressure against the wall at any depth below the ground surface can be expressed as:

$$p'_p = K_p(\gamma z - u) + 2c'\sqrt{K_p}$$

$$K_a = \tan^2\left(45 - \frac{\phi'}{2}\right) - \frac{2c'}{p'_o}\tan^2\left(45 - \frac{\phi'}{2}\right)$$

$$K_p = \tan^2\left(45 + \frac{\phi'}{2}\right) + \frac{2c'}{p'_o}\tan^2\left(45 + \frac{\phi'}{2}\right)$$

(a) Wall Pressures for a Cohesionless Soil and (b) Wall Pressures for Soil with a Cohesion Intercept, with groundwater in both cases

Question 3.6
For the following retaining wall, the angle of wall friction between backfill and wall is negligible. The depth (ft) of tensile crack from the surface based on Rankine Active earth pressure theory is most nearly:

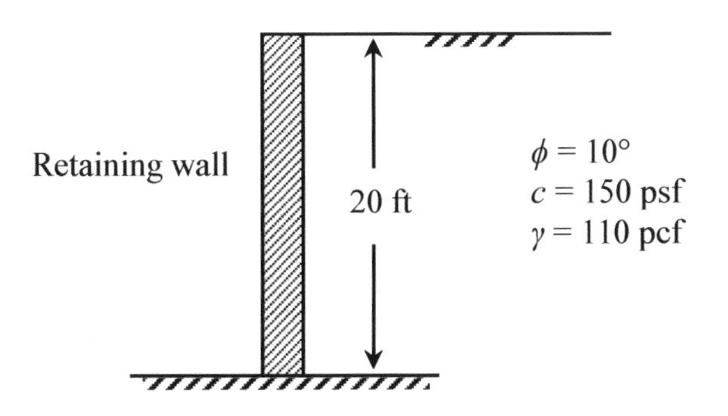

Solution:

$$p_a' = K_a(\gamma z - u) - 2c'\sqrt{K_a}$$

Tensile crack starts when the pressure converts from compression to tension, i.e., $p_a' = 0$

As there is no water, $u = 0$

$$K_a(\gamma z - u) = 2c'\sqrt{K_a}$$

$$z = \frac{2c'}{\gamma\sqrt{K_a}}$$

$$z = \frac{2c'}{\gamma \tan\left(45 - \frac{\phi}{2}\right)}$$

This is the depth, z to which tensile stress develops is known as the depth of tensile crack, because the tensile stress in the soil will eventually cause a crack along the soil–wall interface.

$$\frac{2c'}{\gamma \tan\left(45 - \frac{\phi}{2}\right)} = \frac{2(150\,\text{psf})}{(110\,\text{pcf})\tan\left(45 - \frac{10}{2}\right)} = \underline{3.25\,\text{ft}}$$

Example 3.7
A retaining wall that has a soft, saturated clay backfill is shown in Figure below. For the undrained condition ($\phi = 0$) of the backfill, based on Rankine Active earth pressure theory determine:

a. Maximum depth of the tensile crack
b. Lateral force before the tensile crack occurs
c. Lateral force after the tensile crack occurs

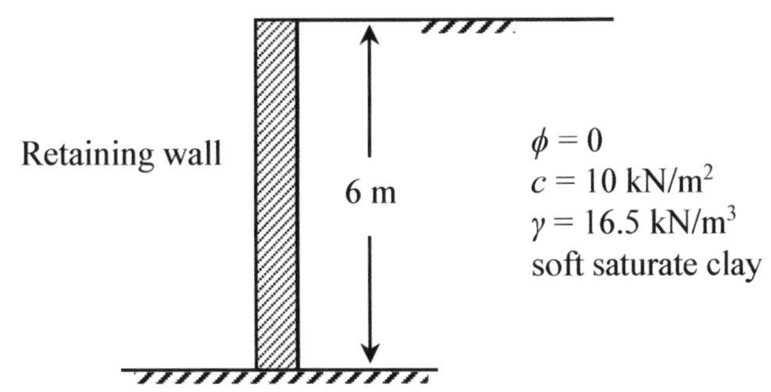

Solution:

Part a.

Rankine's active earth-pressure coefficient, $K_a = \frac{1-\sin\phi'}{1+\sin\phi'} = \frac{1-\sin 0}{1+\sin 0} = 1.0$

The active pressure against the wall, $p_a' = K_a(\gamma z - u) - 2c'\sqrt{K_a}$

$$= (1.0)(\gamma z - 0) - 2c'\sqrt{1.0}$$
$$= \gamma z - 2c'$$

At depth, z = 0, $p_a' = \gamma z - 2c' = 0 - 2\left(10\ \frac{\text{kN}}{\text{m}^2}\right) = -20\ \frac{\text{kN}}{\text{m}^2}$

At depth, z = 6 m, $p_a' = \gamma z - 2c' = \left(16.5\ \frac{\text{kN}}{\text{m}^3}\right)(6\ \text{m}) - 2\left(10\ \frac{\text{kN}}{\text{m}^2}\right) = 79\ \frac{\text{kN}}{\text{m}^2}$

The variation of p_a' with depth is shown in Figure below. The depth of tensile crack can be determined as: $\gamma z - 2c' = 0$

Or, $z = \frac{2c'}{\gamma} = \frac{2\left(10\ \frac{\text{kN}}{\text{m}^2}\right)}{16.5\ \frac{\text{kN}}{\text{m}^3}} = \underline{1.21\text{m}}$

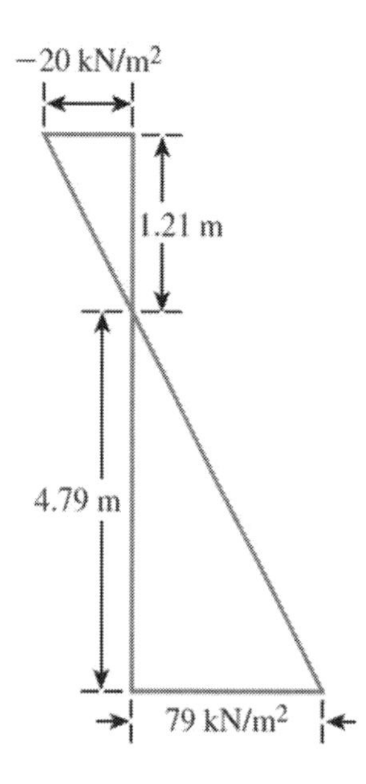

Part b.

Before tensile crack occurs, lateral force

$$P_a' = \frac{1}{2}p_a'z = \frac{1}{2}\left[K_a(\gamma z - u) - 2c'\sqrt{K_a}\right]z = \frac{1}{2}\gamma z^2 - 2c'z$$
$$= \frac{1}{2}\left(16.5\frac{\text{kN}}{\text{m}^3}\right)(6\ \text{m})^2 - 2\left(10\frac{\text{kN}}{\text{m}^2}\right)(6\ \text{m})$$
$$= \underline{177\frac{\text{kN}}{\text{m}}}$$

Part c.

After tensile crack occurs, the top 1.21 m will lose the contact.

Lateral force $P_a' = \frac{1}{2}p_a'z = \; = \frac{1}{2}\left(79\frac{\text{kN}}{\text{m}^2}\right)(6\ \text{m} - 1.21\ \text{m}) = \underline{189.2\frac{\text{kN}}{\text{m}}}$

3.1.3 Coulomb Earth Pressure

The Coulomb theory for determining lateral earth pressure, developed nearly a century before the Rankine theory, assumes that failure occurs in the form of a wedge and that friction occurs between wall and soil. The sides of the wedge are the earth side of the retaining wall and a failure plane that passes through the heel of the wall. Resultant active earth pressure acts on the wall at a point where a line through the wedge's center of gravity and parallel to the failure plane intersects the wall. Coulomb coefficients for sloping wall with wall friction and sloping cohesionless backfill are given below.

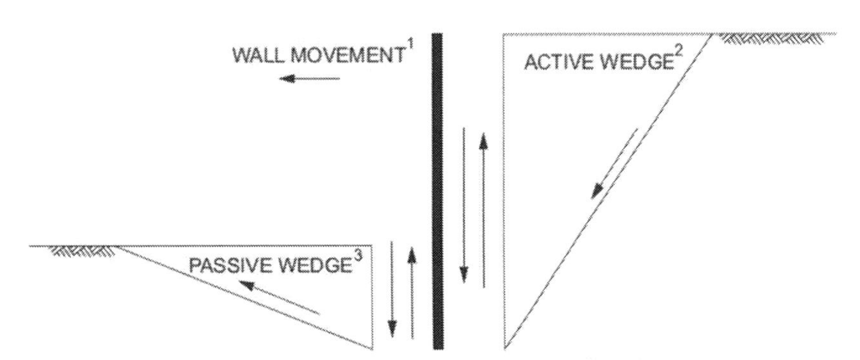

Figure. Wall Friction on Soil Wedges

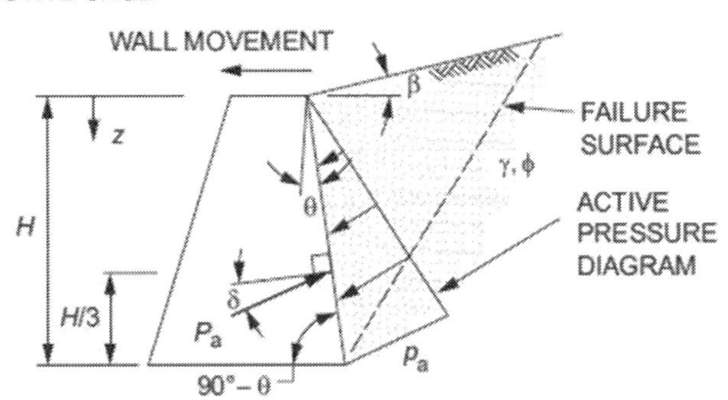

Coulomb active earth pressure coefficient, $K_a = \dfrac{\cos^2(\phi-\theta)}{\cos^2\theta\cos(\theta+\delta)\left[1+\sqrt{\dfrac{\sin(\phi+\delta)\sin(\phi-\beta)}{\cos(\theta+\delta)\cos(\theta-\beta)}}\right]^2}$

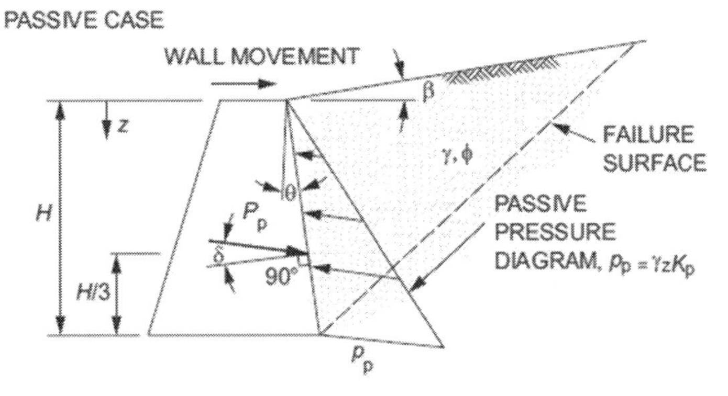

Coulomb passive earth pressure coefficient, $K_p = \dfrac{\cos^2(\theta+\phi)}{\cos^2\theta\cos(\theta-\delta)\left[1-\sqrt{\dfrac{\sin(\phi+\delta)\sin(\phi+\beta)}{\cos(\theta-\delta)\cos(\theta-\beta)}}\right]^2}$

ϕ = friction angle of soil
δ = friction between wall and soil
β = angle of backfill slope (β = 0° for horizontal surface)
θ = angle of wall face (θ = 0° for vertical wall)

Example 3.8
Given for the following sloping wall with wall friction and sloping cohesionless backfill, $\beta = 10°$; $\theta = 5°$; $H = 4$ m; unit weight of soil, $\gamma = 15$ kN/m^3; soil friction angle, $\phi' = 30°$; and $\delta' = 15°$. Estimate the active force, per unit length of the wall following Coulomb theory. Also, state the direction and location of the resultant force.

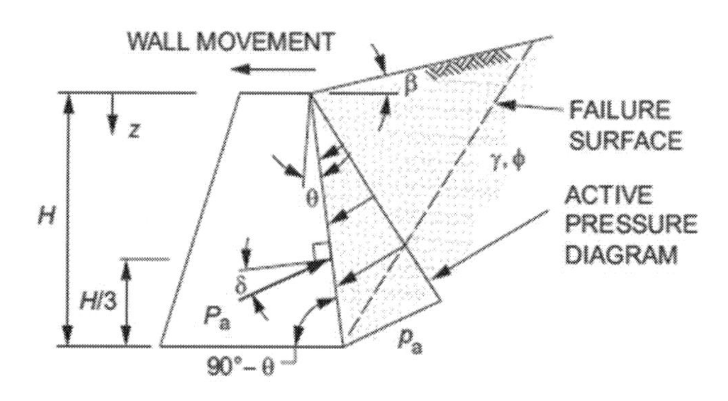

Solution:

$$K_a = \frac{\cos^2(\phi-\theta)}{\cos^2\theta\cos(\theta+\delta)\left[1+\sqrt{\dfrac{\sin(\phi+\delta)\sin(\phi-\beta)}{\cos(\theta+\delta)\cos(\theta-\beta)}}\right]^2}$$

$$= \frac{\cos^2(30-5)}{\cos^2 5\cos(5+15)\left[1+\sqrt{\dfrac{\sin(30+15)\sin(30-10)}{\cos(5+15)\cos(5-10)}}\right]^2}$$

$$= \frac{0.8214}{0.9326\times 2.2749}$$

$= 0.3872$

$P_a = \frac{1}{2}K_a\gamma z^2$ = ½ (0.3872) (15 kN/m^3) (4 m)^2 = 46.5 kN/m^3

The resultant will act at a vertical distance of 1/3 of 4 m = 1.33 m above the bottom of wall and will be inclined at an angle of $\delta' = 15°$ to the back face of the wall.

Example 3.9
For the following retaining wall, the angle of wall friction between backfill and wall is negligible. The active earth pressure per foot of wall (kN/m) by Coulomb theory is most nearly:

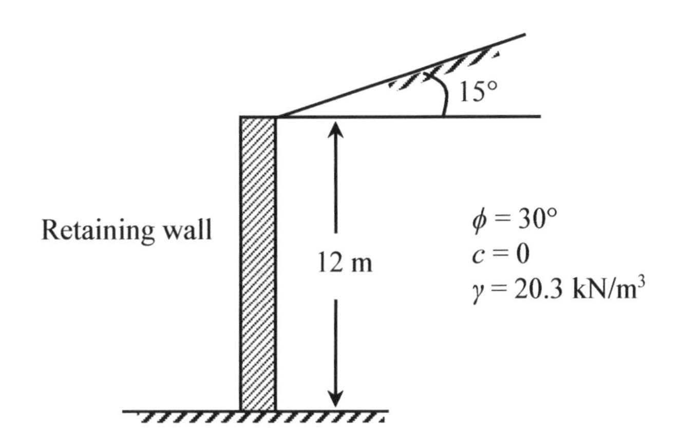

Solution:

ϕ = friction angle of soil = 30°
δ = friction between wall and soil = 0
β = angle of backfill slope = 15°
θ = angle of wall face (θ = 0° for vertical wall)

$$K_a = \frac{\cos^2(\phi-\theta)}{\cos^2\theta\cos(\theta+\delta)\left[1+\sqrt{\frac{\sin(\phi+\delta)\sin(\phi-\beta)}{\cos(\theta+\delta)\cos(\theta-\beta)}}\right]^2}$$

$$= \frac{\cos^2(30-0)}{\cos^2 0\cos(0+0)\left[1+\sqrt{\frac{\sin(30+0)\sin(30-15)}{\cos(0+0)\cos(0-15)}}\right]^2} = \frac{0.75}{1.0\times1.8660} = 0.40$$

$P_a = \frac{1}{2}K_a\gamma z^2$ = ½ (0.40) (20.3 kN/m³) (12.0 m)² = <u>585 kN/m³</u>

The other topics presented in the PE Civil Reference Handbook may be skipped for Breadth Exam.

3.2 Soil Consolidation

This topic is based on Article 3.2 of the PE Civil Handbook. A stress increase caused by the construction of foundations or other loads compresses soil layers. The compression is caused by (a) deformation of soil particles, (b) relocations of soil particles, and (c) expulsion of water or air from the void spaces. In general, the soil settlement caused by loads may be divided into three broad categories:

1. Immediate settlement (or Elastic settlement), which is caused by the elastic deformation of dry soil and of moist and saturated soils without any change in the moisture content. Elastic settlement calculations generally are based on equations derived from the theory of elasticity.
2. Primary consolidation settlement, which is the result of a volume change in saturated cohesive soils because of expulsion of the water that occupies the void spaces.
3. Secondary consolidation settlement, which is observed in saturated cohesive soils and is the result of the plastic adjustment of soil fabrics. It is an additional form of compression that occurs at constant effective stress.

Immediate settlement (or Elastic settlement) is discussed in the next section. Primary consolidation and secondary consolidation settlements are discussed here following the sequence of materials presented in the PE Civil Ref. Handbook. Soil Consolidation is the decrease in volume of soil through the expulsion of water under long term static loading. Soil Consolidation occurs when a stress is applied that causes the soil particles to pack closely together, therefore decreasing its volume. When Soil Consolidation occurs in saturated soil, water is squeezed out. The classical method of soil consolidation, developed by Karl von Terzaghi, uses an oedometer test to determine the soil's compression index.

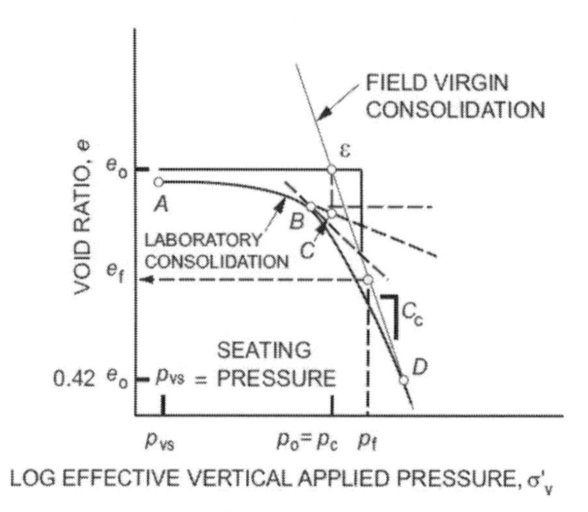

(a) NORMALLY CONSOLIDATED SOIL

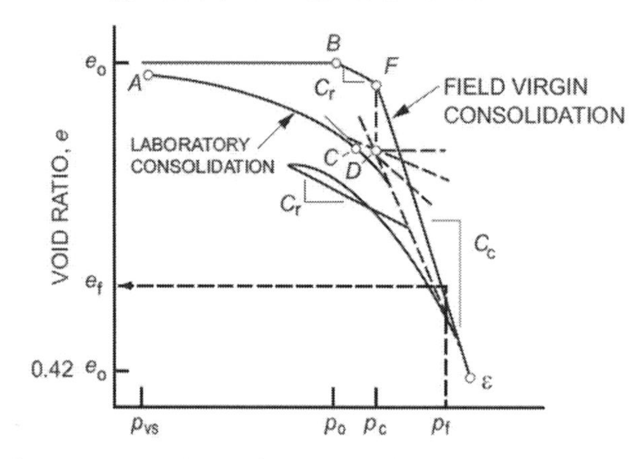

LOG EFFECTIVE VERTICAL APPLIED PRESSURE, σ'_v

(b) OVERCONSOLIDATED SOIL

Figure. Construction of Field Virgin Consolidation Relationships (adapted from USACE, 1994)

3.2.1 Normally Consolidated Soils

A soil that is currently experiencing its highest stress is said to be normally consolidated and. A soil could be considered underconsolidated or unconsolidated immediately after a new load is applied but before the excess pore water pressure has dissipated.

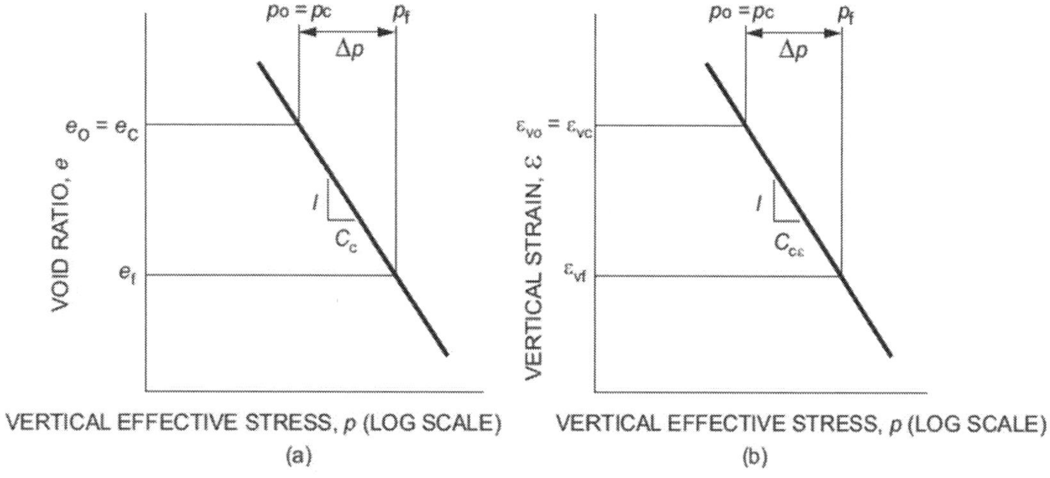

Figure. Typical Consolidation Curve for Normally Consolidated Soil:
(a) Void ratio versus vertical effective stress and
(b) Vertical strain versus vertical effective stress

$$\text{Consolidated settlement } S_C = \left(\frac{C_c}{1+e_o}\right) H_o \log_{10}\left(\frac{p_f}{p_o}\right)$$

$$S_C = \sum_1^n C_{c\varepsilon} H_o \log_{10}\left(\frac{p_f}{p_o}\right)$$

$$\text{Where, } C_{c\varepsilon} = \frac{C_c}{1+e_o}$$

Example 3.10

The 5 ft x 5 ft x 1 ft footing is located in a 32.5 ft (depth) normally consolidated clay layer. The clay layer has a density of 125 lb/ft^3, a compression index (C_c) of 0.27, and an initial void ratio (e_o) of 0.76. The pressure distribution ratio under the footing is 1:1. The applied load on the foundation is 150 kip.

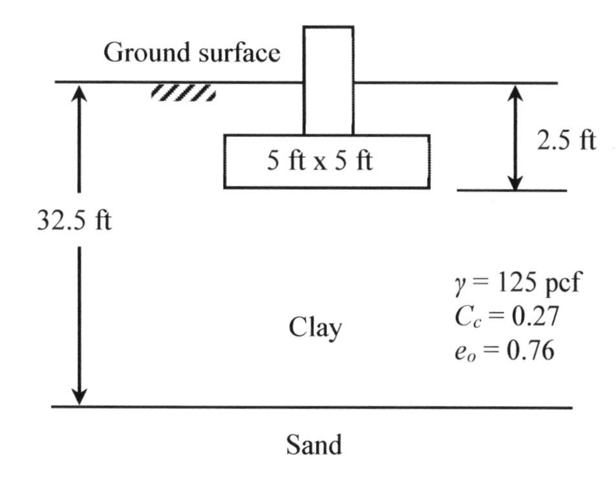

a) What is the effective vertical stress at the midpoint of the clay layer?
b) Calculate the increase in effective vertical stress at the midpoint of the clay layer due to the footing.
c) Determine the settlement (inch) due to consolidation caused by the footing.

Solution:

a. effective vertical pressure at midpoint, $p_o^{/} = \gamma' z$

$= 125\ \text{lb/ft}^3 \times (15\ \text{ft} + 2.5\ \text{ft}) = \underline{2{,}187.5\ \text{lb/ft}^2}$

b. The distributed load area at the midpoint = (15 ft + 5 ft + 15 ft)^2 = 1,225 ft^2

$\Delta p_{\text{midpoint}}$ = Load ÷ Area = 150,000 lb ÷ 1,225 ft^2 = $\underline{122\ \text{lb/ft}^2}$

c. Settlement $S_C = \left(\dfrac{C_c}{1+e_o}\right) H_o \log_{10}\left(\dfrac{p_f}{p_o}\right)$

$$= \left(\frac{0.27}{1+0.76}\right)(30\,\text{ft})\log\left(\frac{2{,}188\ \text{psf} + 122\ \text{psf}}{2{,}188\ \text{psf}}\right) = 0.11\ \text{ft} = \underline{1.3\text{in.}}$$

Note: The term 'H_o' represents the full depth of the clay layer. However, the effective stress and the increased stress are calculated at the mid depth of the layer. In addition, only clay layer gets the consolidation settlement – not the sand layer. Sand settles immediately.

3.2.2 Overconsolidated Soils

The soil which had its load removed is considered to be overconsolidated. This is the case for soils that have previously had glaciers on them. The highest stress that it has been subjected to is termed the preconsolidation stress.

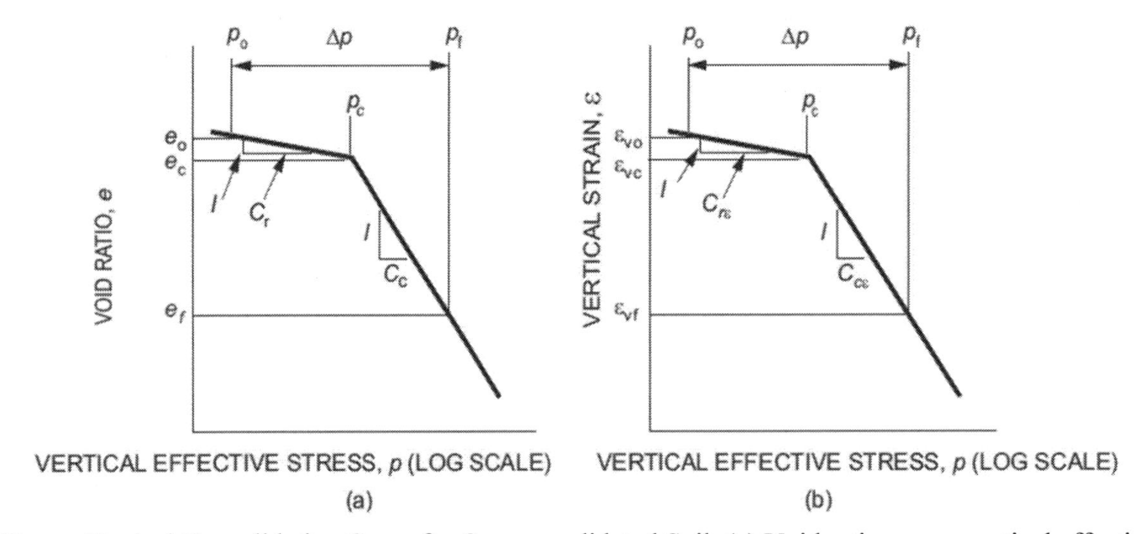

Figure. Typical Consolidation Curve for Overconsolidated Soil: (a) Void ratio versus vertical effective stress and (b) Vertical strain versus vertical effective stress

$$S = \sum_{1}^{n} \frac{H_o}{1+e_o}\left(C_r \log_{10}\frac{p_c}{p_o} + C_c \log_{10}\frac{p_f}{p_c}\right)$$

$$S = \sum_{1}^{n} H_o\left(C_{r\varepsilon} \log_{10}\frac{p_c}{p_o} + C_{c\varepsilon} \log_{10}\frac{p_f}{p_c}\right)$$

where

C_c = coefficient of consolidation (void ratio)
$C_{c\varepsilon}$ = coefficient of consolidation (strain)
C_r = coefficient of reconsolidation (void ratio)
$C_{r\varepsilon}$ = coefficient of reconsolidation (strain)

e_o = initial void ratio of clay soil
H_o = thickness of compressible layer
p_o = initial overburden pressure (= p_c for normally consolidated clay soils)
p_c = preconsolidation pressure
p_f = final overburden pressure = $p_o + \Delta p$
Δp = increase in effective stress

- If both p'_o and $p'_o + \Delta p$ are smaller than p_c, then settlement $S_C = \left(\frac{C_r}{1+e_o}\right) H_o \log_{10}\left(\frac{p_f}{p_o}\right)$
- If $p'_o + \Delta p > p_c > p'_o$, then settlement $S = \frac{H_o}{1+e_o}\left(C_r \log_{10}\frac{p_c}{p_o} + C_c \log_{10}\frac{p_f}{p_c}\right)$
- If both p'_o and $p'_o + \Delta p$ are greater than p_c, then settlement $S_C = \left(\frac{C_c}{1+e_o}\right) H_o \log_{10}\left(\frac{p_f}{p_o}\right)$

Example 3.11
A foundation is to be constructed at a site whose soil profile is shown below. The initial void ratio of the over-consolidated clay layer is 0.9. The compression index of the clay layer is 0.3 and the swell index is 0.05. The pressure increase due to the foundation is calculated to be 60 kPa at the mid-height of the clay layer.

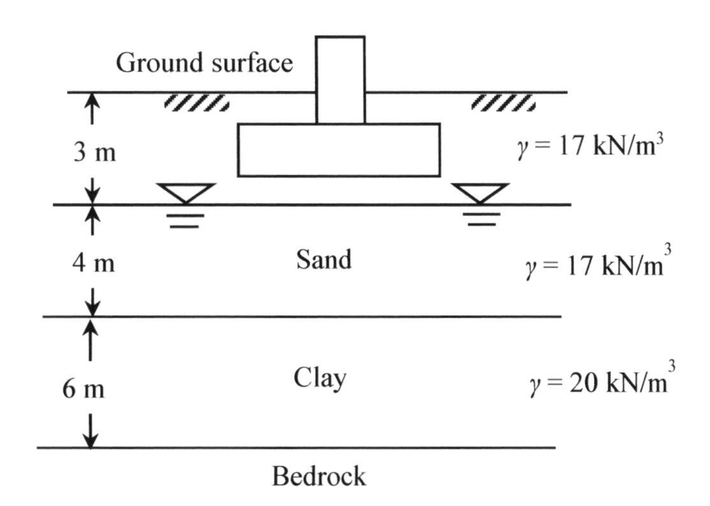

a) For the above soil, calculate the effective over-burden pressure at the mid-height of the clay layer.
b) Calculate the total effective pressure at the mid-height of the clay layer.
c) If the over-consolidated pressure of the clay layer is 130 kPa, calculate the primary consolidation settlement for the clay layer.
d) For the above problem, if the over-consolidation pressure is 100 kPa, calculate the primary consolidation settlement in cm for the clay layer.
e) For the above problem, if the over-consolidation pressure is 200 kPa, calculate the primary consolidation settlement (cm) for the clay layer.

Solution:

Part a. $p'_o = \left(17\,\frac{\text{kN}}{\text{m}^3}\right)(3\text{m}) + \left(17 - 9.81\,\frac{\text{kN}}{\text{m}^3}\right)(4\text{m}) + \left(20 - 9.81\,\frac{\text{kN}}{\text{m}^3}\right)(3\text{m}) = \underline{110.33\text{ kPa}}$

Part b. $p_f = p'_o + \Delta p = 110.33 + 60 = \underline{170.33 \text{ kPa}}$

Part c. $p_c = 130$ kPa

$p'_o + \Delta p > p_c > p'_o$

Consolidation settlement, $S = \sum_{1}^{n} \frac{H_o}{1+e_o}\left(C_r \log_{10} \frac{p_c}{p_o} + C_c \log_{10} \frac{p_f}{p_c} \right)$

$$= \left(\frac{6}{1+0.9}\right)\left((0.05)\log_{10}\left(\frac{130}{110.33}\right) + (0.3)\log_{10}\left(\frac{170.33}{130}\right)\right)$$

$$= 0.0112 \text{ m} + 0.111 \text{ m}$$

$$= \underline{12.2 \text{ cm}}$$

Part d.

$p_c = 100$ kPa

$p'_o > p_c$

$p'_o + \Delta p > p_c$

Both p'_o and $p'_o + \Delta p$ are greater than p_c. So, consolidation settlement,

$$S_C = \left(\frac{C_c}{1+e_o}\right) H_o \log_{10}\left(\frac{p_f}{p_o}\right)$$

$$= \left(\frac{0.3}{1+0.9}\right)(6.0 \text{ m}) \log_{10}\left(\frac{170.33 \text{ kPa}}{110.33 \text{ kPa}}\right) = 0.179 \text{ m} = \underline{17.9 \text{ cm}}$$

Part e.

$p_f = p'_o + \Delta p = 110.33 + 60 = 170.33$ kPa

$p_c = 200$ kPa

Both p'_o and $p'_o + \Delta p$ are smaller than p_c. So, consolidation settlement,

$$S_C = \left(\frac{C_r}{1+e_o}\right) H_o \log_{10}\left(\frac{p_f}{p_o}\right)$$

$$= \left(\frac{0.05}{1+0.9}\right)(6.0 \text{ m}) \log_{10}\left(\frac{170.33 \text{ kPa}}{110.33 \text{ kPa}}\right) = 0.03 \text{ m} = \underline{3 \text{ cm}}$$

Example 3.12

Figure below shows a proposed foundation site, with 10 ft of sand overlying 15 ft of clay with consolidation properties shown. The clay is normally consolidated.

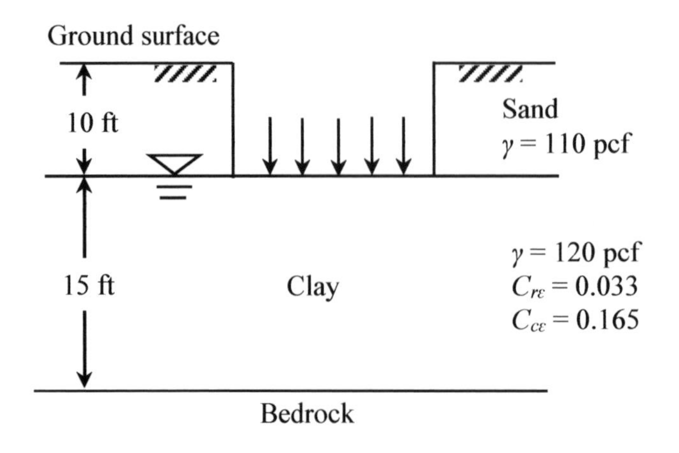

a) Compute the initial effective vertical stress at the middle of the clay layer prior to excavation and construction.
b) After excavation and during construction, the foundation area will be heavily loaded with the structure and equipment so that the effective vertical stress at the middle of the clay layer will be increased to 3,900 psf. Determine the settlement that will occur under these conditions.
c) After construction is completed, the equipment will be removed and the final effective vertical stress at the middle of the clay layer will be 3,200 psf. Determine the settlement that will occur under these conditions.

Solution:

Part a. $p_o' = \left(110\,\frac{\text{lb}}{\text{ft}^3}\right)(10\,\text{ft}) + \left(120 - 62.4\,\frac{\text{lb}}{\text{ft}^3}\right)(7.5\,\text{ft}) = \underline{1{,}532\text{ psf}}$

Part b. $p_f = 3{,}900$ psf

$$\text{As, } C_{c\varepsilon} = \frac{C_c}{1+e_o},\quad S_C = \sum_{1}^{n} C_{c\varepsilon} H_o \log_{10}\left(\frac{p_f}{p_o}\right)$$

$$= (1.65)(15\,\text{ft})\log_{10}\left(\frac{3{,}900\text{ psf}}{1{,}532\text{ psf}}\right)$$

$$= \underline{1.0\,\text{ft}}$$

Part c. p_f will be 3,200 psf and $p_o = 3{,}900$ psf

$$S_C = \sum_{1}^{n} C_{r\varepsilon} H_o \log_{10}\left(\frac{p_f}{p_o}\right)$$

$$= (0.033)(15\,\text{ft})\log_{10}\left(\frac{3{,}200\text{ psf}}{3{,}900\text{ psf}}\right)$$

$$= -0.0425\,\text{ft}$$

(-ve means it will swell by 0.0425 ft)
Final settlement = 1.0 ft – 0.0425 ft = <u>0.96 ft</u>

Example 3.13

Figure below shows a proposed site where an excavation will be made. The 10 ft layer of sand will be removed, so that the top of the 24 ft normally consolidated clay layer will be exposed. Assume full capillarity in the clay only. Assuming 1-D conditions, compute how much the clay layer will deform due to this excavation, in inches. Specify whether this is settlement or heave.

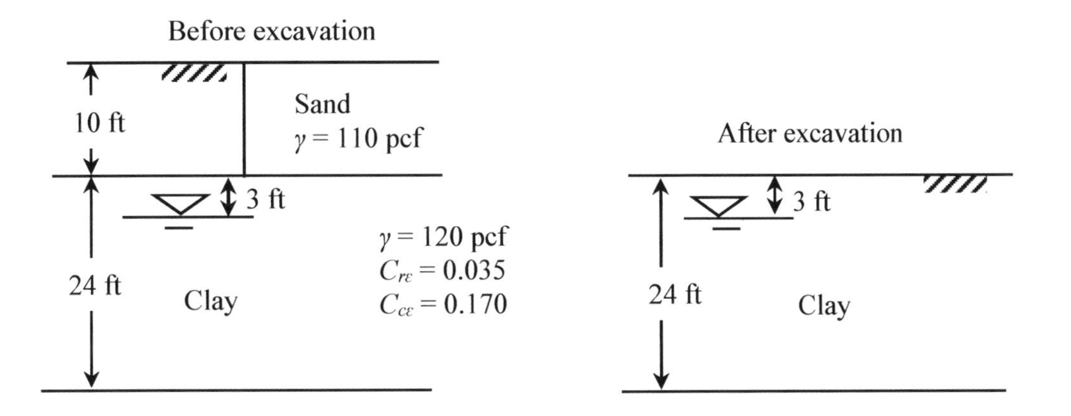

Solution:

Before excavation

$$p_o' = \left(110\ \frac{\text{lb}}{\text{ft}^3}\right)(10\,\text{ft}) + \left(120\ \frac{\text{lb}}{\text{ft}^3}\right)(3\,\text{ft}) + \left(120 - 62.4\frac{\text{lb}}{\text{ft}^3}\right)(9.0\,\text{ft}) = 1{,}978\ \text{psf}$$

After excavation

$$p_o' = \left(120\ \frac{\text{lb}}{\text{ft}^3}\right)(3\,\text{ft}) + \left(120 - 62.4\frac{\text{lb}}{\text{ft}^3}\right)(9.0\,\text{ft}) = 878\ \text{psf}$$

$$S_C = \sum_1^n C_{r\varepsilon} H_o \log_{10}\left(\frac{p_f}{p_o}\right) = (0.035)(24\,\text{ft})\log_{10}\left(\frac{878}{1{,}978}\right) = -0.2963\,\text{ft} = \underline{3.6\text{in.}}$$

(-ve means it will swell by 3.6 in.)

3.2.3 Time Rate of Settlement

In addition to knowing the amount of settlement, it is also important to know the time rate of settlement. For a stratum of clay soil, the time rate of settlement depends in part on a number of factors including but not limited to the soil's compression properties, *in situ* void ratio, and permeability. The effect of all such factors may be combined into one parameter called the *coefficient of consolidation* (c_v). The coefficient of consolidation indicates how rapidly (or slowly) the process of consolidation takes place.

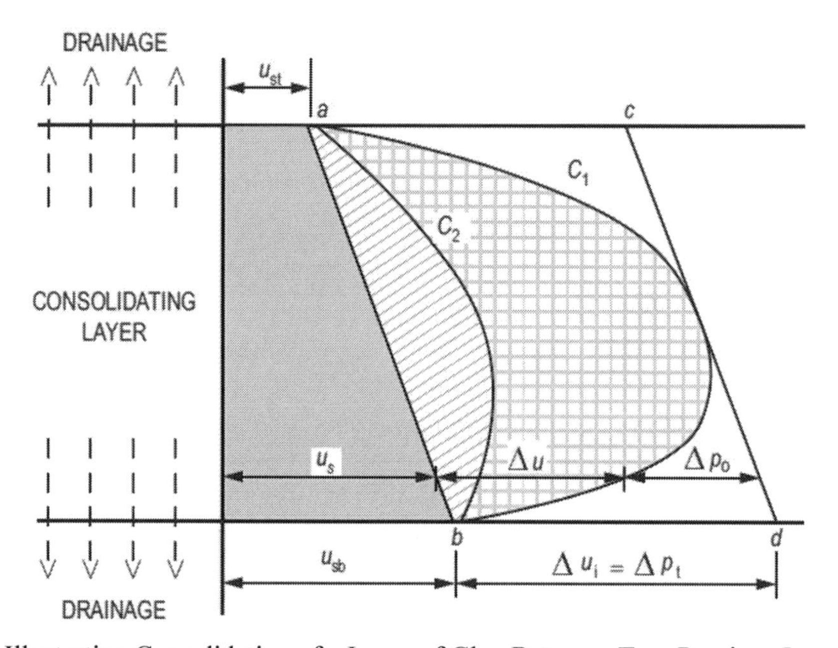

Figure. Diagram Illustrating Consolidation of a Layer of Clay Between Two Pervious Layers (modified, after Terzaghi et alia, 1996)

where

C_1 = excess pore water pressure profile at time 1
C_2 = excess pore water pressure profile at time 2
u_{st} = hydrostatic pore water pressure at top of layer
u_{sb} = hydrostatic pore water pressure at bottom of layer
u_s = hydrostatic pore water pressure at any depth
Δu_i = initial excess pore water pressure
Δu = excess pore water pressure at any depth after time t

$u_t = u_s + \Delta u$ = total pore water pressure at any depth after time t

The time rate of settlement due to primary consolidation can be computed using, $T_v = \dfrac{c_v t}{(H_d)^2}$

$$\text{Or, } t = \frac{T_v (H_d)^2}{c_v}$$

c_v = coefficient of consolidation
H_d = longest distance to drainage boundary [if the clay layer in situ is drained on both top and bottom, half the thickness of the layer should be substituted]
t = time to reach a particular percent of consolidation; percent of consolidation is defined as the ratio of the amount of settlement at a certain time during the process of consolidation to the total settlement due to consolidation
T_v = time factor, a coefficient depending on the particular percent of consolidation

Table. Average Degree of Consolidation, U, Versus Time Factor, T_v, for Uniform Initial Increase in Pore Water Pressure

***U* %**	***T*v**	***U*%**	***T*v**
0	0	80	0.567
10	0.008	90	0.848
20	0.031	93.1	1.0
30	0.071	95.0	1.163
40	0.126	98.0	1.50
50	0.197	99.4	2.0
60	0.287	100	infinite
70	0.403		

Example 3.14
Using the data below, how long will it take for 85% consolidation if the consolidation coefficient (c_v) is 0.20 ft^2/day for a 30-ft clay underlain by an impervious rock?

% Consolidation	T_v
80	0.63
90	0.95

Solution:

From the Percent Consolidation chart, for 85% Consolidation, $T_v = 0.79$
H_d = 30 ft (one way drainage for having underlain by an impervious rock)
c_v = 0.20 ft^2/day

$$t = \frac{T_v (H_d)^2}{c_v}$$

t = (0.79) (30 ft)^2 ÷ 0.20 ft^2/day = 3,555 day

3.2.4 Consolidation Testing

Consolidation test consists of applying the pressure on a thin soil specimen in increments and keeping each pressure increment (Δp) for sufficient time until the consolidation of the soil specimen and measurement of the vertical deformation or void ratio (e) of the soil specimen due to expulsion of pore water. This topic is not specified in the PE Civil Exam Specification. However, it may be worthy to practice. Article 3.8 of the PE Civil Handbook also presented some testing methods for consolidation.

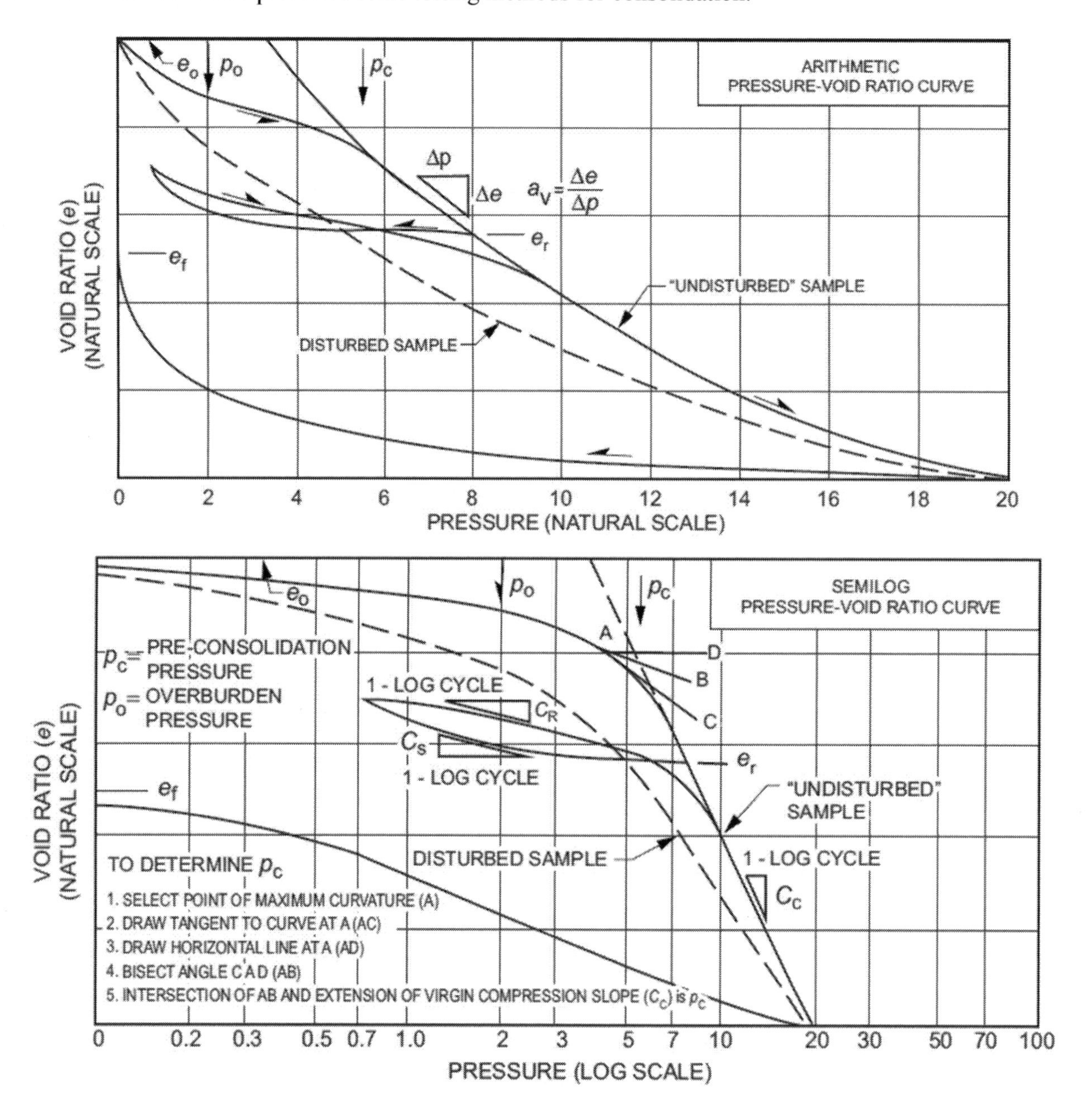

Example 3.15

The following are the results of a laboratory consolidation test:

Pressure (ton/ft²)	Void ratio	Remarks	Pressure (ton/ft²)	Void ratio	Remarks
0.25	1.03	Loading	8.0	0.71	Loading
0.5	1.02		16.0	0.62	
1.0	0.98		8.0	0.635	Unloading
2.0	0.91		4.0	0.655	
4.0	0.79		2.0	0.67	

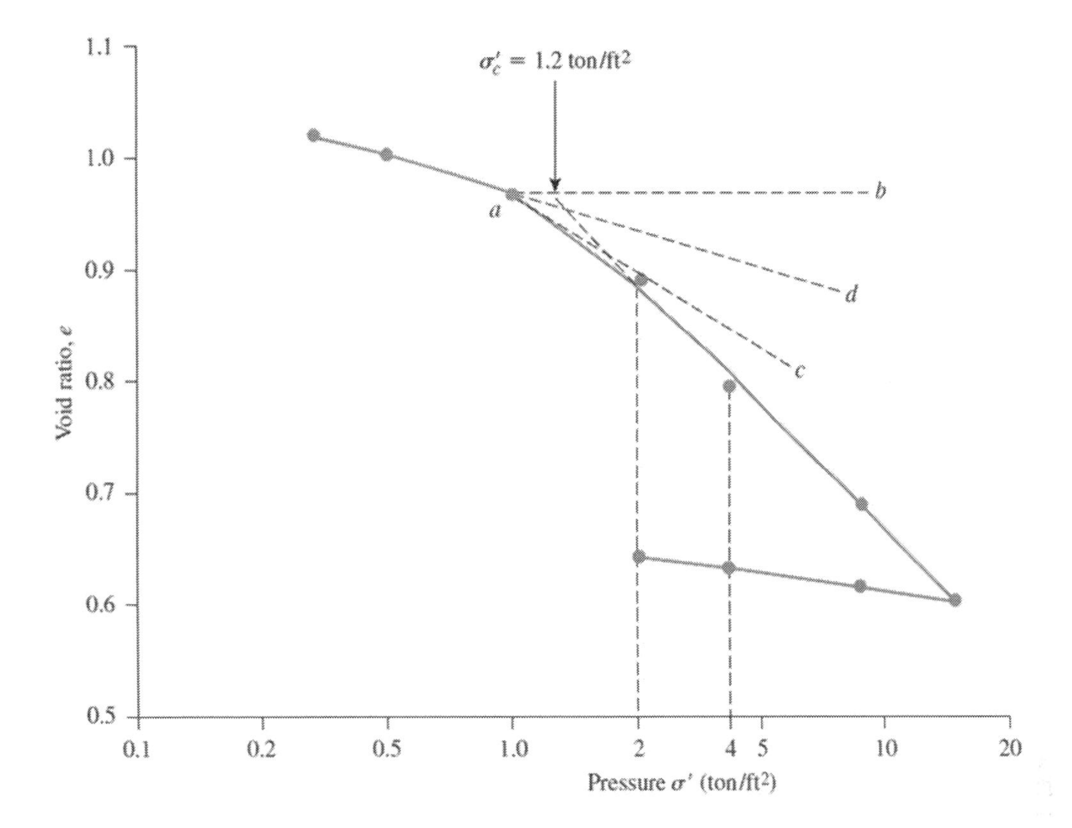

a. Calculate the average compression index and the recompression index

b. On the basis of the average *e*-log*p* plot, calculate the void ratio at 12 ton/ft^2 during loading

Solution:

Part a.

From the loading branch, considering two far points to make it average say 2 tsf to 16 tsf,

$$\text{compression index, } C_c = \frac{e_1 - e_2}{\log\left(\frac{p_2}{p_1}\right)} = \frac{0.91 - 0.62}{\log\left(\frac{16.0 \text{ tsf}}{2.0 \text{ tsf}}\right)} = \underline{0.32}$$

From the unloading branch, considering any two far points to make it average say 8 tsf to 2 tsf, compression index,

$$C_r = \frac{e_1 - e_2}{\log\left(\frac{p_2}{p_1}\right)} = \frac{0.67 - 0.635}{\log\left(\frac{8.0 \text{ tsf}}{2.0 \text{ tsf}}\right)} \approx \underline{0.06}$$

Part b.

Consider, e_1 as 0.91 for 2 tsf, then for 12 tsf:

$$C_c = \frac{e_1 - e_3}{\log\left(\frac{p_2}{p_1}\right)}$$

$$0.32 = \frac{0.91 - e_3}{\log\left(\frac{12.0 \text{ tsf}}{2.0 \text{ tsf}}\right)}$$

$e_3 = \underline{0.66}$

The *coefficient of consolidation* (c_v) can be calculated in different ways. For example, using the time to 50% of primary consolidation, the following equation can be used.

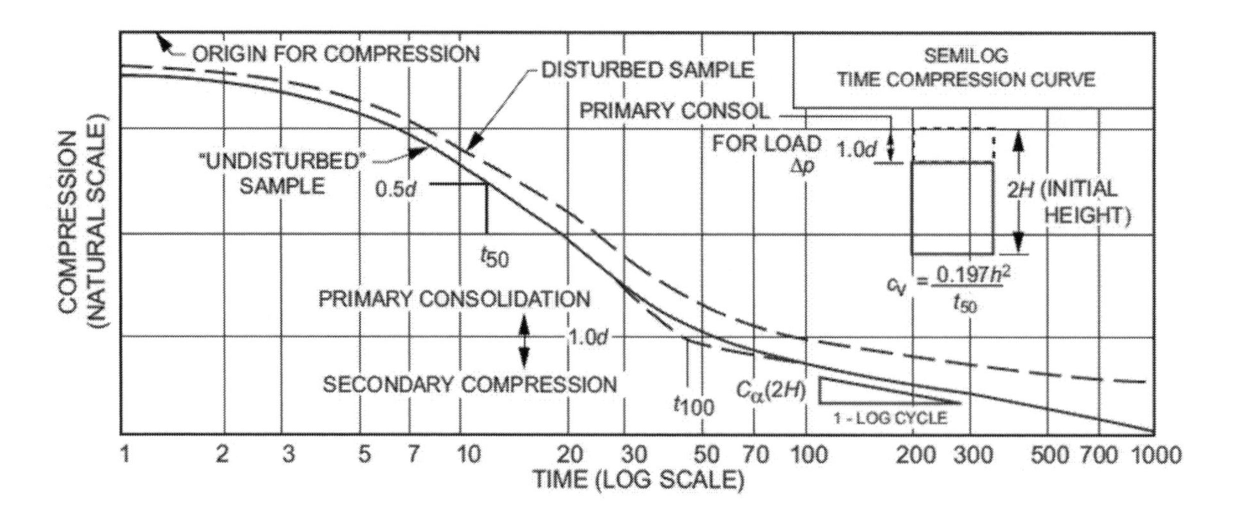

Figure. Consolidation Test Relationships (after NAVFAC, 1986a)

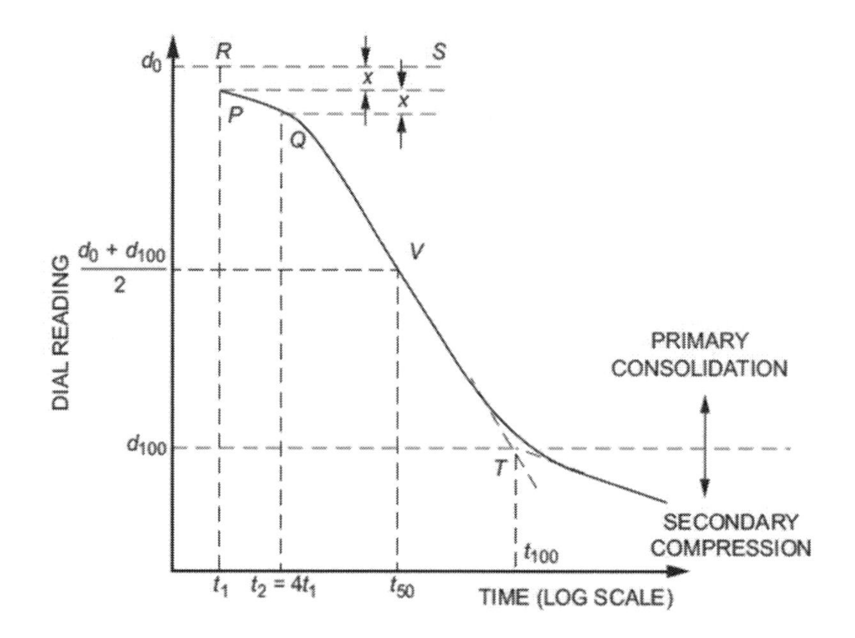

$$c_v = \frac{0.197 H_d^2}{t_{50}}$$

where

c_v = coefficient of vertical consolidation
H_d = thickness of compressible layer
t_{50} = time to 50% of primary consolidation

Example 3.16
During a laboratory consolidation test, the time and dial gauge readings obtained from an increase of pressure on the specimen from 50 kN/m^2 to 100 kN/m^2 are plotted below.

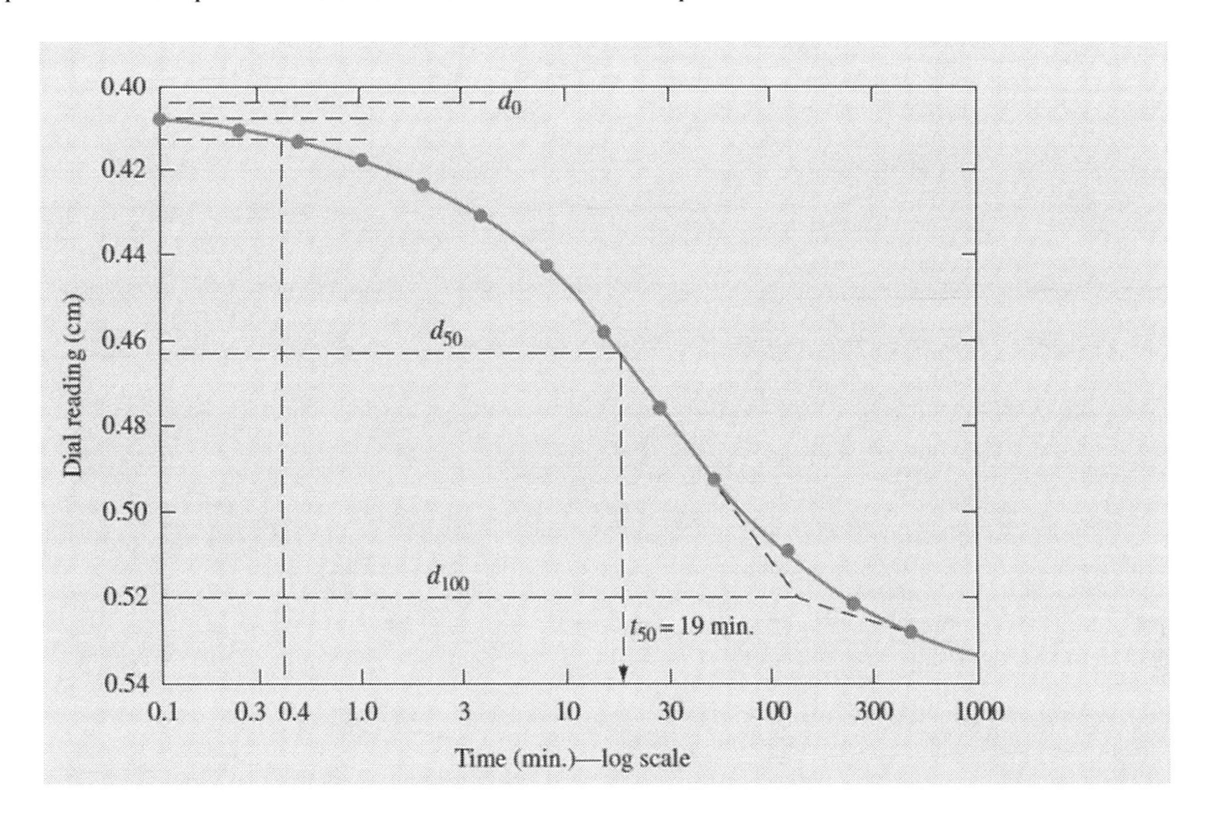

Using the logarithm-of-time method, determine c_v. The average height of the specimen during consolidation was 2.24 cm, and it was drained at the top and bottom.

Solution:

From the curve, t_{50} = 19 min.

$$c_v = \frac{0.197 H_d^2}{t_{50}}$$

Because the clay layer has two-way drainage, H_d = 2.24 /2 cm = 1.12 cm

$$c_v = \frac{0.197(1.12\text{cm})^2}{19\text{ min}} = 0.013\frac{\text{cm}^2}{\text{sec}}$$

Using the time required to 90% of primary consolidation, the following equation can be used to calculate the *coefficient of consolidation* (c_v).

$$c_v = \frac{0.848 H_d^2}{t_{90}}$$

where

c_v = coefficient of vertical consolidation
H_d = thickness of compressible layer
t_{90} = time to 90% of primary consolidation

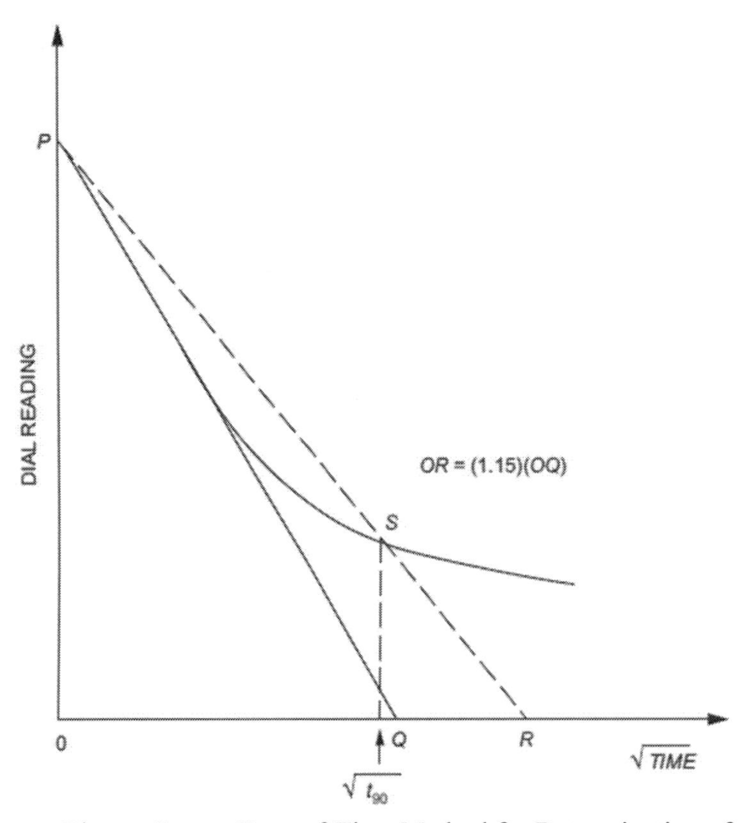

Figure. Square-Root-of-Time Method for Determination of *c*v

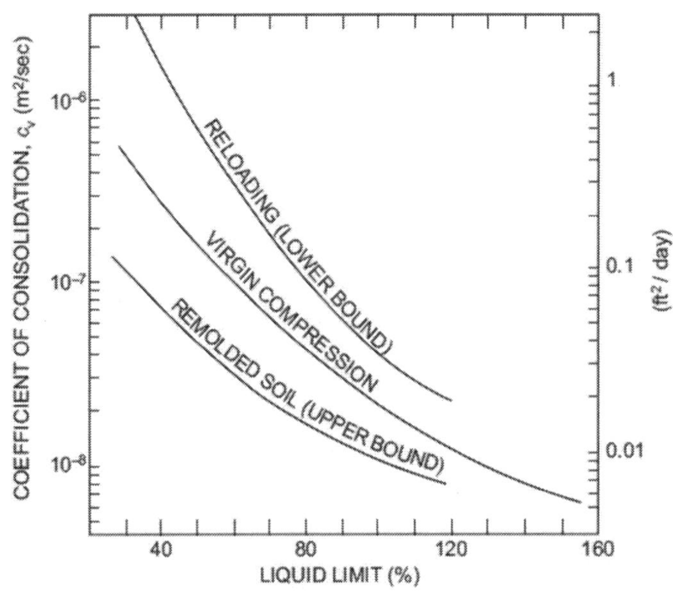

Figure. Approximate Correlations Between c_v and LL (NAVFAC, 1986a). Sometimes, instead of giving The *coefficient of consolidation* (c_v) the problem may give you liquid limit and soil type with which you can find the *coefficient of consolidation* (c_v). It also shows that the *coefficient of consolidation* (c_v) decreases with increase in liquid limit.

Example 3.17
A 3-m-thick layer (double drainage) of saturated clay under a surcharge loading underwent 90% primary consolidation in 75 days. Find the coefficient of consolidation (cm^2/sec) of clay for the pressure range.

Solution:

$$c_v = \frac{0.848 H_d^2}{t_{90}}$$

Because the clay layer has two-way drainage, H_d = 3 /2 m = 1.5 m = 1.5 x 100 cm

$$c_v = \frac{0.848(1.5 \times 100\ \text{cm})^2}{75 \times 24 \times 60 \times 60\ \text{sec}} = \underline{0.00294 \frac{\text{cm}^2}{\text{sec}}}$$

Example 3.18
Which of the following statements is FALSE for consolidation of soil?

A. For specimens drained at both top and bottom, H_d equals one-half the average height of the specimen during consolidation.
B. Compressive deformation generally results from reduction in soil's solid volume accompanied by rearrangement of soil grains.
A. For specimens drained on only one side, H_d equals the average height of the specimen during consolidation.
B. Soil with higher liquid limit takes longer time for consolidation

Solution:

Option B is not accurate. Compressive deformation generally results from reduction in void volume, accompanied by rearrangement of soil grains and compression of the material in the voids.

3.2.5 Secondary Consolidation

After primary consolidation has ended (i.e., all water has been extruded from the voids in a fine-grained soil) and all primary consolidation settlement has occurred, soil compression (and additional associated settlement) continues very slowly at a decreasing rate. This phenomenon is known as secondary compression and perhaps results from plastic readjustment of soil grains due to new stresses in the soil and progressive breaking of clayey particles and their interparticle bonds. Coefficient of secondary consolidation can be presented as:

$$C_{\alpha\varepsilon} = \frac{\Delta\varepsilon}{\Delta(\log t)}$$

$$C_{\alpha e} = \frac{\Delta e}{\Delta(\log t)}$$

$$C_{\alpha\varepsilon} = \frac{C_{\alpha e}}{1+e_o}$$

$C_{\alpha\varepsilon}$ = coefficient of secondary consolidation (strain)
$C_{\alpha e}$ = coefficient of secondary consolidation (void ratio)
e_o = initial void ratio
t = time

Then, the secondary consolidation, $S_s = (\Delta\varepsilon \text{ or } \Delta e) H$

Example 3.19
A foundation is to be built on a sand deposit underlain by a highly compressible clay layer 5.0 m thick. The clay layer's natural water content is 80%. Primary consolidation is estimated to be complete in 10 yr. Coefficient of secondary consolidation (strain) is 0.015. Calculate the secondary compression settlement expected to occur from 10 to 70 year after construction of the foundation.

Solution:

$$C_{\alpha\varepsilon} = \frac{\Delta\varepsilon}{\Delta(\log t)}$$

$$\Delta\varepsilon = C_{\alpha\varepsilon}\Delta(\log t) = (0.015)\log\left(\frac{70\,\text{year}}{10\,\text{year}}\right) = 0.0127$$

Secondary consolidation, $S_s = (\Delta\varepsilon \text{ or } \Delta e)H$ = 0.0127 (5.0 m) = 0.064 m = <u>64 mm</u>

3.3 Effective and Total Stresses

This topic is based on Article 3.3 of the PE Civil Handbook. Effective stress is the force carried by the solids in soil and is the force that keeps sand, soil, or gravel rigid.

3.3.1 Shear Strength Effective Stress

This topic has been covered in Chapter 7.

3.3.2 Undrained Shear Strength of Clays

Relationship between the ratio of undrained shear strength to effective overburden pressure and plasticity index for normally consolidated and overconsolidated clays is shown below. The author does not believe that this topic is very important for the Breadth exam. You may have a look at it.

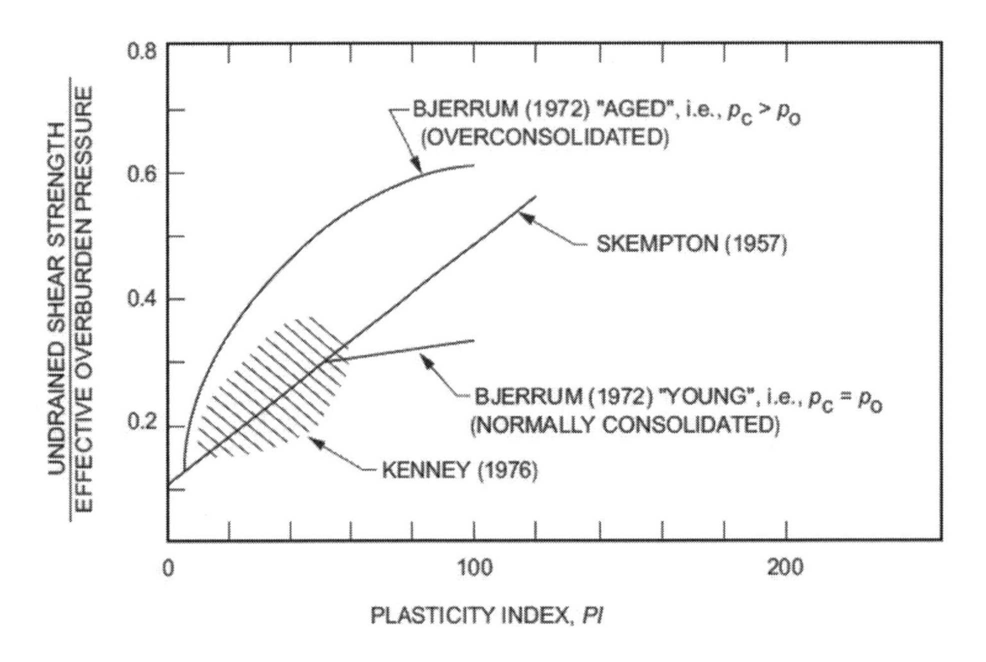

3.3.4 Drained Shear Strength of Clays

The drained shear strength is the shear strength of the soil when pore fluid pressures, generated during the course of shearing the soil, are able to dissipate during shearing. It also applies where no pore water exists in the soil (the soil is dry) and hence pore fluid pressures are negligible. Relationship Between ϕ' and PI (after Terzaghi et alia, 1996) is shown below. The author does not believe that this topic is very important for the Breadth exam. You may have a look at it.

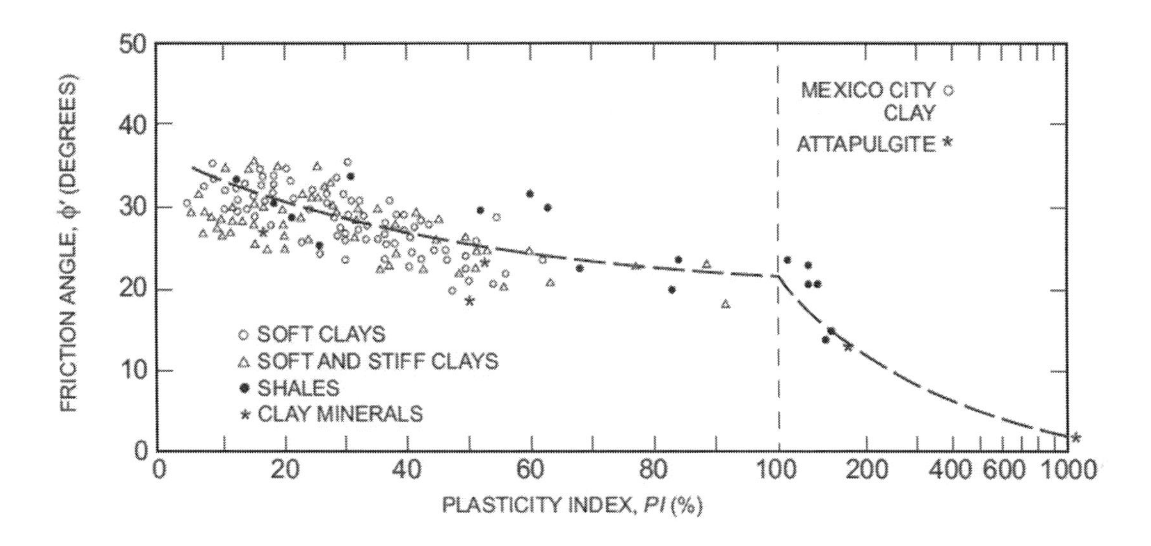

3.4 Bearing Capacity

This topic is based on Article 3.4 of the PE Civil Handbook. Bearing Capacity is a measure of a soil's ability to support applied loads. A soil's bearing capacity is the maximum average contact pressure between the foundation and the soil which should not allow a shear failure.

3.4.1 Bearing Capacity Theory

The basic principles governing bearing capacity theory as developed by Terzaghi can be better followed by referring to Figure below. As load is applied, the footing undergoes a certain amount of settlement as it is pushed downward, and a wedge of soil directly below the footing's base moves downward with the footing. The soil's downward movement is resisted by shear resistance of the foundation soil along slip surfaces and by the weight of the soil in sliding wedges. For each set of assumed slip surfaces, the corresponding load that would cause failure can be determined.

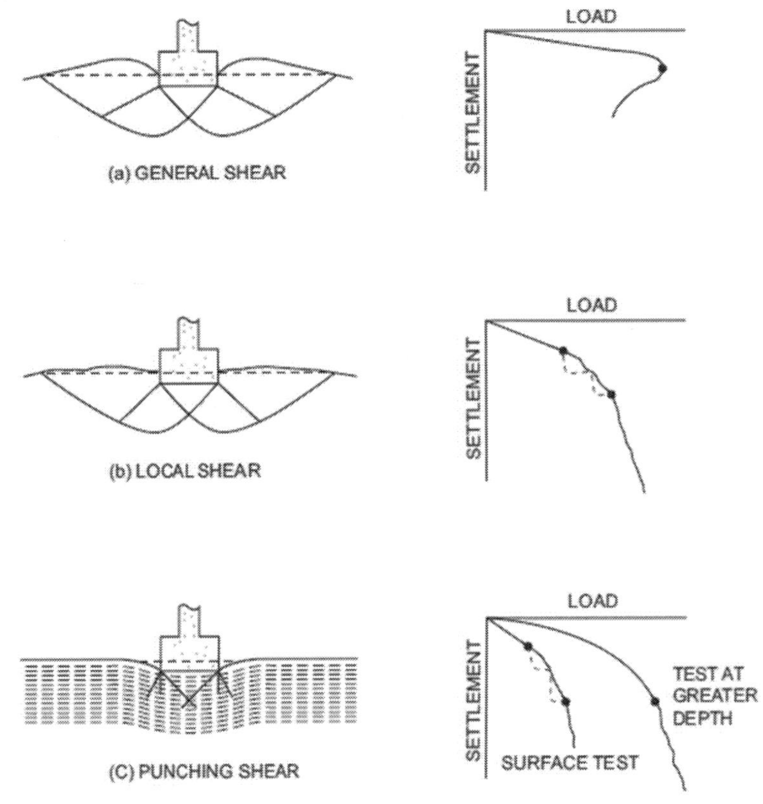

Figure. Modes of Bearing Capacity Failure: (a) General shear (b) Local shear (c) Punching shear

Bearing capacity refers to the ability of a soil to support or hold up a foundation and structure. The *ultimate bearing capacity* of a soil refers to the loading per unit area that will just cause shear failure in the soil. It is given the symbol q_{ult}. The *allowable bearing capacity* (symbol q_a) refers to the loading per unit area that the soil is able to support without unsafe movement. It is the "design" bearing capacity. The allowable load is equal to allowable bearing capacity multiplied by area of contact between foundation and soil. The allowable bearing capacity is equal to the ultimate bearing capacity divided by the factor of safety. A factor of safety of 2.5 to 3 is commonly applied to the value of q_{ult}. Care must be taken to ensure that a footing design is safe with regard to (1) foundation failure (collapse) and (2) excessive settlement.

3.4.2 Bearing Capacity Equation for Concentrically Loaded Strip Footings

Ultimate bearing capacity of strip footing, $q_{ult} = cN_c + qN_q + 0.5\gamma B_f N_\gamma$
Total surcharge at base of the footing, $q = q_{appl} + \gamma_a D_f$

$$N_q = e^{\pi \tan\phi} \tan^2\left(45 + \frac{\phi}{2}\right)$$

$N_c = 2 + \pi = 5.14$ for $\phi = 0°$

$N_c = \left(N_q - 1\right)\cot\phi$ for $\phi > 0°$

$N_\gamma = 2\left(N_q - 1\right)\tan\phi$

where

c = cohesion of the soil
q = total surcharge at base of the footing
q_{appl} = applied surcharge at surface
γ_a = unit weight of soil above base of footing
D_f = depth of footing
γ = unit weight of soil

B_f = width of footing
N_q = bearing capacity factor for surcharge
N_c = bearing capacity factor for cohesion
N_γ = bearing capacity factor for soil weight

Example 3.20
A strip of wall footing 3 ft wide is located 3.5 ft below the ground surface. Supporting soil has a unit weight of 125 lb/ft^3. The results of laboratory tests on the soil samples indicate that the supporting soil's cohesion and angle of internal friction are 1,200 lb/ft^2 and 25°, respectively. Groundwater was not encountered during subsurface soil exploration. Determine the allowable bearing capacity, using a factor of safety of 3.

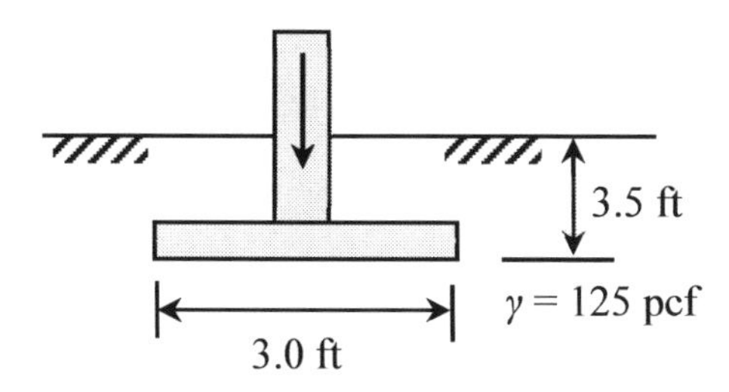

Solution:

Ultimate bearing capacity of strip footing, $q_{ult} = cN_c + qN_q + 0.5\gamma B_f N_\gamma$
Applied surcharge at surface, $q_{appl} = 0$
Total surcharge at base of the footing, $q = q_{appl} + \gamma_a D_f = 0 + 0.125$ kcf x 3.5 ft = 0.4375 ksf

$$N_q = e^{\pi \tan\phi} \tan^2\left(45 + \frac{\phi}{2}\right) = e^{\pi \tan 25} \tan^2\left(45 + \frac{25}{2}\right) = 10.7$$

$$N_c = \left(N_q - 1\right)\cot\phi = \left(10.7 - 1\right)\cot 25 = 20.8$$

$$N_\gamma = 2\left(N_q - 1\right)\tan\phi = 2\left(10.7 - 1\right)\tan 25 = 9.0$$

$q_{ult} = cN_c + qN_q + 0.5\gamma B_f N_\gamma$
= 1.2 ksf x 20.8 + 0.4375 ksf x 10.7 + 0.5 x 0.125 kcf x 3.0 x 9.0
= 31.3 ksf

Allowable bearing pressure, $q_{all} = q_{ult}$ / FS = 31.3 ksf / 3 = 10.4 ksf

Bearing capacity equation for concentrically loaded square or rectangular footings,

$$q_{ult} = cN_c s_c + qN_q s_q + 0.5\gamma B_f N_\gamma s_\gamma$$

Shape Correction Factors (AASHTO, 2004 with 2006 Interims)

Factor	Friction Angle	Cohesion Term (s_c)	Unit Weight Term (s_γ)	Surcharge Term (s_q)
Shape Factors, s_c, s_γ, s_q	$\phi = 0$	$1 + \left(\frac{B_f}{5L_f}\right)$	1.0	1.0
	$\phi > 0$	$1 + \left(\frac{B_f}{L_f}\right)\left(\frac{N_q}{N_c}\right)$	$1 - 0.4\left(\frac{B_f}{L_f}\right)$	$1 + \left(\frac{B_f}{L_f}\tan\phi\right)$

Table. Bearing Capacity Factors

ϕ	N_c	N_q	N_γ	ϕ	N_c	N_q	N_γ
0	5.14	1.0	0.0	23	18.1	8.7	8.2
1	5.4	1.1	0.1	24	19.3	9.6	9.4
2	5.6	1.2	0.2	25	20.7	10.7	10.9
3	5.9	1.3	0.2	26	22.3	11.9	12.5
4	6.2	1.4	0.3	27	23.9	13.2	14.5
5	6.5	1.6	0.5	28	25.8	14.7	16.7
6	6.8	1.7	0.6	29	27.9	16.4	19.3
7	7.2	1.9	0.7	30	30.1	18.4	22.4
8	7.5	2.1	0.9	31	32.7	20.6	26.0
9	7.9	2.3	1.0	32	35.5	23.2	30.2
10	8.4	2.5	1.2	33	38.6	26.1	35.2
11	8.8	2.7	1.4	34	42.2	29.4	41.1
12	9.3	3.0	1.7	35	46.1	33.3	48.0
13	9.8	3.3	2.0	36	50.6	37.8	56.3
14	10.4	3.6	2.3	37	55.6	42.9	66.2
15	11.0	3.9	2.7	38	61.4	48.9	78.0
16	11.6	4.3	3.1	39	67.9	56.0	92.3
17	12.3	4.8	3.5	40	75.3	64.2	109.4
18	13.1	5.3	4.1	41	83.9	73.9	130.2
19	13.9	5.8	4.7	42	93.7	85.4	155.6
20	14.8	6.4	5.4	43	105.1	99.0	186.5
21	15.8	7.1	6.2	44	118.4	115.3	224.6
22	16.9	7.8	7.1	45	133.9	134.9	271.8

Question 3.21

A square footing 2 m by 2 m is to be constructed at 1.22 m below the ground surface, as shown below. The groundwater table is located 1.82 m below the ground surface. The subsoil consists of a uniform, medium dense, cohesionless soil with the following properties:

Unit weight of soil = 18.53 kN/m^3
Angle of internal friction = 32°
Cohesion = 0

If a factor of safety of 2.5 is used, the foundation soil's allowable bearing capacity (kN/m^2) is most nearly:

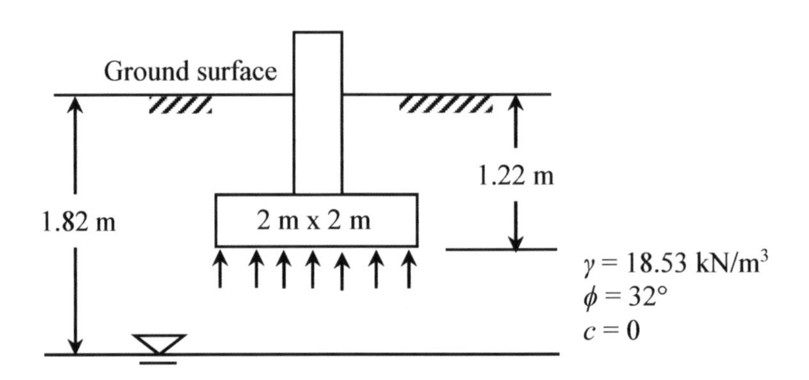

Solution:

From the handbook table, for $\phi = 32°$, $N_c = 35.5$, $N_q = 23.2$, $N_\gamma = 30.2$.
For square footing, $q_{ult} = cN_c s_c + qN_q s_q + 0.5\gamma B_f N_\gamma s_\gamma$
As $c = 0$, discard the term, $cN_c s_c$
$q = q_{appl} + \gamma_a D_f = 0 + (18.53 \text{ kN/m}^3)(1.22 \text{ m}) = 22.61 \text{ kN/m}^2$

$$\text{Shape factor } s_q = 1 + \left(\frac{B_f}{L_f}\tan\phi\right) = 1 + \left(\frac{2\text{m}}{2\text{m}} \times \tan 32\right) = 1.62$$

$$\text{Shape factor } s_\gamma = 1 - 0.4\left(\frac{B_f}{L_f}\right) = 1 - 0.4 \times \left(\frac{2\text{m}}{2\text{m}}\right) = 0.6$$

If the water table is below the base of the footing but less than distance B below the base, a linearly interpolated value of effective unit weight should be used in the $\gamma B_f N_\gamma$ terms. This concept is not clear in the PE Civil Handbook. For the $\gamma B_f N_\gamma$ term:
$\gamma = 18.53 \text{ kN/m}^3 (0.6 \text{ m} / 2.0 \text{ m}) + (18.53 - 9.81)(1.4 \text{ m} / 2.0 \text{ m}) = 11.66 \text{ kN/m}^3$
$q_{ult} = qN_q s_q + (0.5 \text{ x } 0.6)\, \gamma B_f N_\gamma$
$= (22.61 \text{ kN/m}^3)(23.2)(1.62) + (0.5 \text{ x } 0.6)(11.66 \text{ kN/m}^3)(2 \text{ m})(30.2)$
$= 850 \text{ kN/m}^2 + 211 \text{ kN/m}^2$
$= 1{,}061 \text{ kN/m}^2$
$q_{all} = q_{ult} / \text{FS} = 1{,}061 / 2.5 = 424 \text{ kN/m}^2 \approx \underline{420 \text{ kN/m}^2}$

Normal footing becomes eccentrically load footing when there is an eccentricity in the loading or when there is a bending moment at the connection of footing and the column. The eccentricity could be in one direction or in both directions. The contact area of the footing decreases due to the eccentricity which results in the decrease in bearing capacity of supporting soil. For one-way eccentricity, only one dimension decreases.

Reduced width, $B'_f = B_f - 2e_B$
Reduced length, $L'_f = L_f - 2e_L$
Reduced area, $A' = B'_f L'_f$

where

B_f = footing width
B'_f = effective footing width
L_f = footing length
L'_f = effective footing length
e_B = eccentricity in the B_f direction
e_L = eccentricity in the L_f direction

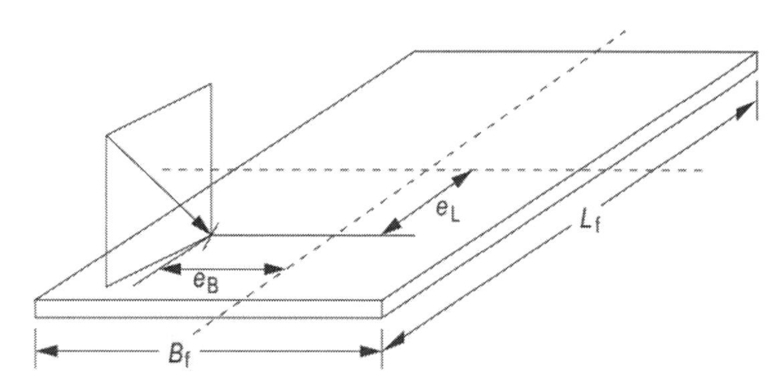

Figure. Notations for Footings Subjected to Eccentric, Inclined Loads (after Kulhawy, 1983)

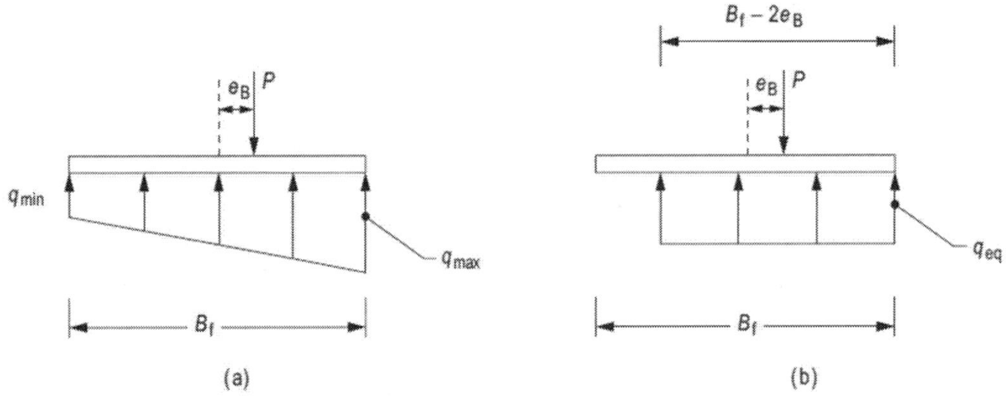

Figure. Eccentrically Loaded Footing with: (a) Linearly varying pressure distribution (structural design)
(b) Equivalent uniform pressure distribution (sizing the footing)

Example 3.22

A rectangular footing 5 ft by 7.5 ft is loaded as shown below. Calculate the equivalent uniform pressure.

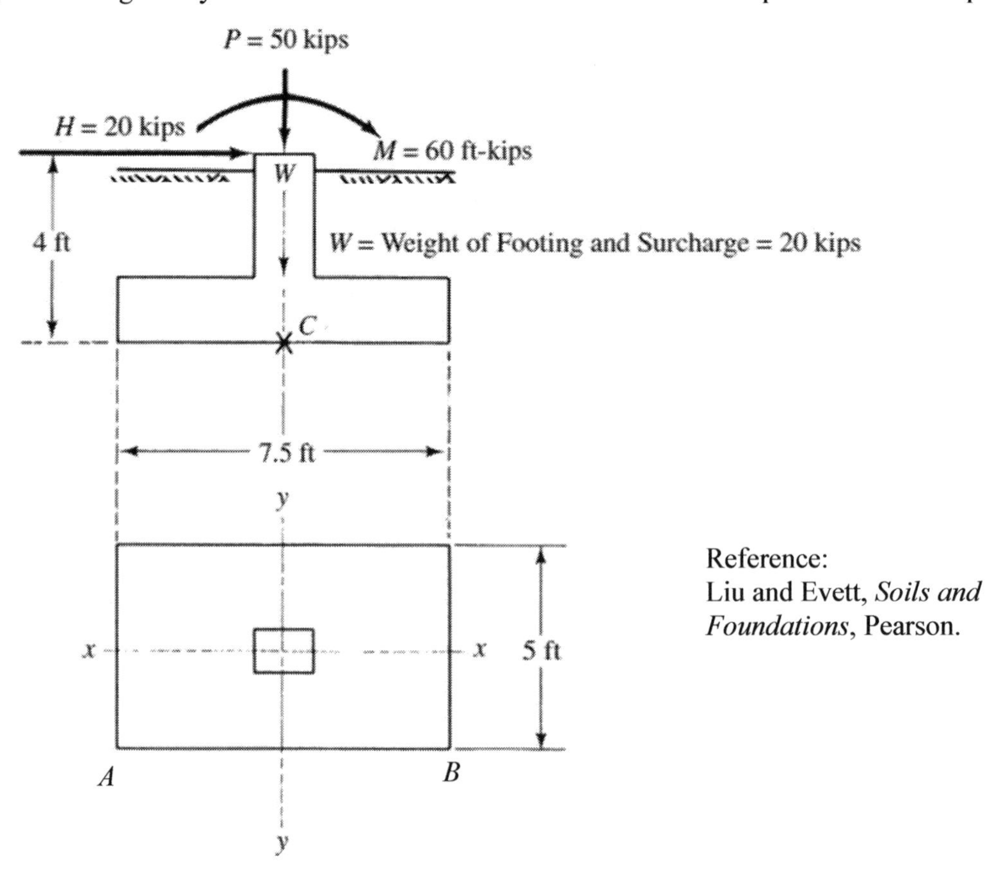

Reference:
Liu and Evett, *Soils and Foundations*, Pearson.

Solution:

Vertical compressive load, $Q = P + W =$ 50 kip + 20 kip of weights = 70 kip
One-way moment, $M =$ 20 kip x 4 ft + 60 kip.ft = 140 kip.ft
One-way eccentricity, e = 140 ft.kip / 70 kip = 2 ft
B_f = footing width = 7.5 ft
B'_f = effective footing width = 7.5 ft – 2 x 2.0 ft = 3.5 ft
L_f = footing length = 5.0 ft

$$q_{eq} = \frac{Q}{A'} = \frac{Q}{L_f B'_f} == \frac{70\,\text{kip}}{5.0\,\text{ft} \times 3.5\,\text{ft}} = \underline{4.0\ \text{ksf}}$$

3.4.3 Frost Depth

The frost line, also known as frost depth or freezing depth - is most commonly the depth to which the groundwater in soil is expected to freeze. The frost depth depends on the climatic conditions of an area, the heat transfer properties of the soil and adjacent materials, and on nearby heat sources. Approximate Frost Depth Map for United States is shown in figure below. See that the north-side of the country has larger frost depth.

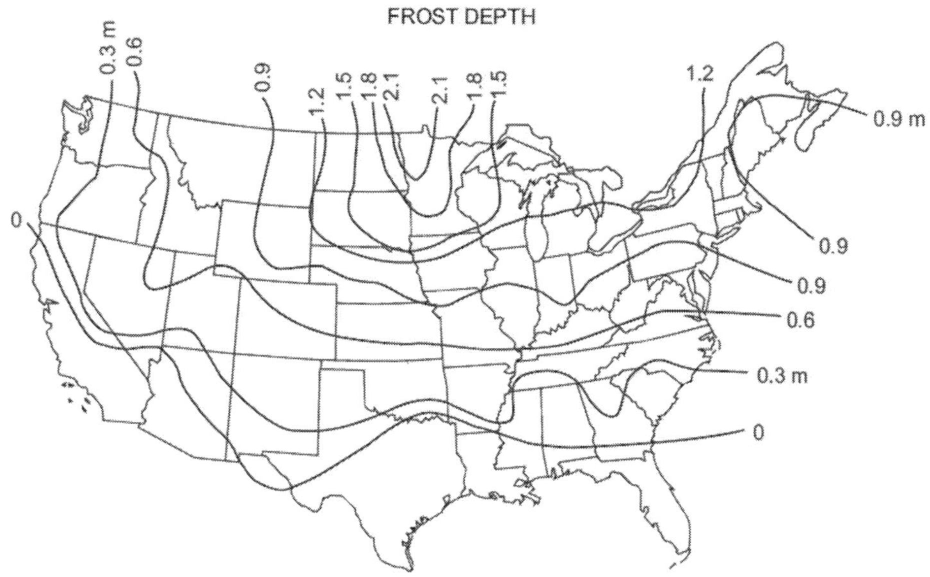

Figure. Approximate Frost Depth Map for United States (Bowles, 1996); 1 m = 3.28 ft

3.5 Foundation Settlement

This topic is based on Article 3.5 of the PE Civil Handbook. Foundation Settlement is the vertical downward movement of a structure's foundation as a result of compression in the underlying soil caused by the increased load of the structure. Foundation settlement is caused by one or more of the following:

- Elastic compression of the foundation and the underlying soil.
- Inelastic compression of the underlying soils.
- Lowered ground water.
- Vibrations due to pile driving and local blasting.
- Seasonal swelling and shrinkage of expansive clays.
- Ground movement on earth slopes such as surface erosion or landslide.
- Excavation on adjacent properties.
- Underground erosion.

Settlement of structures on fine-grained soil generally consists of three phases. The first phase is known as immediate settlement, or volume distortion settlement. Immediate settlement occurs rapidly after load is applied. Caused by soil volume distortion, immediate settlement is typically completed quickly and constitutes a relatively small amount of total settlement in fine-grained soils. Subsequent to immediate settlement, primary consolidation settlement occurs, the result of primary consolidation. (These are commonly referred to simply as consolidation settlement and consolidation, respectively.) Primary consolidation occurs due to extrusion of water from the voids as a result of increased loading. Primary consolidation settlement is very slow and continues over a long period of time. After primary settlement has ended, soil compression and additional associated settlement continue at a very slow rate, the result of plastic readjustment of soil grains due to new, changed stresses in the soil and progressive breaking of clayey particles and their inter-particle bonds. This phenomenon is known as secondary compression, and associated settlement is called secondary compression settlement.

3.5.1 Stress Distribution

Vertical Stress below a uniform load for Continuous and Square Footings can be determined utilizing Figure below.

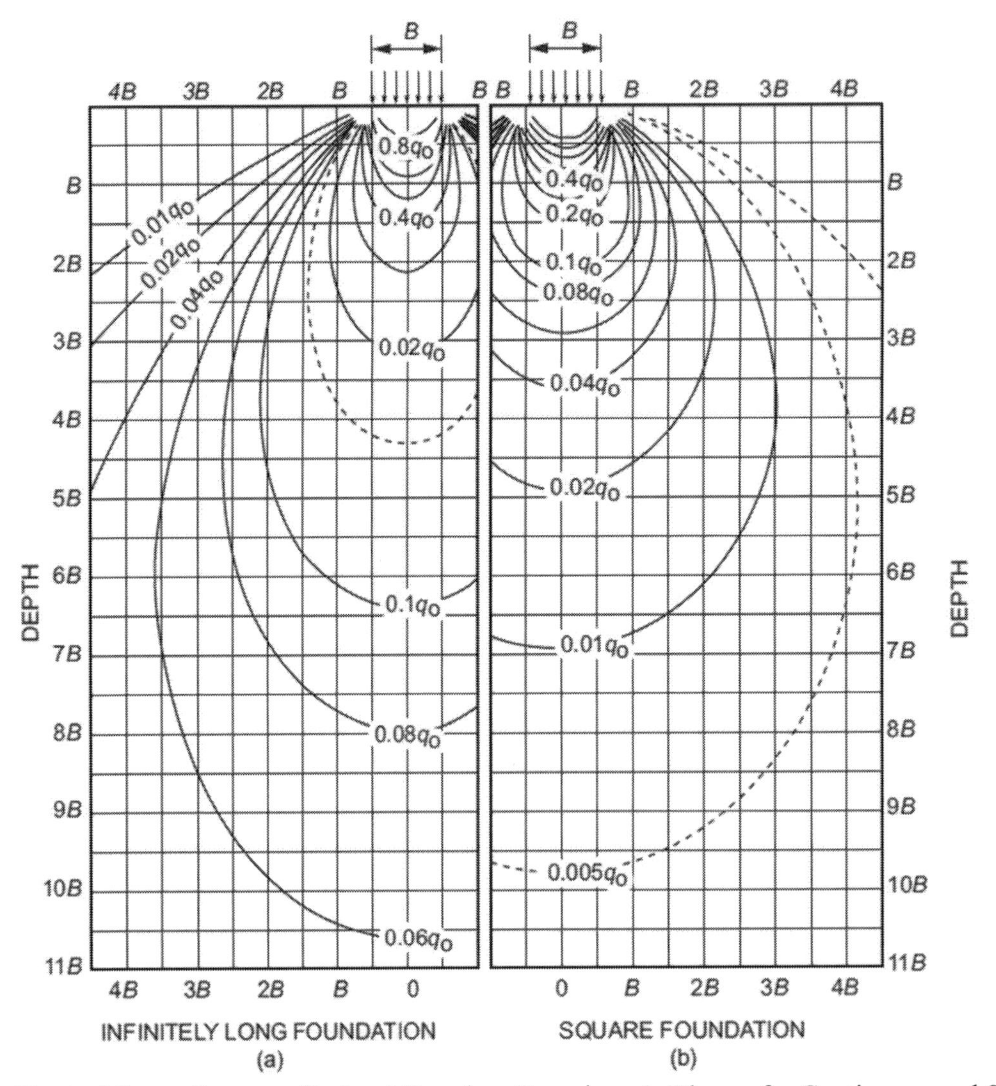

Figure. Vertical Stress Contours (Isobars) Based on Boussinesq's Theory for Continuous and Square Footings (modified after Sowers, 1979; AASHTO, 2002)

Example 3.23

A 1.5-m by 1.5-m footing located 1 m below the ground surface as shown in Figure below carries a load of 650 kN (including column load and weight of footing and soil surcharge). Calculate the net vertical stress increment due to this load at a depth of 5 m below the center of the footing (i.e., at point A in figure).

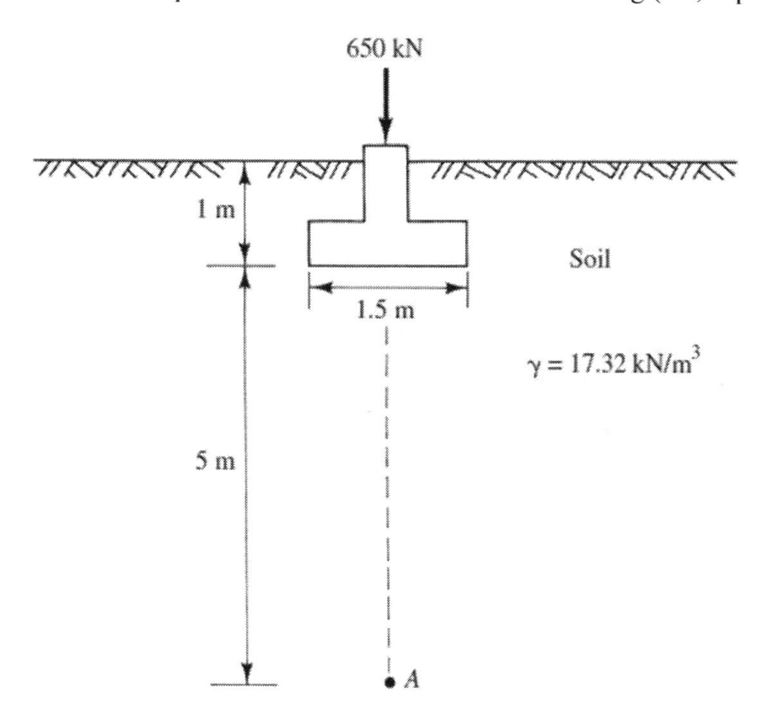

Solution:

$$\text{Applied stress at surface, } q_o = \frac{650\,\text{kN}}{(1.5\,\text{m})(1.5\,\text{m})} - \left(17.32\frac{\text{kN}}{\text{m}^3}\right)(1\,\text{m}) = 272\frac{\text{kN}}{\text{m}^2}$$

$B = 1.5$ m

Depth = 5 m / 1.5 m of $B = 3.33B$

From Chart, stress $\approx 0.05q_o = 0.05$ (272 kN/m^2) =13.6 kN/m^2

The approximate method is based on the assumption that the area (in a horizontal plane) of stress below a concentrated load increases with depth, as shown in Figure below. With the 2:1 slope shown, it is apparent that at any depth z, both L and B are increased by the amount z. Accordingly, stress at depth z is given by:

$$\Delta p = \frac{P}{(B+z)(L+z)}$$

Because P, L, and B are constants for a given application, it is obvious that the stress at depth z (p) decreases as depth increases. This method should be considered crude at best. It may be useful for preliminary stability analysis of footings; however, for settlement analysis the approximate method may likely not be accurate enough, and a more accurate approach based on elastic theory (discussed later in this section) may be required.

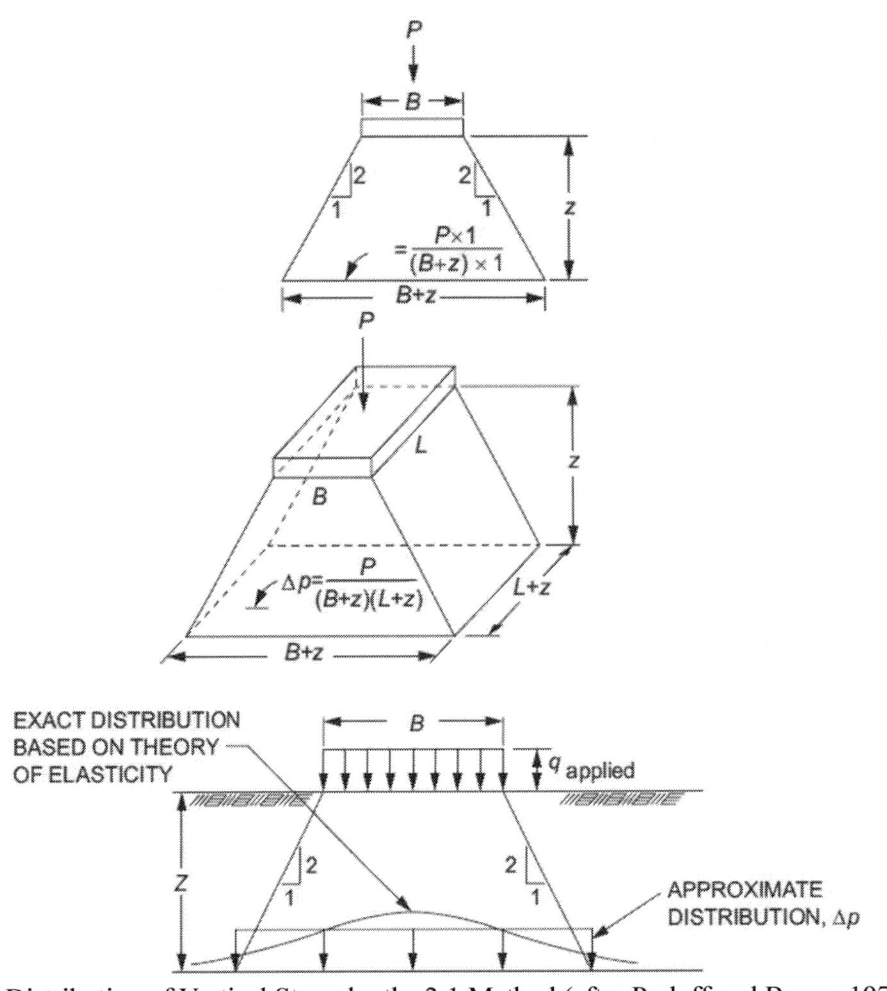

Figure. Distribution of Vertical Stress by the 2:1 Method (after Perloff and Baron, 1976)

Example 3.24
A 3.5-m by 2.5-m rectangular area carries a uniform load of 250 kPa on earth surface. Determine the stress level at 4-m from the surface.

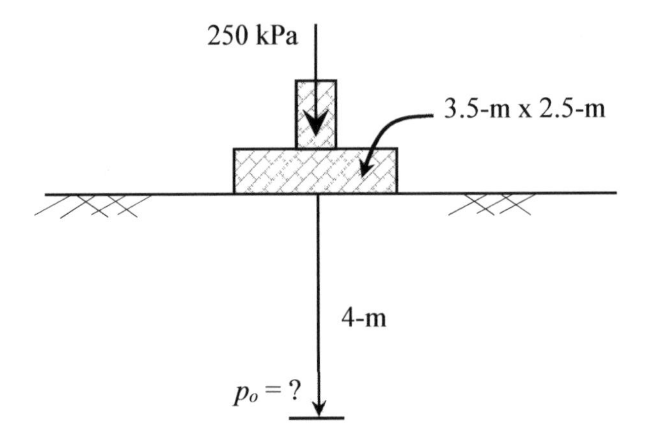

Solution:

Applied concentrated load, P = Stress x Loading Area = 250 kN/m^2 x (3.5-m x 2.5-m)^2 = 2,188 kN

The vertical stress on a plane at 4-m-depth of a circular loading:

$$\Delta p = \frac{P}{(B+z)(L+z)} = \frac{2{,}188\,\text{kN}}{(2.5+4)(3.5+4)\,\text{m}^2} = 45\frac{\text{kN}}{\text{m}^2}$$

Example 3.25
A 10-ft diameter footing applies 2.5 ksf load on surface. Determine the stress level at 12 ft from the surface.

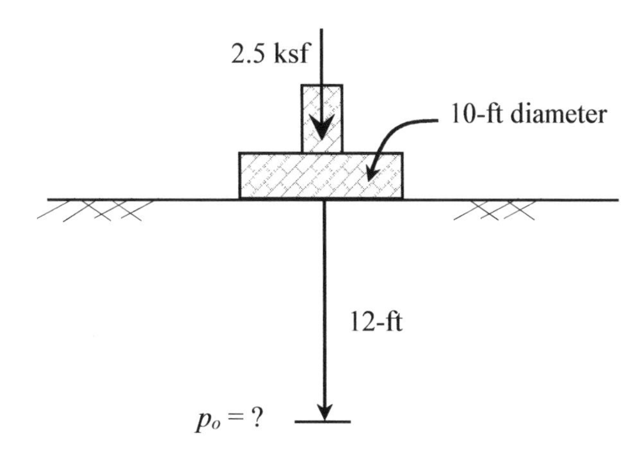

Solution:

Applied concentrated load, P = Stress x Loading Area = 2.5 ksf x π/4 (10-ft)^2 = 196.35 kip
Pressure diameter at 12-ft deep = $D + z$ = 10 ft + 12 ft = 22 ft
The vertical stress on a plane at 12-ft-depth of a circular loading:

$$\Delta p = \frac{P}{\frac{\pi}{4}(D+z)^2} = \frac{196.35\text{ kip}}{\frac{\pi}{4}(22\text{ ft})^2} = \underline{0.52\text{ ksf}}$$

Two methods are very popular to calculate the immediate settlement:

a) Elastic Method
b) Schmertmann's Method

The primary consolidation and secondary consolidation are already discussed in previous sections.

3.5.2 Elastic Method

As noted previously, immediate settlement occurs rapidly, perhaps within hours or days after load is applied. It is caused by soil volume distortion, and it usually constitutes only a small amount of total settlement in fine-grained soils. Immediate settlement may be estimated based on the linear theory of elasticity as follows:

$$\delta_v = \frac{C_d \Delta p B_f \left(1-\upsilon^2\right)}{E_m}$$

where

δ_v = vertical settlement at surface
C_d = shape and rigidity factors (see following table)
Δp = change in stress at base of footing
B_f = footing diameter or width
υ = Poisson's ratio of soil or rock
E_m = elastic or Young's modulus of soil or rock

Shape and Rigidity Factors, C_d, for Calculating Settlements of Points on Loaded Areas at the Surface of a Semi-Infinite, Elastic Half Space

Shape	**Center**	**Corner**	**Middle of Short Side**	**Middle of Long Side**	**Average**
Circle	1.00	0.64	0.64	0.64	0.85
Circle (rigid)	0.79	0.79	0.79	0.79	0.79
Square	1.12	0.56	0.76	0.76	0.95
Square (rigid)	0.99	0.99	0.99	0.99	0.99
Rectangle (length/width):					
1.5	1.36	0.67	0.89	0.97	1.15
2	1.52	0.76	0.98	1.12	1.30
3	1.78	0.88	1.11	1.35	1.52
5	2.10	1.05	1.27	1.68	1.83
10	2.53	1.26	1.49	2.12	2.25
100	4.00	2.00	2.20	3.60	3.70
1,000	5.47	2.75	2.94	5.03	5.15
10,000	6.90	3.50	3.70	6.50	6.60

Elastic Constants of Various Soils (after AASHTO 2004, with 2006 interims)

Soil Type	**Typical Range of Young's Modulus Values, E_s (tsf)**	**Poisson's Ratio, *n***
Clay:		
Soft sensitive	25–150	0.4–0.5 (undrained)
Medium stiff to stiff	150–500	
Very stiff	500–1,000	
Loess Silt	150–600 20–200	0.1–0.3 0.3–0.35
Fine Sand:		
Loose	80–120	0.25
Medium dense	120–200	
Dense	200–300	
Sand:		
Loose	100–300	0.20–0.36
Medium dense	300–500	
Dense	500–800	0.30–0.40
Gravel:		
Loose	300–800	0.20–0.35
Medium dense	800–1,000	
Dense	1,000–2,000	0.30–0.40
Estimating E_s from SPT *N*-value		
Soil Type		***Es* (tsf)**
Silts, sandy silts, slightly cohesive mixtures Clean fine to medium sands and slightly silty sands Coarse sands and sands with little gravel Sandy gravel and gravels		$4 N1_{60}$ $7 N1_{60}$ $10 N1_{60}$ $12 N1_{60}$
Estimating E_s (tsf) from q_c Static Cone Resistance		
Sandy soils	$2q_c$ where (q_c is in tsf)	

Note: 1 tsf = 95.76 kPa

Example 3.26
A 3-m diameter rigid circular footing is resting on a deep clay deposit with the following parameters:

- The footing is to carry a concentrated load of 1800 kN
- The undrained elastic modulus of clay is estimated to be 40 MPa
- Assume Poisson's ratio of the clay is 0.40

The expected immediate vertical settlement (mm) at surface along the center of the footing is most nearly:

Solution:

C_d = shape and rigidity factors (from table) = 0.79 for rigid circular footing at the center
Δp = change in stress at base of footing = 1,800 kN / [π(1.5 m)^2] = 255 kPa
B_f = footing diameter = 3 m
v = Poisson's ratio of soil = 0.40
E_m = elastic or Young's modulus of soil or rock = 40,000 kPa

$$\delta_v = \frac{C_d \Delta p B_f \left(1-\upsilon^2\right)}{E_m} = \frac{0.79(255\text{ kPa})(3.0\text{m})\left(1-0.40^2\right)}{40,000\text{kPa}} = 0.013\text{m} = \underline{13\text{ mm}}$$

3.5.3 Settlement (Schmertmann's Method)

This is a method for estimating foundation settlement on sand and gravel was developed by Schmertmann (1970). Settlement on sand is not amenable to Solution: based on laboratory tests, largely because of the problem of obtaining undisturbed soil samples for sandy soils for laboratory testing. Instead, settlement on sand is generally calculated by empirical means. The Schmertmann method evaluates settlement on sand using a semiempirical strain influence factor where settlement on sand can be calculated by:

$$S_i = C_1 C_2 \Delta p \sum_{i=1}^{n} \Delta H_i$$

$$\Delta H_i = H_c \left(\frac{I_z}{XE_s}\right)$$

S_i = settlement of foundation t years after construction
I_z = strain influence factor for soil zone z depth below foundation (dimensionless)
H_c = thickness of layer
n = number of soil layers within zone of strain influence
Δp = net applied stress at foundation depth
E_s = elastic modulus of soil layer
X = factor for shape of footing
  X = 1.25 for L_f/B_f (axisymmetric) and X = 1.75 for $L_f/B_f \geq 10$ (plane strain)
  Interpolate for $1 < L_f/B_f < 10$

C_1 = correction factor for strain relief due to embedment, $C_1 = 1 - 0.5\left(\frac{p_o}{\Delta p}\right) \geq 0.5$

p_o = effective in situ overburden stress at the foundation depth
C_2 = correction factor to incorporate time dependent (creep) increase in settlement,

$C_2 = 1 + 0.2\log_{10}\left(\frac{t}{0.1}\right)$

t = time years
The variation of the strain influence factor (Iz) with depth below the foundation is shown Figure below. The relationship of Figure below was developed on the basis of theory and model studies for vertical strain in sands below foundations as a function of depth.

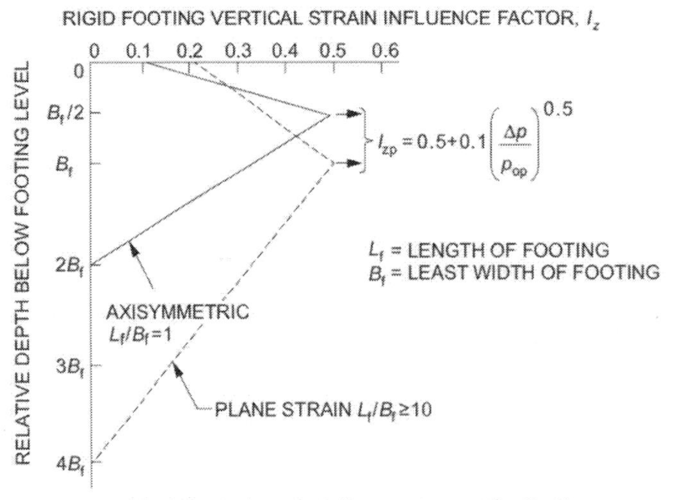

Simplified Vertical Strain Influence Factor Distributions

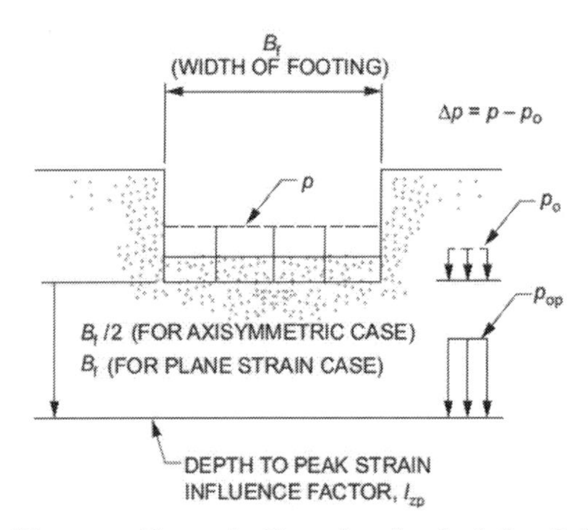

Figure Explanation of Pressure Terms in Equation for I_{zp} (after Schmertmann et al, 1978)

Question 3.27

A proposed square footing 2 m by 2 m carrying a total load of 800 kN is to be constructed on a sand deposit. The depth of the footing will be 1 m below the ground surface, and the unit weight of the sand is 17.5 kN/m^3. The modulus of elasticity of the sand was determined to be 10,000 kN/m^3 throughout. The modulus of elasticity of the sand and strain influence factors (I_z) of different layers are listed. Using Schmertmann's method, estimate the settlement of the footing four years after construction, using four 1-m-thick sublayers.

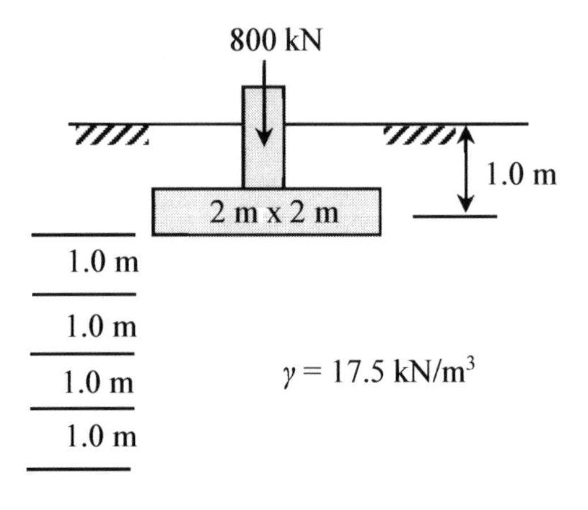

Layer Number	Layer thickness H_c (m)	Depth from Footing Base to Layer Center (m)	Elastic modulus of soil layer (kN/m^2), E_s	Strain influence factors, I_z	Shape Factor, X	$\Delta H_i = H_c\left(\frac{I_z}{XE_s}\right)$
1	1.0	0.5	10,000	0.300	1.25	3.00 x 10^{-5}
2	1.0	1.5		0.417	1.25	4.17 x 10^{-5}
3	1.0	2.5		0.250	1.25	2.50 x 10^{-5}
4	1.0	3.5		0.083	1.25	0.83 x 10^{-5}
						$\sum \Delta H_i$ = 10.50 x 10^{-5}

Solution:

$$S_i = C_1 C_2 \Delta p \sum \Delta H_i = C_1 C_2 \Delta p \sum H_c\left(\frac{I_z}{XE_s}\right)$$

Overburden stress at the bottom of footing, p_o = 17.5 kN/m^3 x 1.0 m = 17.50 kN/m^2

Applied stress at the bottom of footing, p = 800 kN / (2 m x 2 m) = 200 kN/m^2

Net stress at foundation depth is the applied stress minus the stress release due to excavation.

Net stress at foundation depth, $\Delta p = p - p_o$ = 200 kN/m^2 – 17.50 kN/m^2= 182.50 kN/m^2

$$C_1 = 1 - 0.5\left(\frac{p_o}{\Delta p}\right) = 1 - 0.5\left(\frac{17.50\ \text{kN}/\text{m}^2}{182.50\ \text{kN}/\text{m}^2}\right) = 0.952$$

$$C_2 = 1 + 0.2\log_{10}\left(\frac{t}{0.1}\right) = 1 + 0.2\log_{10}\left(\frac{4\,\text{yr}}{0.1}\right) = 1.32$$

$$S_i = C_1 C_2 \Delta p \sum H_c\left(\frac{I_z}{XE_s}\right) = (0.952)\,(1.32)\,(182.5\ \text{kN/m}^2)\,(10.5 \times 10^{-5}\ \text{m}^3\text{/kN}) = 0.024\ \text{m}$$

= 24 mm

3.6 Slope Stability

This topic is based on Article 3.6 of the PE Civil Handbook. Slope stability is the potential of soil covered slopes to withstand and undergo movement. Stability is determined by the balance of shear stress and shear strength. A previously stable slope may be initially affected by preparatory factors, making the slope conditionally unstable. Triggering factors of a slope failure can be climatic events can then make a slope actively unstable, leading to mass movements. Mass movements can be caused by increase in shear stress, such as loading, lateral pressure, and transient forces. Alternatively, shear strength may be decreased by weathering, changes in pore water pressure, and organic material.

The stability number method is also based on the premise that resistance of a soil mass to sliding results from cohesion and internal friction of the soil along the failure surface. In this method the failure surface is assumed to be a circular arc (see Figure below). A parameter called the stability number (N_o) is introduced, which groups factors affecting the stability of soil slopes. The stability number (N_o) is related to factor of safety as follows:

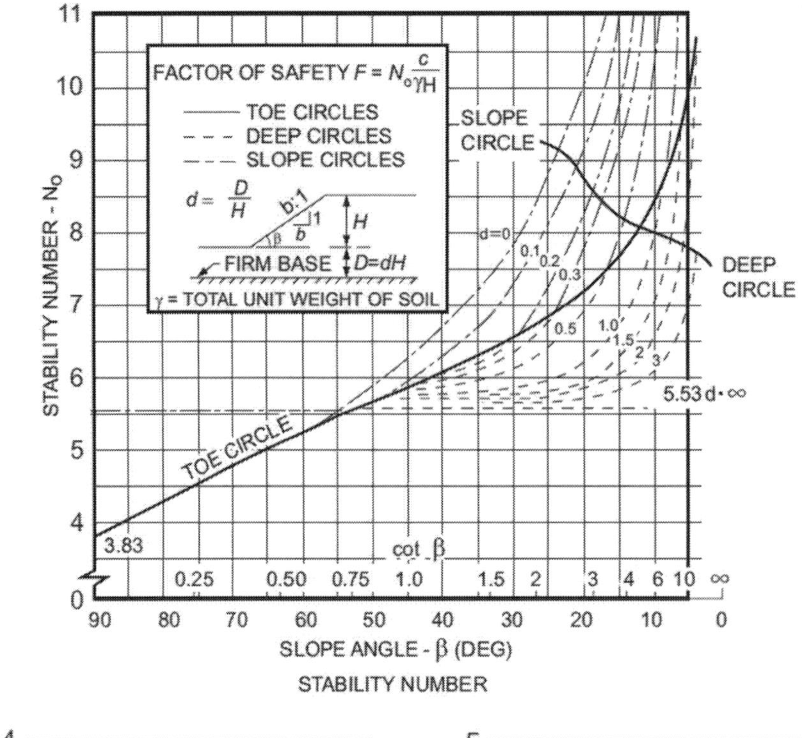

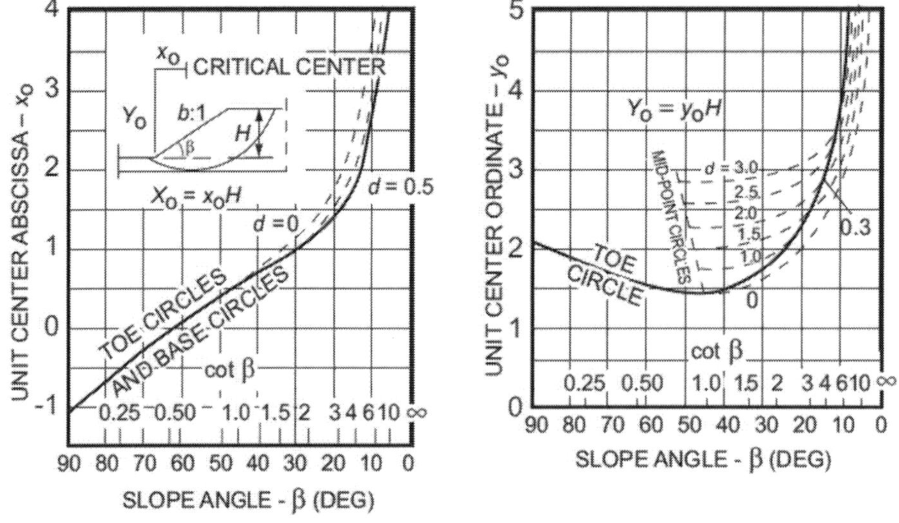

CENTER COORDINATES FOR CRITICAL CIRCLE

Figure. Stability Charts for $\phi = 0$ Soils

γ = unit weight of soil
H = height of cut
c = cohesion of soil

Example 3.28
An 8 ft deep trench is required to be dug in soil with the following parameters:

- cohesion = 130 lb/ft^2
- unit weight = 115 lb/ft^3
- stability number = 4.89

Is this trench safe considering no factor of safety?

Solution:

$$\text{Factor of safety } = N_o \frac{c}{\gamma H}$$

Critical Height, $H = (c \times N_o) \div \gamma$
Soil cohesion, c = 130 lb/ft^2
Stability number, N_o = 4.89
Unit weight, γ = 115 lb/ft^3

Therefore, H = (130 lb/ft^2 x 4.89) ÷ 115 lb/ft^3 = 5.53 ft < 8 ft; trench is unsafe.

Example 3.29
A soil slope with friction angle (ϕ) of 0 is shown below. The cohesion and unit weight of the soil are listed. The safety factor for the failure surface shown is desired to be at least 2.0.

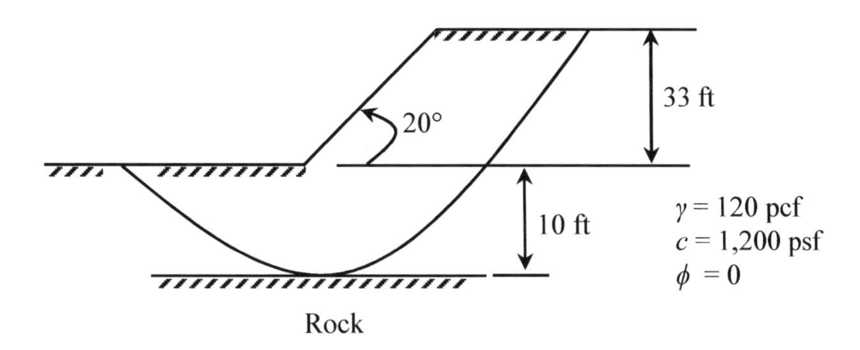

Is this slope safe?

Solution:

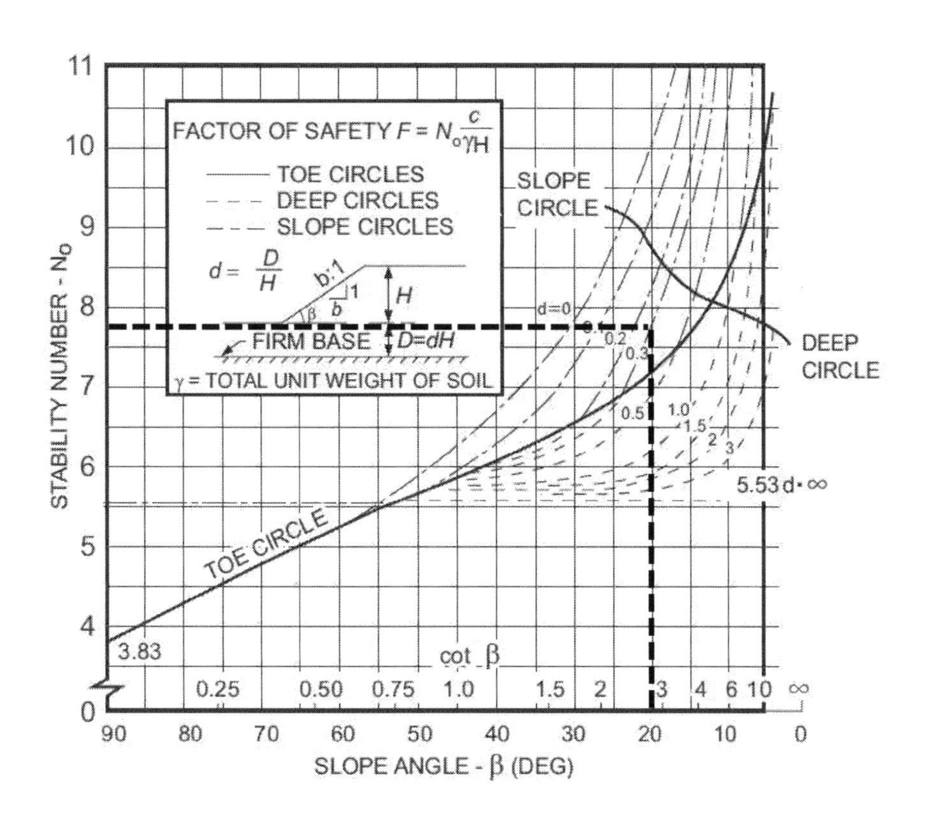

Depth factor, $d = D / H =$ 10 ft / 33 ft = 0.3

With $\beta = 20°$ and $d = 0.3$, from the handbook figure, required $N_o = 7.65$

Factor of Safety $= N_o \dfrac{c}{\gamma H}$ = 7.65 x 1,200 psf / (120 pcf x 33 ft) = 2.32 (> 2.0, SAFE!)

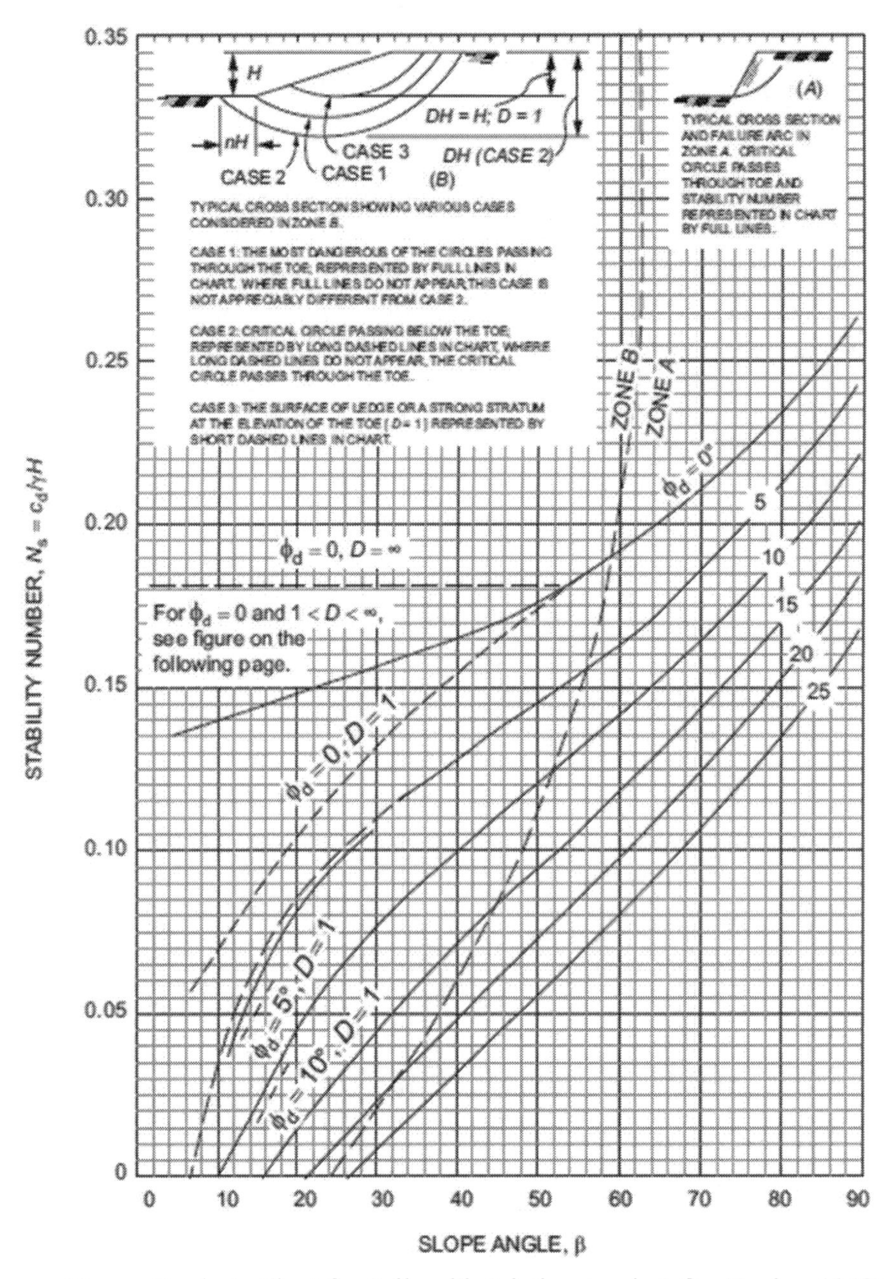

Figure. Taylor's Chart for Soils with Friction Angle (after Taylor, 1948)

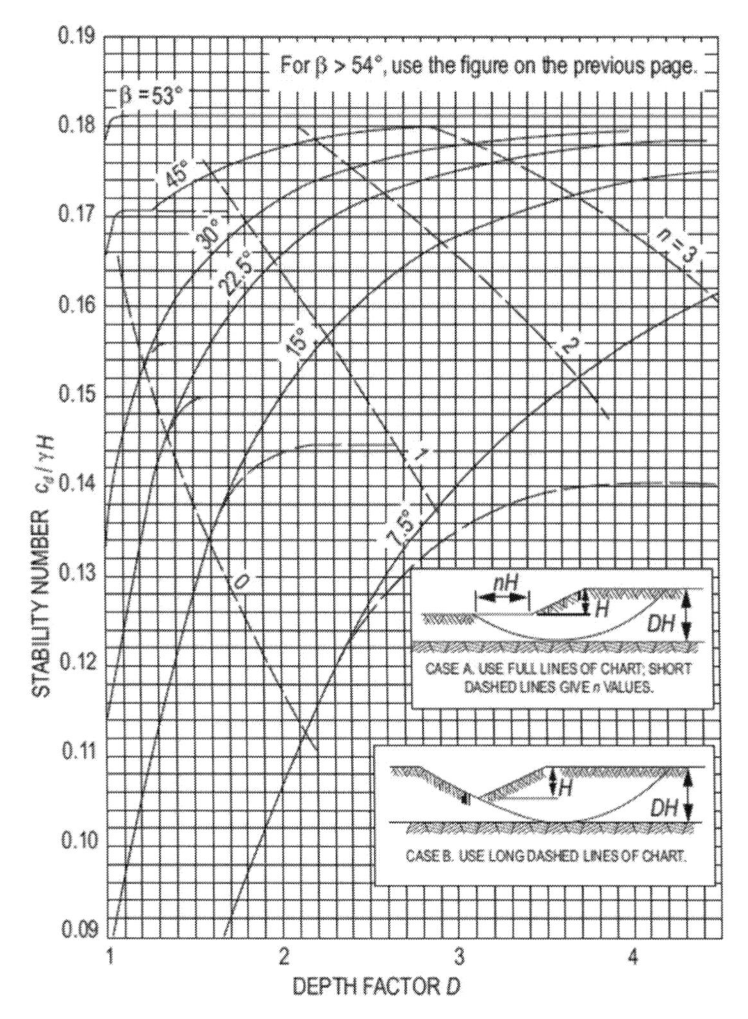

Figure. Taylor's Chart for $\phi' = 0$ Conditions for Slope Angles (β) less than 54°

Example 3.30

A soil slope with friction angle (ϕ) of 20° is shown below. The cohesion and unit weight of the soil are listed. The safety factor for the failure surface shown is desired to be at least 1.5.

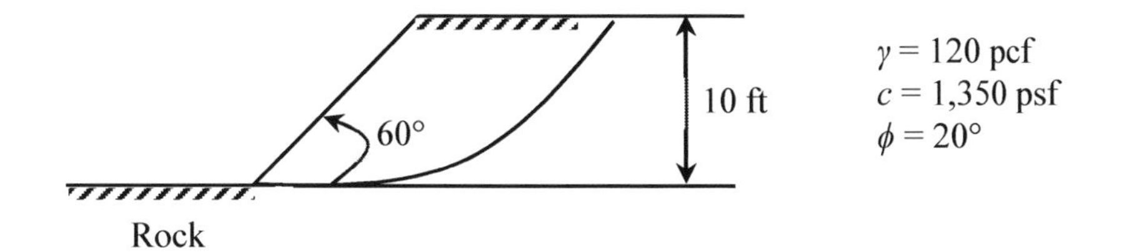

Is this slope safe?

Solution:

DH = 10 ft

H = 10 ft

Therefore, D = 1.0

With $\beta = 60°$ and $D = 1.0$, from the handbook figure, required $N_s = 0.09$

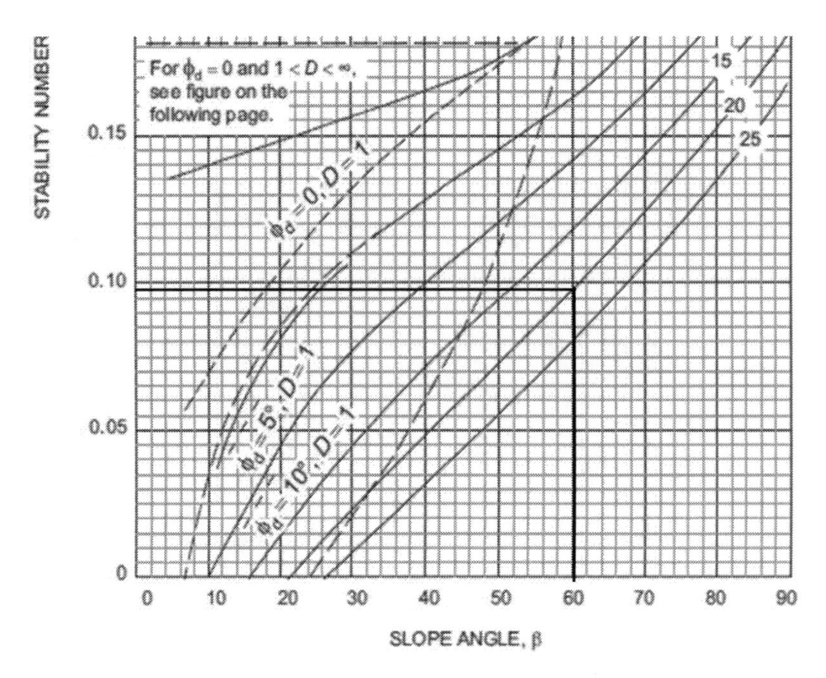

Factor of Safety $= N_s \dfrac{c_d}{\gamma H}$ = 0.09 x 1,350 psf / (120 pcf x 10 ft) = 0.10 (<< 1.5, UNSAFE!)

3.7 Soil Classification and Boring Log Interpretation

This topic is not specified in the PE Civil Breadth (morning) exam. However, the author believes it is a good idea to study this topic as well being very common topic among many areas of civil engineering, especially Unified Soil Classification System (USCS) and AASHTO Classification System. Chapter 7 discusses this topic. See Article 3.7 of the PE Civil Handbook.

Again to remind you that about 50% of the questions will be non-mathematical based. Therefore, revise the basic concepts of each topic. Make sure you are familiar with all the symbols in the Handbook, and try to know equations are available at which chapters. Your breadth exam questions will also depends on your selected depth area. For example, construction depth students may see more construction related questions in the breadth exam.

Chapter 4
Structural Mechanics

This chapter is primarily based on Article 1.6 of the PE Civil Handbook which talks about statics, strength of materials, some structural analysis, etc. Some basics of structural design is also included. Considering the breadth exam, no deep study is required. However, considering your depth selection, some deep level question may arrive. For example, if you choose Structural Depth, then your questions from this section may be deeper compared to a candidate with Water/Environment Depth.

4.1 Dead and Live Loads

Dead Loads are relatively constant over time and include the weight of the structure and immovable items such as walls, ceilings, floors, roof, finishes, built-in furniture, mechanical, electrical, plumbing, etc. Dead loads are also known as permanent or static loads. Live Loads are either temporary, of short duration, or moving loads and include all the forces that are variable during normal operation. A special category of live loads are environmental loads such as Wind, Snow, Rain, Ice, Seismic, Thermal, etc. Gravity loads are the dead loads on the structure. Gravity loads are typically permanent loads once construction is complete. Rain, movable furniture, people, etc. are transient, not permanent, and therefore fall into the live load category.

Knowledge on tributary is important to calculate the loads. Although 'Tributary Areas' is specified in the Structural Depth exam, it is a good idea to study this topic. There are two different ways that slab load is transferred to beam: one-way system and two-way system. These are explained using the following figure. Let us consider the following slab with beams all around.

- If, $\frac{\text{Length}}{\text{Width}} > 2.0$, then the load distribution is one-way; the slab load is to be carried by both longer beams equally.
- If, $\frac{\text{Length}}{\text{Width}} \leq 2.0$, then the load distribution is two-way; beams all around are to be carry the load.

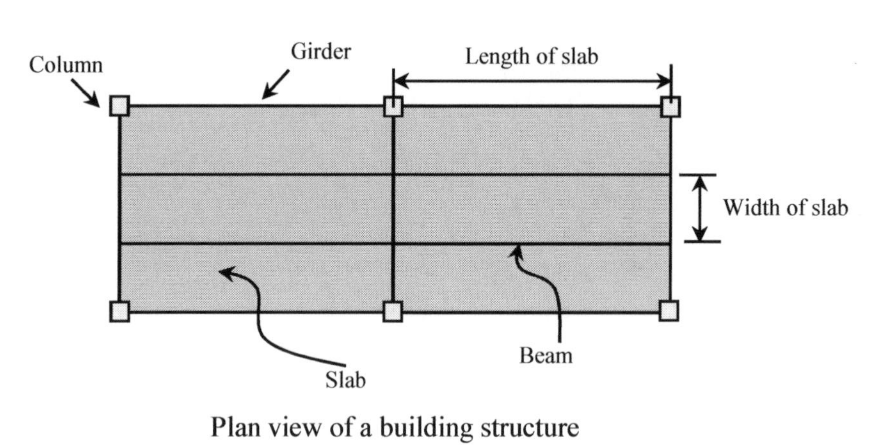

Plan view of a building structure

Column

Beam/girder

Profile of a building structure

This theory is not listed in the PE Civil Handbook but more about basics of load calculation. Try to revise the basics of most theories as about 50% of the questions will be theory based or do not need computations.

4.1.1 One-Way Load System

For one-way load system $\left(\frac{\text{Length}}{\text{Width}} > 2.0\right)$, the slab load is distributed as shown in figure below. Beam, B-2 will carry load 50% of each slab as shown by gray color. Beams, B-1 and B-3 will carry load 50% of the slab as shown by the dotted region. The girder, in the left and in the right will not carry any load directly from slab. However, the girders will have its self-weight and the concentrated load at its mid span from the interior beam. The exterior beam will transfer the load directly to the column. The column load at the lower story will be cumulative of the load from its story and all of the stories above.

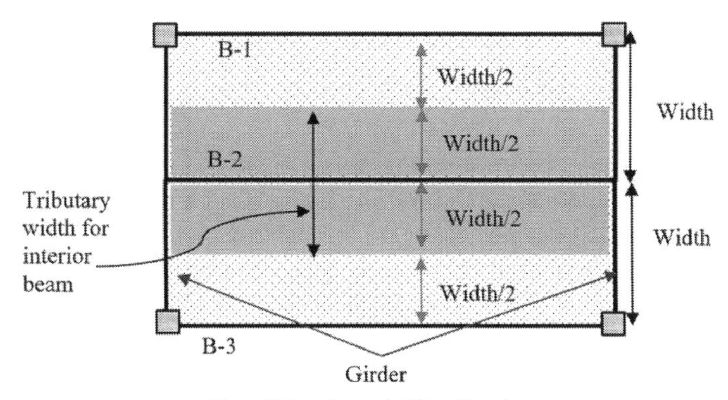

One-Way Load Distribution

Let us see an example of one-way load transfer system based on the above figure.

Example 4.1
Let us assume the following in the above figure:

Width of slab = 10 ft
Length of beam = 22 ft
Slab load = 2 ksf (including the self-weight)

What is most nearly the load and draw it for the interior beam, B-2?

Solution:

Length-to-width ratio of the slab = 22/10 = 2.2 >2; so one-way load distribution.
Tributary width of the beam = (10/2)+(10/2) = 10 ft.
Load on interior beam = 2 ksf (10 ft) = 20 kip/ft. The load distribution can be drawn as shown in figure below.

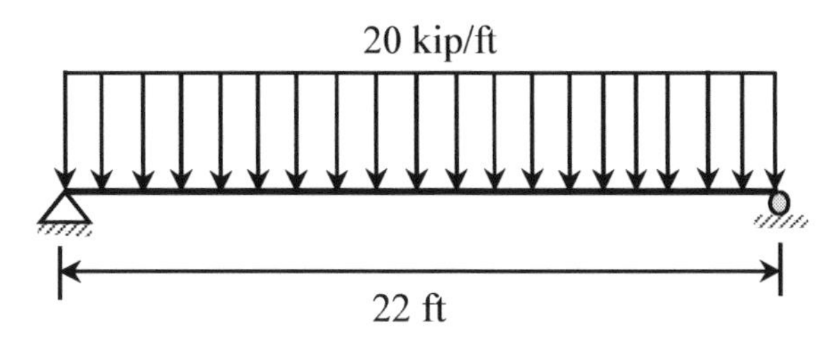

Load on interior Beam, B-2

4.1.2 Two-Way Load System

For two-way load system $\left(\dfrac{\text{Length}}{\text{Width}} \leq 2.0\right)$, the slab load is distributed is shown in figure below. Beam, B-2 will carry load 50% of each slab not up to full length. The girder, in the left and in the right will carry some load directly from slab. The area of this load determined by drawing 45° lines from each corner. The exterior beam will transfer the load directly to the column. The column load at the lower story will be cumulative of the load from its story and all of the story above.

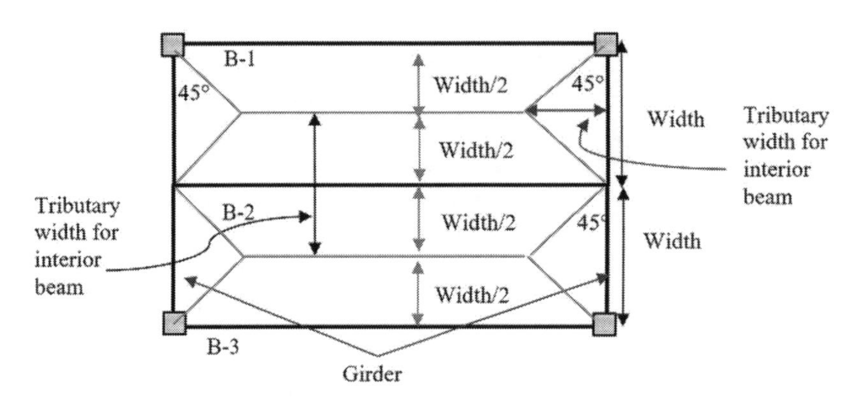

Two-way Load Distribution

Let us see an example of two-way load transfer system based on the above figure.

Example 4.2
Let us assume the following in the above figure:

Width of slab = 10 ft
Length of beam = 15 ft
Slab load = 2 ksf (including the self-weight)

What is most nearly the load and draw it for the interior beam, B-2?

Solution:

Length-to-width ratio of the slab = 15/10 = 1.5<2; so two-way load distribution.
Tributary width of the beam = (10/2) + (10/2) = 10 ft.
Load on interior beam = 2 ksf (10 ft) = 20 kip/ft up to middle (15 - 2x5) = 5 ft, uniformly decreases to zero at the ends. Therefore, the load distribution can be drawn as shown in figure below.

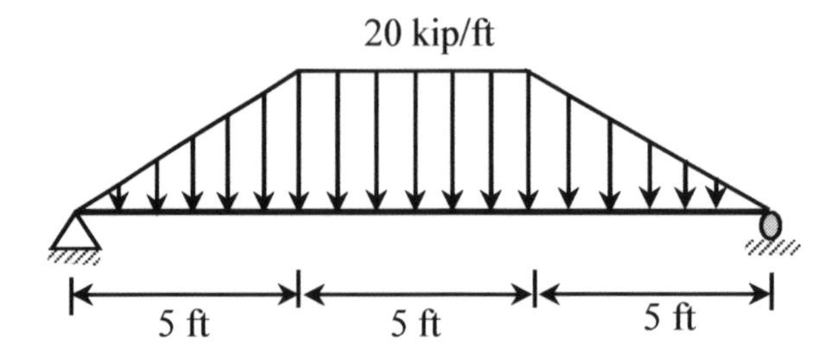

Load on Interior beam, B-2

Remember: One-way load tracing system is more common in real structures as beams are placed closely.

Example 4.3

A 30 ft x 30 ft flat roof is supported by 9 columns (each 15 ft apart). The roof weighs 120 lb/ft^2. The gravity load on each column is most nearly:

Solution:

Roof area = 30ft x 30ft = 900 ft^2

Total weight of roof = 900 ft^2 x 120 lb/ft^2 = 108,000 lb

Since the columns are equally spaced, each one supports a 10 ft x 10 ft area that weighs 10 ft x 10 ft = 12,000 lb

Example 4.4

Using the floor framing plan shown below, determine the following:

- Tributary width and tributary area of a typical interior beam
- Tributary width and tributary area of a typical spandrel or perimeter beam
- Tributary area of a typical interior girder
- Tributary area of a typical spandrel girder
- Tributary area of a typical interior column
- Tributary area of a typical corner column
- Tributary area of a typical exterior column

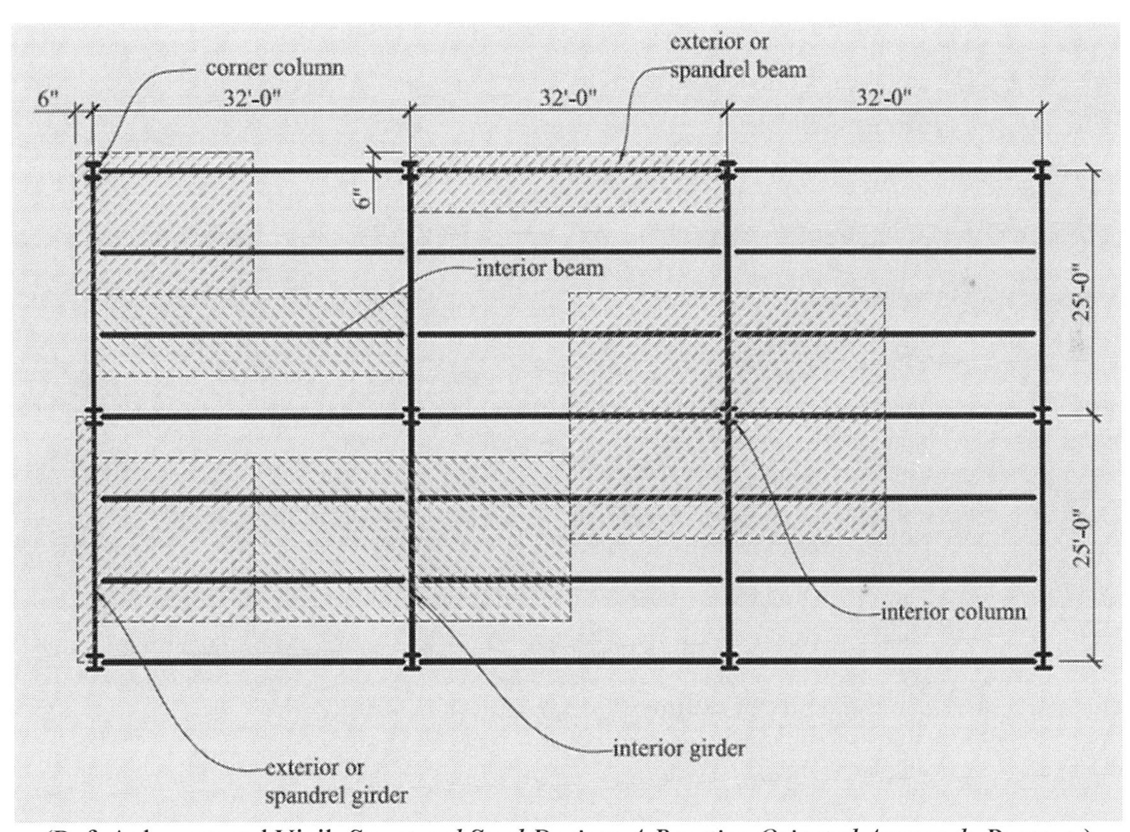

(Ref: Aghayere and Vigil, *Structural Steel Design: A Practice-Oriented Approach*, Pearson.)

The tributary area is already shaded here to help understanding. In real exam, it should not be shaded.

Solution:

Member	Tributary Width (TW)	Tributary Area (A_T)
Typical Interior Beam	25 ft./3 spaces = 8.33 ft.	(8.33 ft.) (32 ft.) = 267 ft.^{2}
Typical Spandrel Beam	(25 ft./3 spaces)/2 + 0.5 [ft.] edge distance = 4.67 ft.	(4.67 ft.) (32 ft.) = 150 ft.^{2}
Typical Interior Girder	—	$\left(\frac{267}{2}\text{ ft.}^2\right)$(4 beams) = 534 ft.^{2}
Typical Spandrel Girder	—	(0.5 ft. edge dist) (25 ft.) + $\left(\frac{267}{2}\text{ ft.}^2\right)$(2 beams) = 280 ft.^{2}
Typical Interior Column	—	(32 ft.) (25 ft.) = 800 ft.^{2}
Typical Corner Column	—	(32 ft./2 + 0.5 ft. edge distance) × (25 ft./2 + 0.5 ft. edge distance) = 215 ft.^{2}
Typical Exterior Column (long side of building)	—	(32 ft./2 + 0.5 ft. edge distance) (25 ft.) = 413 ft.^{2}
Typical Exterior Column (short side of building)	—	(25 ft./2 + 0.5 ft. edge distance) (32 ft.) = 416 ft.^{2}

4.2 Trusses

A truss is a structure where members are pin-connected at their ends, and loads act only at the joints. Due to this configuration, all members in a truss are two-force members meaning that they carry only tension or compression. All forces acting on the truss must be applied at the nodes. The self-weight of the member is either neglected or assumed, acting at the ends only. As pin-connected members, the members cannot sustain the moment.

4.2.1 Zero-Force Members

Some of the members in a truss are zero-force members. This means the member is not designed to carry any load. However, this member is provided for safety if the load conditions change and to provide additional stability. There are two rules to identify the zero-force members:

Rule 1. If two non-collinear members form an unloaded joint both are zero-force members.
Rule 2. If three members form an unloaded joint of which two are collinear, then the third member is a zero-force member.

A two-force body in static equilibrium has two applied forces that are equal in magnitude, opposite in direction, and collinear. A question on finding zero-force member was a guarantee in the FE exam. If there is a question from truss, it might be finding zero-force member again.

Example 4.5

Find out the zero-force member(s) of the truss shown in figure below.

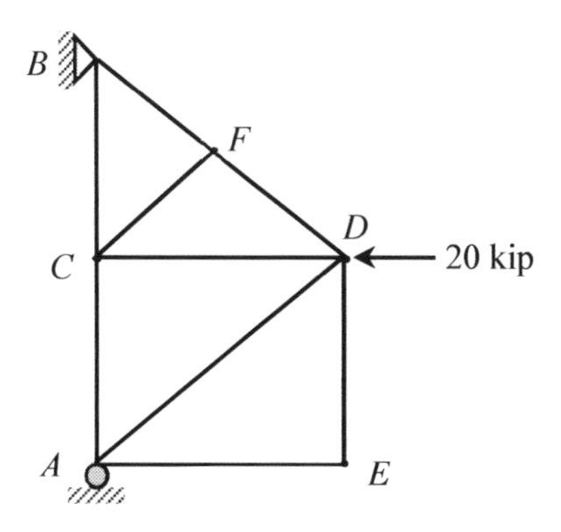

Solution:

AE and *ED* are zero-force members, according to Rule 1.

CF is zero-force member, according to Rule 2. Once *CF* is a zero-force member, *CD* is also a zero-force member too, according to Rule 2.

Example 4.6

Find out the zero-force member(s) of the truss shown in figure below.

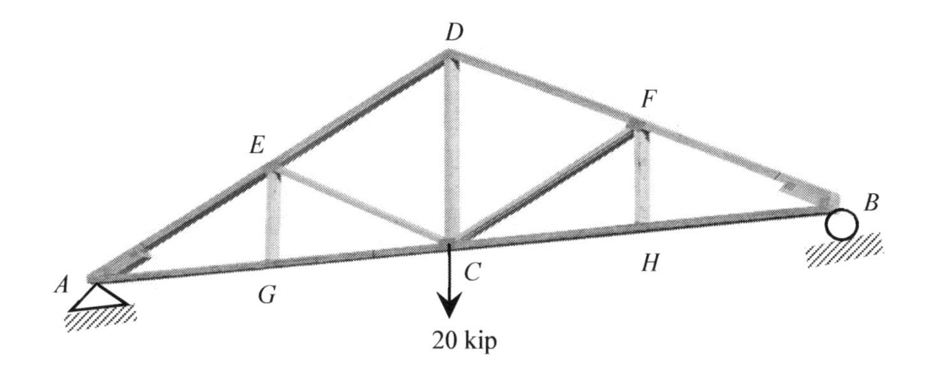

Solution:

GE and *HF* are zero-force members according to Rule 2. Once they are zero-force members, *CE* and *CF* are also zero-force members according to Rule 2.

Example 4.7

Find out the zero force member(s) of the truss shown in figure below.

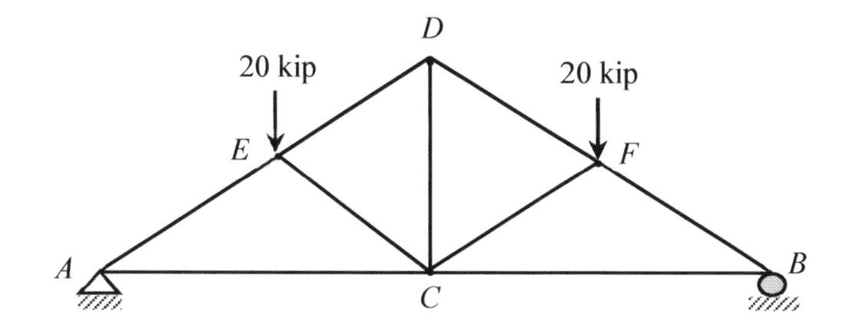

Solution:

None of the members is a zero-force member.

Joints *A*, *B*, *E*, and *F* have a load. Therefore, members associated with these joints might have forces. Joint *D* has three members with no load; however, no two members are linear. So, the associated three members may not be zero-force members. Joint *C* has five members; nothing can be decided from this joint.

4.2.2 Direct-Force Members

The concept of the direct-force member is not well known; it is merely proposed by the authors. There may be some members that carry the applied load directly without distributing it to other members. This happens when a force is applied at a joint along the member and other member(s) connected to the joint are perpendicular to the load and the original member. For example, see below. The truss has three loads at three joints, *G*, *C* and *H*. Let us analyze them one by one. The load in the joint *G* is along the member *GE,* and the other two members (*GA* and *GC*) connected to the joint *G* are perpendicular to the load and the member GE. Therefore, *GE* is the direct-force member for the 2-kip load. As the force (2-kip) is applied away from the member *GE*, the force in the member *GE* is 2 kip (tension).

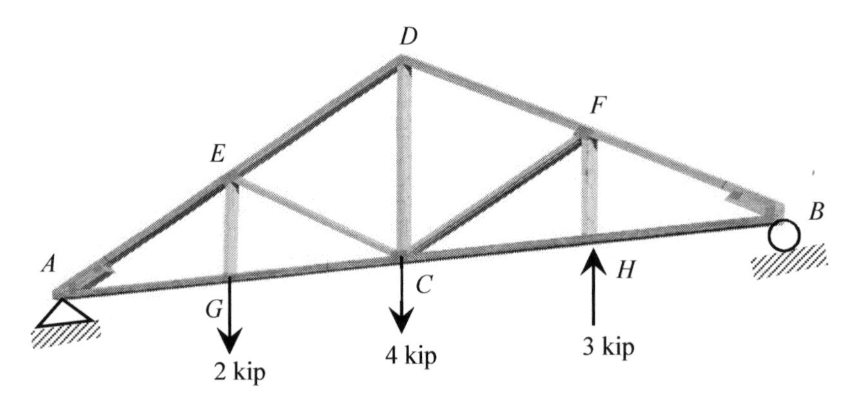

A truss to clarify the direct-force members.

Now, let us consider the joint *C*. It has a 4-kip load along the member *CD*. Two members connected to the joint *C* (*CG* and *CH*) are perpendicular to the load and the member *CD*. However, there are two other members (*CE* and *CF*) which are connected to the joint *C* and are not perpendicular to the load and the member *CD*. Therefore, *CD* is not a direct-force member and the force in the member *CD* cannot be determined in this way. Now, let us consider the joint *H*. It has a 3-kip load along the member *HF*. Two members connected to the joint *C* (*HC* and *HB*) are perpendicular to the load and the member *HF*. Therefore, *HF* is the direct-force member for the 3-kip load. As the force (3-kip) is applied toward the member *HF*, the force in the member *HF* is 3 kip (compression).

4.2.3 Method of Joints

In the method of joints, each joint is considered as an equilibrium problem, which involves a concurrent force system. A free-body diagram of each joint is constructed and two force equations of equilibrium are written to solve for the two unknown member forces. More clearly, a free-body diagram of the joint is drawn to determine the forces in members connected to a joint. While drawing the free-body diagram, the force in each member is commonly assumed tension. An arrow away from member represents the tension force. After the computation, if the force yields a negative sign, it means a compression force. The equilibrium equations ($\sum F_x = 0$ and $\sum F_y = 0$) are applied. Note that if the joint has more than two members, then the forces cannot be determined as only two equilibrium equations ($\sum F_x = 0$ and $\sum F_y = 0$) can be applied. In this case, a neighbor joint is considered to determine the connected member's force. Note that the reactions of the support may not be required, but determining such may help for certain cases. Let us review the steps for the joint method:

Step 1. Isolate a joint from the truss that contains no more than two unknowns.

Step 2. Draw a free-body diagram of the joint and solve for the two unknown member forces by satisfying the horizontal and vertical conditions of equilibrium.

Step 3. Select another joint (usually adjacent to the joint just completed) that contains no more than two unknowns and solve the two conditions of equilibrium.

Step 4. Continue this process until all joints have been solved.

Example 4.8

Determine the member forces of the plane truss shown below.

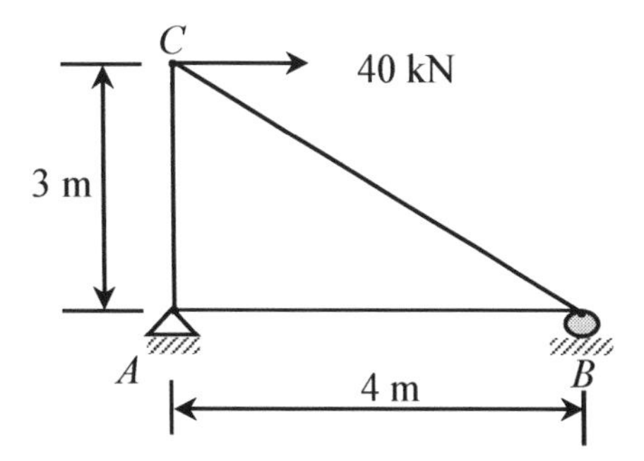

Solution:

The problem did not specify which method to use. Commonly, no specific method is recommended. We will use the joint method here to explain this method. Once you learn the section method, you can use any or mix of both methods. Whatever method you use, the results must be the same. Consider the free-body diagram of the joint C as shown below. The reason for choosing this joint is that it has only two unknown forces (two members). If we select the other joints, they have two unknown forces each and the support reactions. It is assumed in the free-body diagram that all the members are in tension. An arrow away from member represents the tension force.

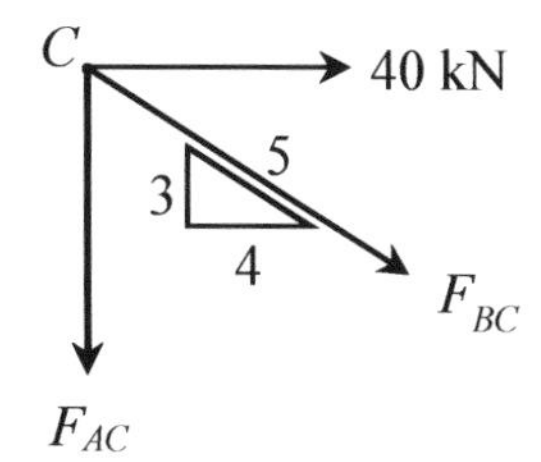

Free-body diagram of the joint C

$$\sum F_x = 0\ (\rightarrow +ve)$$

$$F_{BC}\left(\frac{4}{5}\right) + 40\text{ kN} = 0$$

$$F_{BC} = -50\text{ kN}$$

$$\sum F_y = 0\ (\downarrow +ve)$$

$$F_{BC}\left(\frac{3}{5}\right) + F_{AC} = 0$$

$$F_{AC} = -(-50)\left(\frac{3}{5}\right)\text{ kN} = 30\text{ kN}$$

The force F_{BC} is negative, meaning it is in compression.

Consider the joint B as shown below. We already obtained the force F_{BC}. There are only two unknowns left at joint B, i.e., F_{AB} and B_y. We do not need to find B_y.

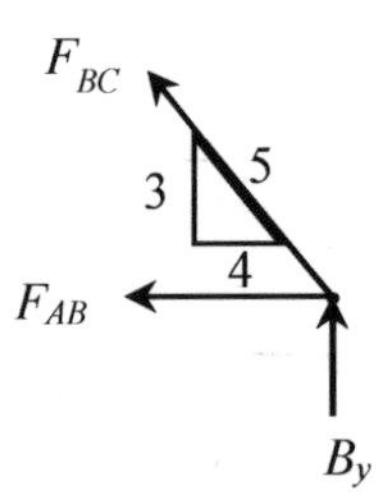

Free-body diagram of the joint B of the truss

$$\sum F_x = 0 \; (\leftarrow +ve)$$

$$F_{BC}\left(\frac{4}{5}\right) + F_{AB} = 0$$

$$F_{AB} = -F_{BC}\left(\frac{4}{5}\right)$$

$$F_{AB} = -(-50)\left(\frac{4}{5}\right) = 40 \text{ kN}$$

Answers:

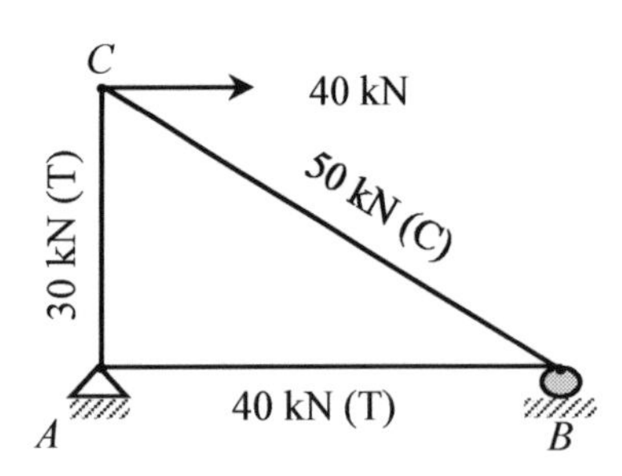

Remember: the symbols F_{AB} and F_{BA} carry the same meaning. It is the force at AB member, tension or compression. The symbol F_{AB} does not mean the force from A to B or vice versa.

Example 4.9

Determine the member forces of the plane truss shown below.

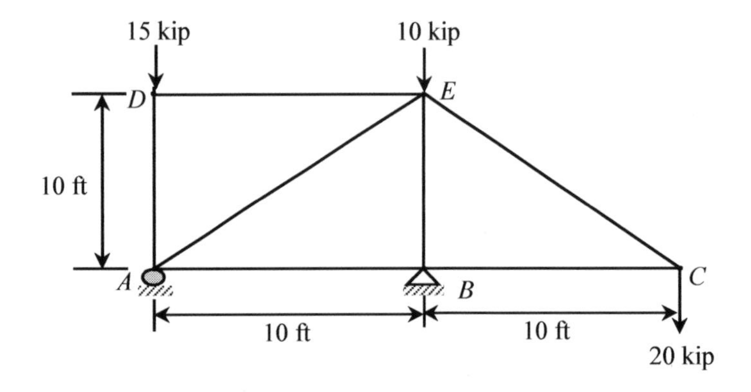

Solution:
We will use the joint method. Considering the joint C as shown below. The reason for choosing this joint is that it has only two unknown forces (two members). If we select the other joints, they have more than two unknown forces each except the joint D. We could also consider joint D at the beginning, as it has only two unknown forces and then we proceed from that joint.

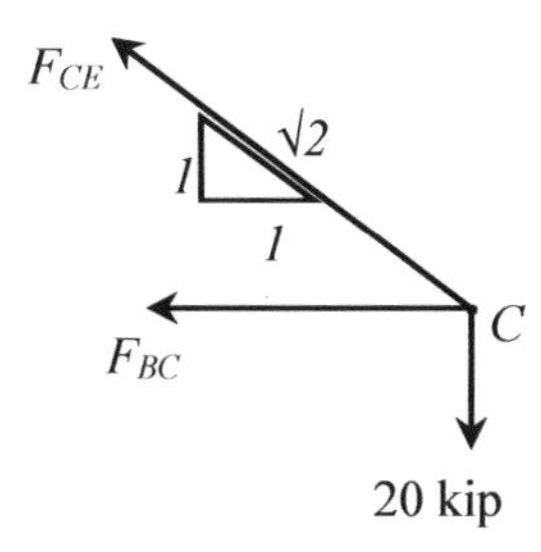

Free-body diagram of the joint C of the truss

$$\sum F_y = 0 \, (\uparrow +ve)$$

$$F_{CE}\left(\frac{1}{\sqrt{2}}\right) - 20\,\text{kip} = 0$$

$$F_{CE} = 20\sqrt{2}\,\text{kip}$$

$F_{CE} = 28.3$ kip (Tension)

$$\sum F_x = 0 \, (\rightarrow +ve)$$

$$-F_{CB} - F_{CE}\left(\frac{1}{\sqrt{2}}\right) = 0$$

$$F_{CB} = -F_{CE}\left(\frac{1}{\sqrt{2}}\right)$$

$$F_{CB} = (-28.3\,\text{kip})\left(\frac{1}{\sqrt{2}}\right)$$

$F_{CB} = -20$ kip

Now, consider the whole truss (figure below).

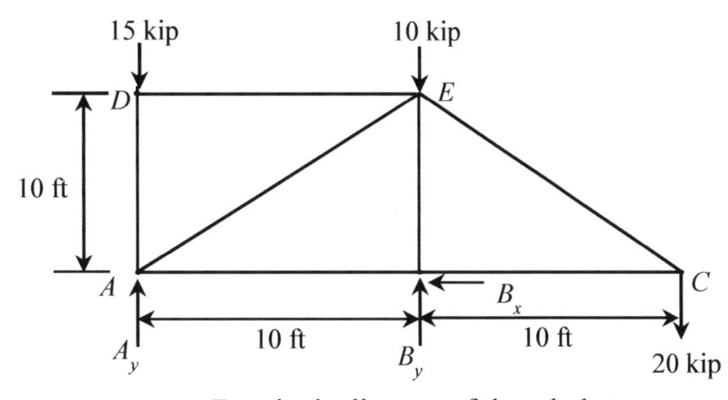

Free-body diagram of the whole truss

$\sum M \text{ at } A = 0 \quad (↲ + ve)$

$10 \text{ kip } (10 \text{ ft}) + 20 \text{ kip } (20 \text{ ft}) - B_y\, (10 \text{ ft}) = 0$
$100 \text{ kip.ft} + 400 \text{ kip.ft} - 10B_y \text{ ft} = 0$
$500 \text{ kip.ft} - 10B_y \text{ ft} = 0$
$10B_y \text{ ft} = 500 \text{ kip.ft}$
$B_y = 50 \text{ kip}$

$\sum F_y = 0 \left(\uparrow +ve\right)$

$A_y + B_y - 15 \text{ kip} - 10 \text{ kip} - 20 \text{ kip} = 0$
$A_y = -B_y + 15 \text{ kip} + 10 \text{ kip} + 20 \text{ kip}$
$A_y = -50 \text{ kip} + 15 \text{ kip} + 10 \text{ kip} + 20 \text{ kip}$
$A_y = -5 \text{ kip}$

Consider the joint *B* as shown below:

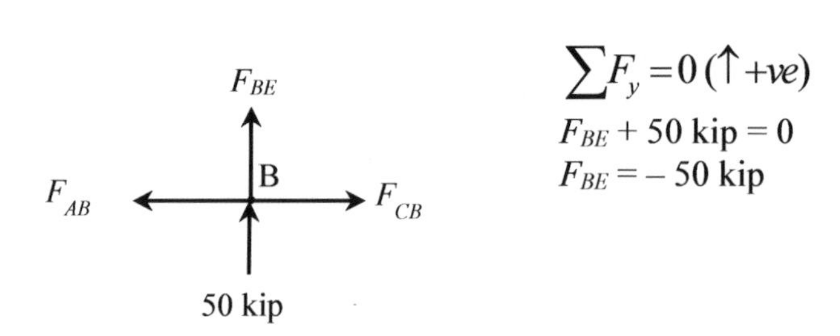

$\sum F_y = 0 \left(\uparrow +ve\right)$
$F_{BE} + 50 \text{ kip} = 0$
$F_{BE} = -50 \text{ kip}$

Free-body diagram of the joint *B* of the truss

$\sum F_x = 0 \left(\rightarrow + ve\right)$

$-F_{AB} + F_{CB} = 0$
$F_{AB} = F_{CB}$
$F_{AB} = -20 \text{ kip}$

Consider the joint *D* as shown in figure below:

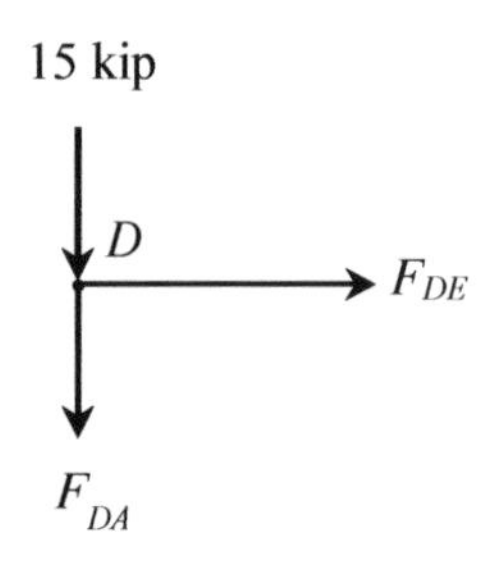

Free-body diagram of the joint *D* of the truss

$\sum F_y = 0 \left(\uparrow +ve\right)$

$F_{DA} + 15 \text{ kip} = 0$
$F_{DA} = -15 \text{ kip}$

We can also find F_{DA} using visual inspection, $F_{DA} = -15$ kip (direct force)

$\sum F_x = 0 \left(\rightarrow + ve\right)$

$F_{DE} = 0$

Consider the joint *A* as shown below:

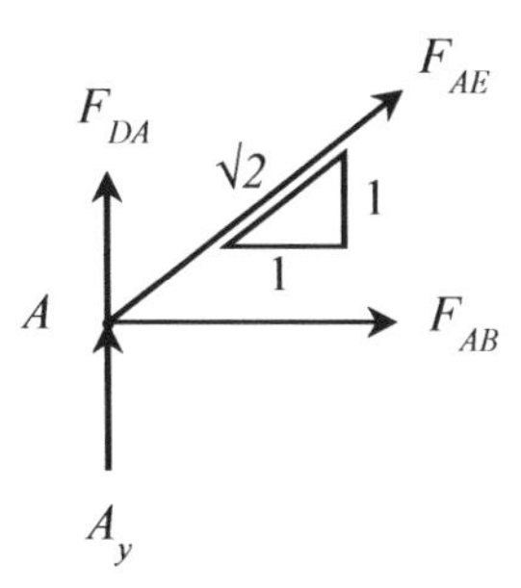

Free-body diagram of the joint D of the truss

$\sum F_x = 0 \ (\rightarrow +ve)$

$$F_{AB} + F_{AE}\frac{1}{\sqrt{2}} = 0$$

$$F_{AE} = -F_{AB}\sqrt{2}$$

$$F_{AE} = -(-20\text{kip})\sqrt{2}$$

$$F_{AE} = 28.3 \text{ kip}$$

Answers:

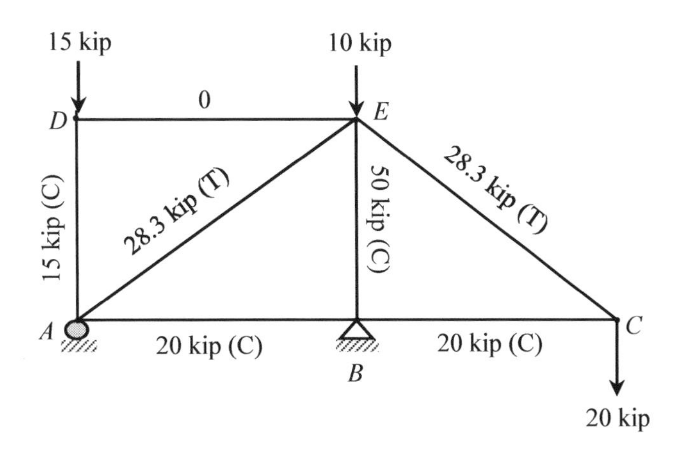

Remember: Finding out the support reactions is not always required. For many cases, member forces can be determined without finding the support reactions. Also, the questions in the exam will not be as big as this example.

4.2.4 Method of Sections

The second method of analysis is called the section method. The method of sections is a particularly useful analysis technique when only a few selected member forces in a truss are desired. In the method of sections, an imaginary section cut is passed through the truss, cutting three members, which includes at least one of the members of interest. The truss is now cut into two parts and a free-body diagram is constructed of either section. Since all forces in the free-body diagram are not concurrent at a common point, this constitutes a rigid body type problem and three equations of equilibrium may be written. These three equations of equilibrium can solve for only three unknown member forces. Note: no more than three unknown members are permitted to be cut for any section passing through the truss.

Example 4.10
Determine the member forces for the truss shown in figure below.

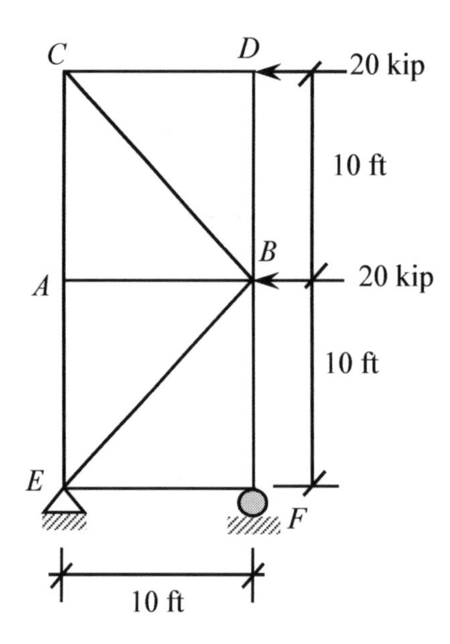

Solution:

By visual inspection:

$F_{CD} = -20$ kip (direct force)

$F_{AB} = 0$ (zero-force member)

It is always a good idea to find out the zero-force members or direct-force members at the beginning of solving the truss. This will reduce the number of unknowns. Consider the free-body diagram of a section of the truss as shown in figure below. Note that you can cut any section of the truss. However, the cut should be made in a way that is helpful.

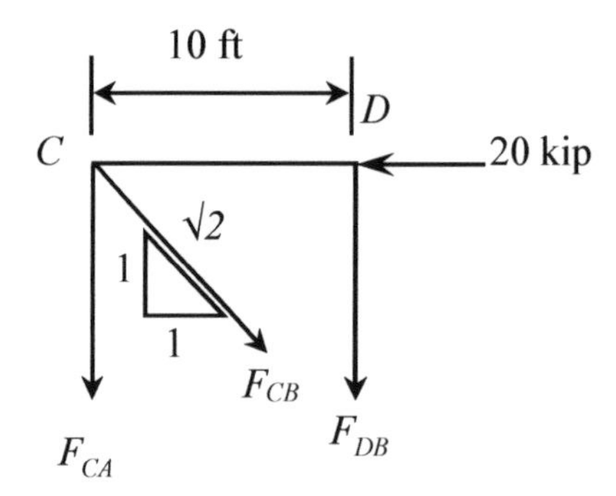

$$\sum F_x = 0 \; (\rightarrow +ve)$$

$$F_{CB}\left(\frac{1}{\sqrt{2}}\right) - 20\,\text{kip} = 0$$

$F_{CB} = 20\sqrt{2}$ kip

$F_{CB} = 28.28$ kip

$$\sum M \text{ at } C = 0 \; (\lrcorner + ve)$$

$F_{DB} = 0$

$\sum F_y = 0 \ (\downarrow +ve)$

$$F_{CA} + F_{DB} + F_{CB}\left(\frac{1}{\sqrt{2}}\right) = 0$$

$$F_{CA} = -F_{DB} - F_{CB}\left(\frac{1}{\sqrt{2}}\right)$$

$$F_{CA} = -0 - 28.28\,\text{kip}\left(\frac{1}{\sqrt{2}}\right)$$

$F_{CA} = -\ 20$ kip

Consider the free-body diagram of a section of the truss as shown in figure below.

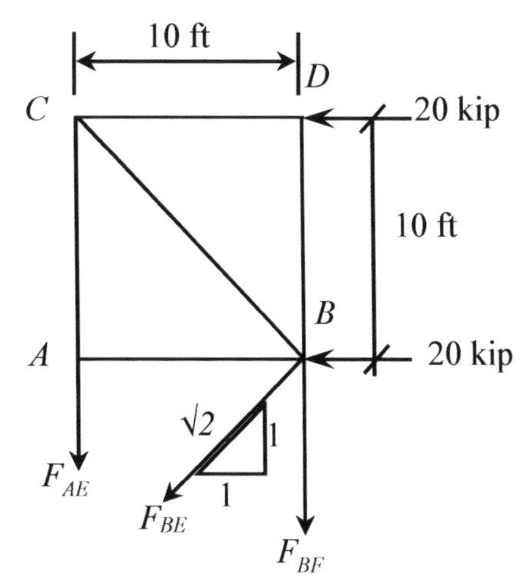

$\sum F_x = 0 \ (\leftarrow +ve)$

$$F_{BE}\left(\frac{1}{\sqrt{2}}\right) + 20\,\text{kip} + 20\,\text{kip} = 0$$

$$F_{BE}\left(\frac{1}{\sqrt{2}}\right) = -40\,\text{kip}$$

$F_{BE} = -\ 40\sqrt{2}$ kip
$F_{BE} = -\ 56.6$ kip

$\sum M$ at B = 0 (Assume a counter-clockwise moment is positive)
F_{AE} (10 ft) + 20 kip (10 ft) = 0
F_{AE} (10 ft) + 200 kip.ft = 0
$F_{AE} = -\ 20$ kip

$\sum F_y = 0 \ (\uparrow +ve)$

$$-F_{AE} - F_{BF} - F_{BE}\left(\frac{1}{\sqrt{2}}\right) = 0$$

$$F_{BF} = -F_{AE} - F_{BE}\left(\frac{1}{\sqrt{2}}\right)$$

$$F_{BF} = -(-20\,\text{kip}) - (-56.6\,\text{kip})\left(\frac{1}{\sqrt{2}}\right)$$

$$F_{BF} = 60\,\text{kip}$$

Consider the joint F as shown in figure below.

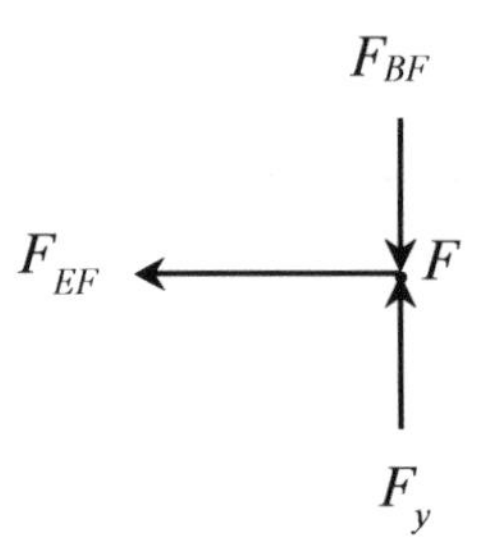

$$\sum F_x = 0 \ (\rightarrow +ve)$$

$$F_{EF} = 0$$

Answer:

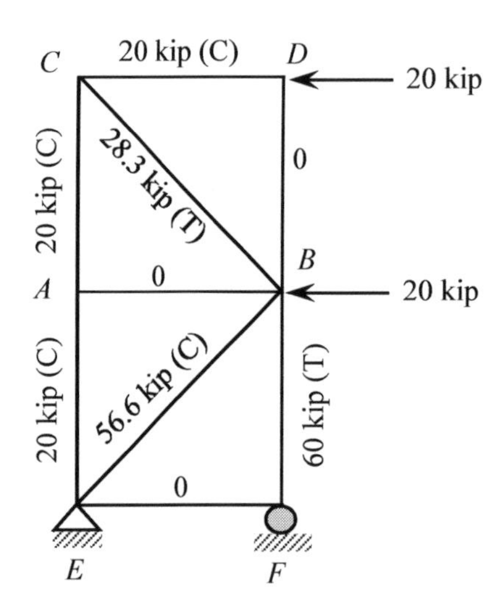

Remember: there is no restriction on which method (joint or section) to be used to solve a truss unless it is specified in the exam. Whatever method is used, the answer (solution) must be the same.

Example 4.11

The truss shown in figure below is supporting two loads. Determine the member force at CF.

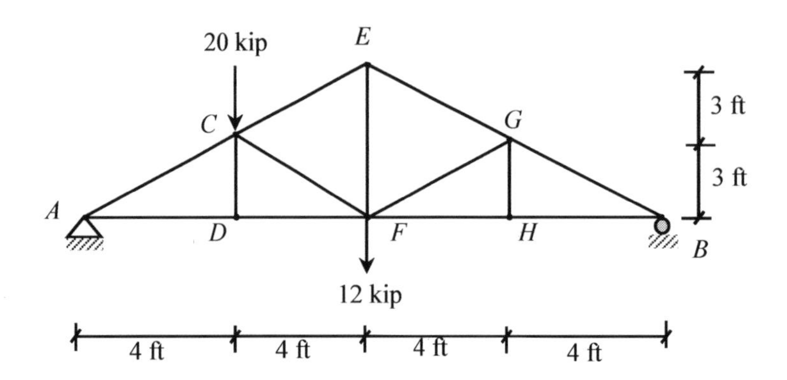

Solution:

First, considering the joint – D as shown in figure below, and applying $\sum F_y = 0$, it is found that CD is a zero-force member. The second rule of the zero-force members also supports that CD is a zero-force member – if three members form an unloaded joint of which two are collinear, then the third member is a zero-force member. Next, consider the left of the a–a cut section:

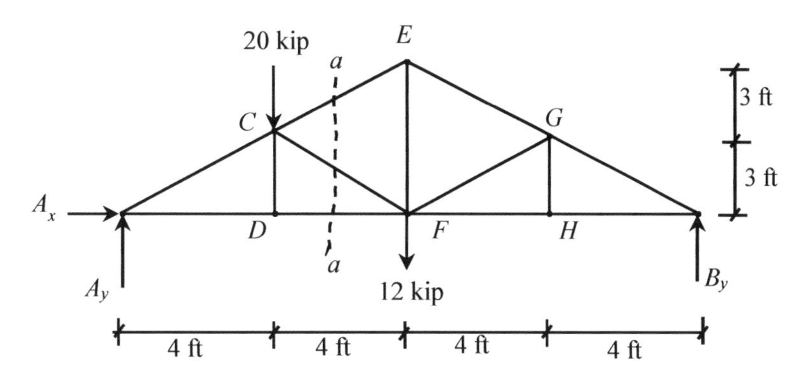

Consider the left side of the section a-a, as shown in figure below.

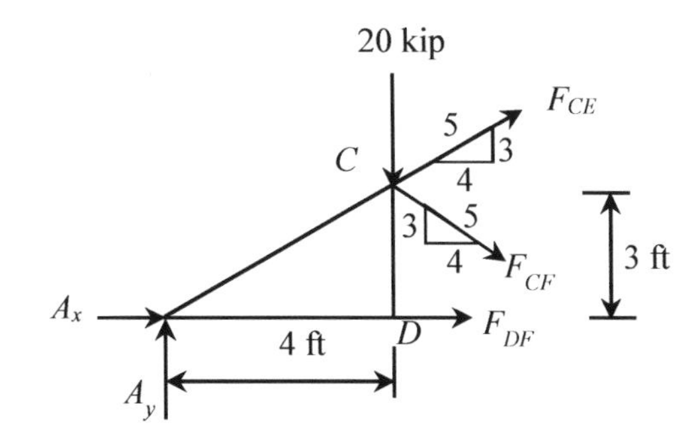

$\sum M$ at $A = 0$ (assuming clockwise moment is positive)

$$20 \text{ kip } (4 \text{ ft}) + F_{CF} (3/5)(4 \text{ ft}) + F_{CF} (4/5)(3 \text{ ft}) = 0$$
$$80 \text{ kip.ft} + 2.4\, F_{CF} + 2.4\, F_{CF} \text{ ft} = 0$$
$$4.8\, F_{CF} \text{ ft} = -\,80 \text{ kip.ft}$$
$$F_{CF} = -16.67 \text{ kip}$$

Remember: you can cut anywhere in any shape while using the section method. A wise cut can reduce the solution time. It is always advised to think a lot before cutting a section.

4.2.5 Determinacy and Stability

A structure is said to be stable if its support restraints and member organization are such that it does not collapse due to external loading from any direction and of any kind. Stability can be assessed by mathematical calculation, and by visual inspection. The following symbols have been used here to discuss this phenomenon.

m = number of members
r = number of independent reactions
j = number of joints

For plane truss (2D truss), the following formulations (Table below) can be used to justify the stability (external) and determinacy of a plane truss.

Table 4.1 Stability and determinacy of a plane truss

Static Analysis	**Classification**
$m + r < 2j$	Unstable
$m + r = 2j$	Stable and statically determinate
$m + r > 2j$	Stable and statically indeterminate

To justify the internal stability of truss, it must be accessed visually. Both the support restraints and member arrangement must be such that it can resist both horizontal and vertical loads either anticipated or accidental. The bar arrangement must be such that it must have at least one diagonal (i.e., triangular) so that it does not squeeze.

Example 4.12
Determine the determinacy and the stability of the truss shown below.

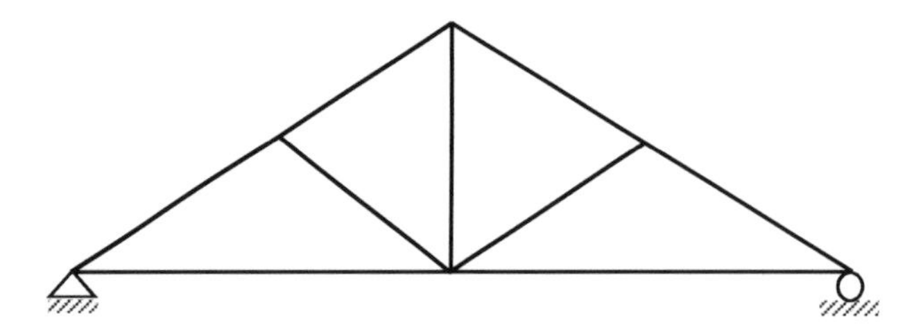

Solution:

Number of member, $m = 9$	$m + r = 12$
Number of reaction, $r = 3$	$2j = 12$
Number of joint, $j = 6$	$m + r = 2j$

As $m + r = 2j$, the structure is determinate and stable.

Example 4.13
Determine the determinacy and the stability of the truss shown in Figure 4.35.

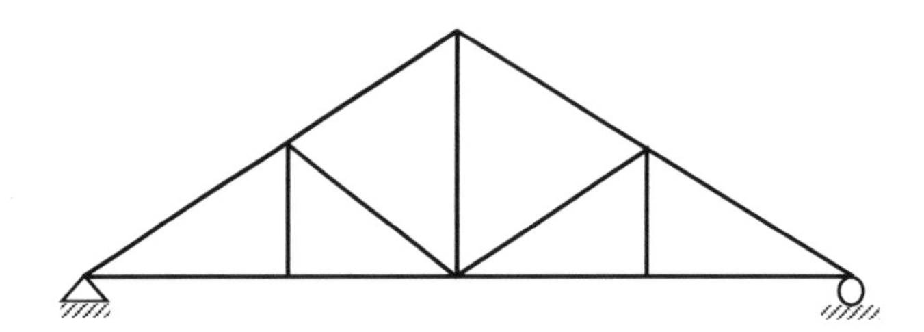

Solution:

Number of member, $m = 13$	$m + \mathrm{r} = 16$
Number of reaction, $r = 3$	$2j = 16$
Number of joint, $j = 8$	$m + r = 2j$

As $m + r = 2j$, the structure is determinate and stable.

4.3 Bending

This topic is based on Article 1.6 of the PE Civil Handbook.

4.3.1 Bending in Non-composite Beam

When positive bending occurs in beam, it bends downward. The bottom fiber gets tensile stress and the top fiber gets compressive stress as shown below.

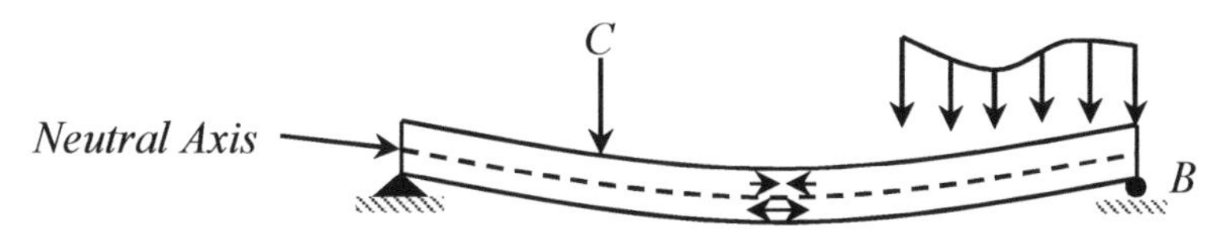

If the member is within the linear-elastic region, then the bending stress diagram along the section can be shown as follows –

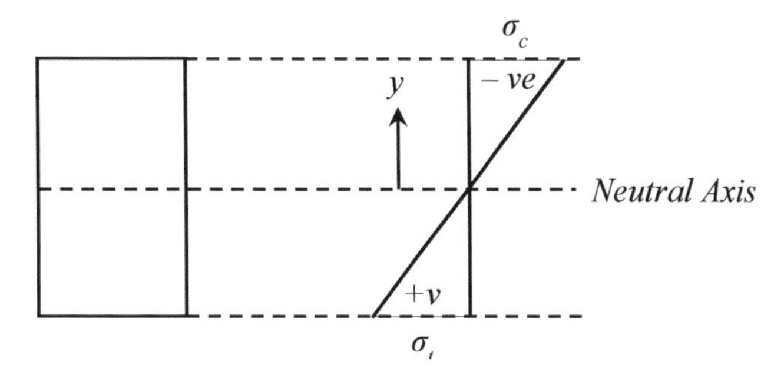

where y is the distance from the neutral axis to the point of interest. For rectangular section, the neutral axis is located at the centroid. Thus, the neutral axis is located at equal distance from the top or the bottom fiber. The bending stress is always linear and zero at the neutral axis. It can be expressed as –

$$\sigma = \frac{My}{I}$$

where σ is the bending stress; M is the applied moment; I is the moment of inertia and y is the any distance from the neutral axis. The bending stress increases as the distance from the neutral axis increases; thus the maximum bending stress occurs at the extreme fiber of the beam. The maximum tensile bending stress can be calculated as –

$$\sigma = \frac{Mc}{I}$$

where c is the distance from the neutral axis to the bottom fiber. Similarly, the maximum compressive bending stress can be calculated as –

$$\sigma = \frac{Mc}{I}$$

where c is the distance from the neutral axis to the top fiber.

Example 4.14

Determine the developed maximum bending stress in the beam shown in figure below.

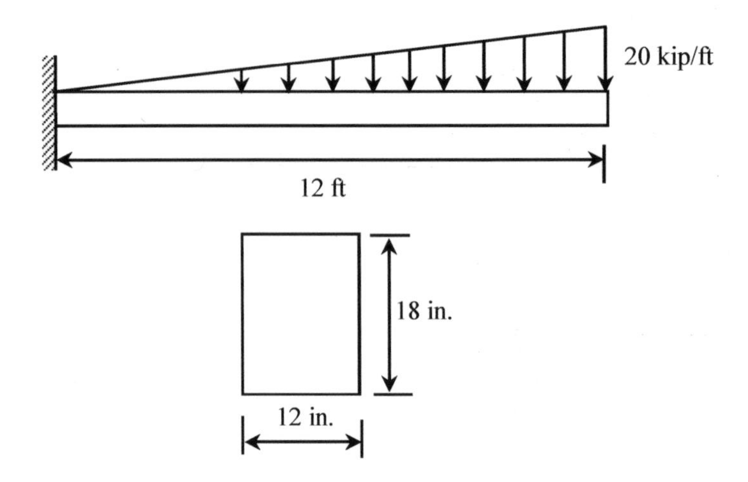

Solution:

Developed maximum moment at the support, M_{max} = Force (distance)
= [½(20 kip)(12 ft)] [8 ft] = 960 kip.ft

Moment of inertia, $I = \dfrac{bh^3}{12} = \dfrac{12\text{in.}(18\text{in.})^3}{12} = 5{,}832\text{ in.}^4$

Distance from the neutral axis to the top/bottom fiber, $c = 9$ in.

Developed maximum stress, $\sigma = \dfrac{Mc}{I} = \dfrac{(960\text{x}12\text{kip.in.})\ (9\text{in.})}{5{,}832\ \text{in.}^4} = \underline{17.8\text{ ksi}}$

Example 4.15

Determine the developed maximum bending stress in the beam shown in figure below. Article 1.6 of the PE Civil Handbook may need to be used.

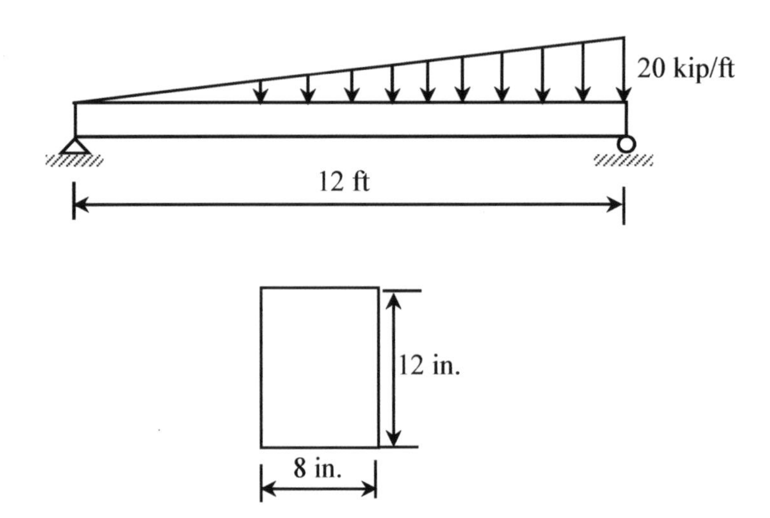

Solution:

PE Civil Handbook, Article 1.6

Maximum moment, $M_{\max} = \dfrac{w_o L^2}{9\sqrt{3}} = \dfrac{\left(20\ \dfrac{\text{kip}}{\text{ft}}\right)(12\text{ ft})^2}{9\sqrt{3}} = 185\text{ ft.kip}$

Moment of inertia, $I = \frac{bh^3}{12} = \frac{8\,\text{in.}(12\,\text{in.})^3}{12} = 1{,}152\ \text{in.}^4$

Distance from Neutral axis to extreme point, $c = 6$ in.

Maximum bending stress, $\sigma = \frac{Mc}{I} = \frac{(185 \times 12\,\text{kip.in.})\,(6\,\text{in.})}{1{,}152\ \text{in.}^4} = \underline{11.6\ \text{ksi}}$

Example 4.16

A beam section, shown below has a maximum positive moment of 100 kip.ft. Determine the developed maximum compressive and the tensile bending stress at the section. The neutral axis is 3 in. below the top fiber.

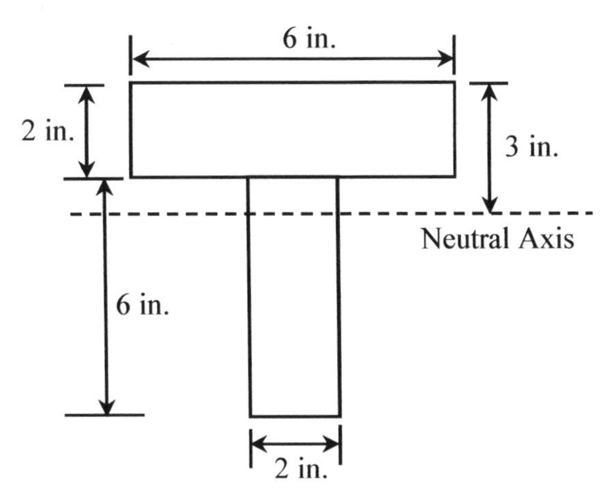

Solution:

Moment of inertia,

$$I = \frac{2\,\text{in.}(6\,\text{in.})^3}{12} + (2\,\text{in.})(6\,\text{in.})(5\,\text{in.} - 3\,\text{in.})^2 + \frac{6\,\text{in.}(2\,\text{in.})^3}{12} + (2\,\text{in.})(6\,\text{in.})(7\,\text{in.} - 5\,\text{in.})^2 = 136\ \text{in.}^4$$

Positive moment causes compressive stress at the top fiber. So, the maximum compressive bending stress, $\sigma_c = \frac{Mc}{I} = \frac{(100 \times 12)\,\text{kip.in.}\ (3\,\text{in.})}{136\ \text{in.}^4} = \underline{26.5\ \text{ksi}}$

Positive moment causes tensile stress at the bottom fiber. So, the maximum tensile bending stress,

$$\sigma_t = \frac{Mc}{I} = \frac{(100 \times 12)\,\text{kip.in.}\ (5\,\text{in.})}{136\ \text{in.}^4} = \underline{44.1\ \text{ksi}}$$

In the above-mentioned bending stress equation, the term I and c are constant for a section. Thus, a new term, section modulus (s) is very often used as $s = \frac{I}{c}$. Then, the bending stress in a beam due to moment is:

$$\sigma = \frac{Mc}{I} = \frac{M}{s}$$

where $S = \frac{I}{c}$ = section modulus. If the allowable bending stress, σ_{all} is known from laboratory testing or provided by the manufacturer, then, the required section modulus (s_{req}) can be calculated as:

$$s_{req} = \frac{M}{\sigma_{all}}$$

Now, from the section catalogue, a section can be chosen which has s_{req} equal or more than required. This is the design philosophy for bending. Sometimes, 'f' is used instead of 'σ' to express bending stress. The summary of design steps are as follows:

Step 1. Calculate the maximum moment (M) in the member.
Step 2. Find out the allowable bending strength (stress) from laboratory testing or manufacturer.
Step 3. Calculate the required section modulus (s_{req})
Step 4. Choose a section from the catalog which satisfies s_{req}

Example 4.17
The allowable bending stress of steel W-beam is 30 ksi. The maximum moment calculated from the analysis is 500 kip-ft. Is W18 x 40 section (which has section modulus of 68.4 in.^{3}) adequate for this bending stress?

Solution:

Section Modulus required, $s_{req} = \frac{M}{\sigma_{all}} = \frac{500 \text{ kip.ft } (12 \text{ in/ft})}{30 \text{ ksi}} = 200 \text{ in}^3$

W18 x 40 section has $S_x = 68.4$ in.^{3} which is less than the required. Therefore, this section is not adequate for this beam.

4.3.2 Bending Stress in Composite Beam

The bending stresses in a beam composed of dissimilar materials (material 1 and material 2) where $E_1 > E_2$ are:

$$\sigma_1 = n\frac{My}{I_T}$$

$$\sigma_2 = \frac{My}{I_T}$$

I_T = the moment of inertia of the transformed section

n = the modular ratio, $\frac{E_1}{E_2}$

E_1 = elastic modulus of material 1
E_2 = elastic modulus of material 2

The modulus section is transformed into a section composed of a single material. The centroid and then the moment of inertia are found on the transformed section for use in the bending stress equations.

Example 4.18
The following beam is composed of wood and two steel plates at the top and at the bottom of wood as shown. The beam has a maximum moment of 100 kip-in. Determine the maximum bending stress developed in the steel plates and the wood section.

$E_s = 210$ GPa, $E_w = 21$ GPa.

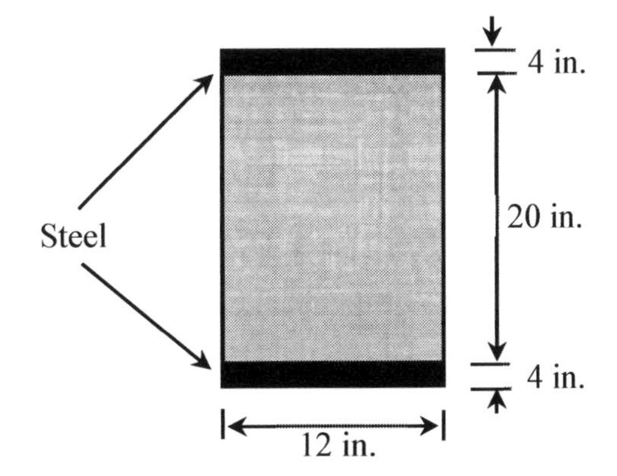

Solution:

$$n = \frac{E_s}{E_w} = \frac{210}{21} = 10$$

4 in.

20 in.

54 in.

4 in.

$12n = 12(10) = 120$ in.

Moment of Inertia, $I = \frac{120\text{in.}(28\text{in.})^3}{12} - 2\frac{54\text{in.}(20\text{in.})^3}{12} = 147{,}520 \text{ in.}^4$

Distance from neutral axis to the extreme of steel plate, c = 14 in.

Maximum bending stress in steel, $\sigma = n\frac{Mc}{I} = 10\frac{100 \text{ kip.in.}(14\text{in.})}{147{,}520 \text{ in.}^4} = 0.095 \text{ ksi} = \underline{95 \text{psi}}$

Maximum bending stress in wood, $\sigma = \frac{My}{I} = \frac{100 \text{ kip.in.}(10\text{in.})}{147{,}520 \text{ in.}^4} = 0.0068 \text{ ksi} = \underline{6.8 \text{psi}}$

4.4 Shear

This topic is based on Article 1.6 of the PE Civil Handbook.

4.4.1 Transverse Shear

Shear stress occurs due to the shear force in the beam section. In the following beam with any arbitrary loading, let us consider a very small element from the beam as shown in figure below. At that element the shear force V can be shown as shown considering the equilibrium of the element.

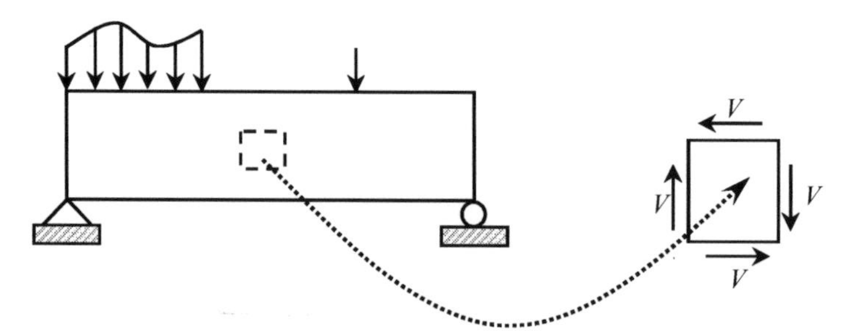

Concept of Shear Force in an Arbitrary Beam

The shear stress diagram is oval shaped with the maximum value at the neutral axis as shown in figure below. It shows that shear stress is zero at the upper and the lower ends and the maximum at the neutral axis or at the centroid. This is true for any kind of section. Maximum shear stress at the cross-section of a beam at a point is considered the maximum shear stress at the top or bottom sides of the beam.

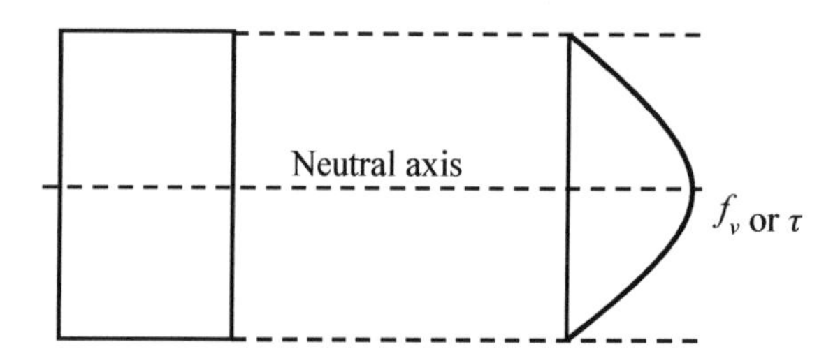

Shear stress (τ) can be expressed as $\tau = \dfrac{VQ}{Ib}$

V = Shear force at the concern point

I = Moment of inertia of the section

b = width or thickness of the section at the concern point

$Q = A'\bar{y}'$ (A' = area of the section above or below the concern point, $\bar{y}'$= centroid of this area (A') with respect to the neutral axis as shown below.

To elaborate, let us assume that shear stress is required to be determined at P-line in the following rectangular section. Then, A' is the area above the P-line. In the following figure area above the P-line has been considered. $\bar{y}'$ is the centroid of the shaded area as shown.

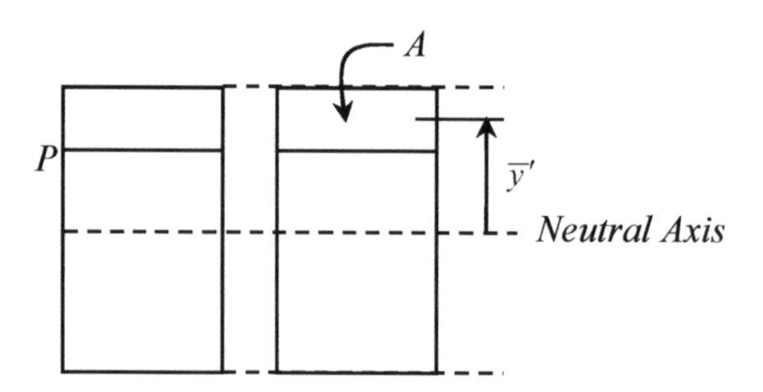

Again to remind you, shear stress is the maximum at the neutral axis and zero at the top and the bottom fibers. Let us determine the maximum shear-stress in a rectangular section of width, b and height, h.

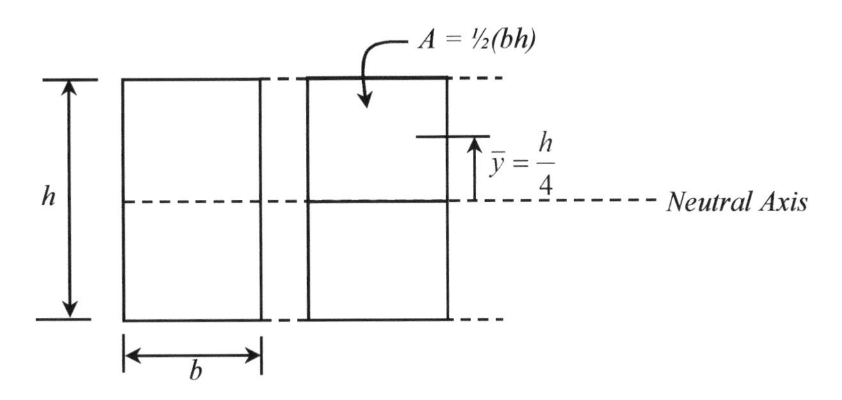

Maxim stress for rectangular section, $\tau_{max} = \frac{VQ}{Ib} = \frac{V(A'\bar{y}')}{\left(\frac{bh^3}{12}\right)b} = \frac{V\left(\frac{1}{2}bh\right)\left(\frac{h}{4}\right)}{\left(\frac{bh^3}{12}\right)b} = 1.5\frac{V}{bh} = 1.5\frac{V}{A}$

Therefore, for rectangular section, the maximum shear stress can be expressed as $\tau = 1.5\frac{V}{A}$. This equation is not listed in the PE Civil Reference Handbook. However, it is worthy to memorize this equation as it saves a lot of time. Remember, this equation is valid for rectangular section only.

Example 4.19
A 12 ft simply supported beam is having a uniformly distributed load of 3 kip/ft as shown below. The cross-section of the beam is 12 in x 18 in. What is most nearly the maximum shear stress developed in the following beam?

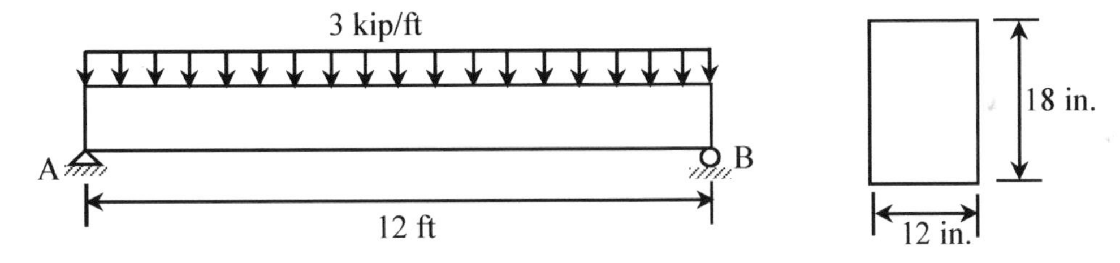

Solution:

$$\text{Maximum shear force, } V_{max} = \frac{wL}{2} = \frac{\left(3\frac{\text{kip}}{\text{ft}}\right)(12\text{ ft})}{2} = 18\text{ kip}$$

$$\text{Maximum shear stress, } \tau_{max} = \frac{VQ}{Ib} = 1.5\frac{V}{A} = 1.5\frac{18\text{ kip}}{(12\text{ in.})(18\text{ in.})} = 0.125\text{ ksi} = \underline{125\text{psi}}$$

Example 4.20

A 16 ft simply supported beam is having a uniformly distributed load of 4 kip/ft as shown below. The cross-section of the beam is a T-section with 18 in x 2 in flange and 18 in x 2 in web. Determine the maximum shear stress developed in the beam.

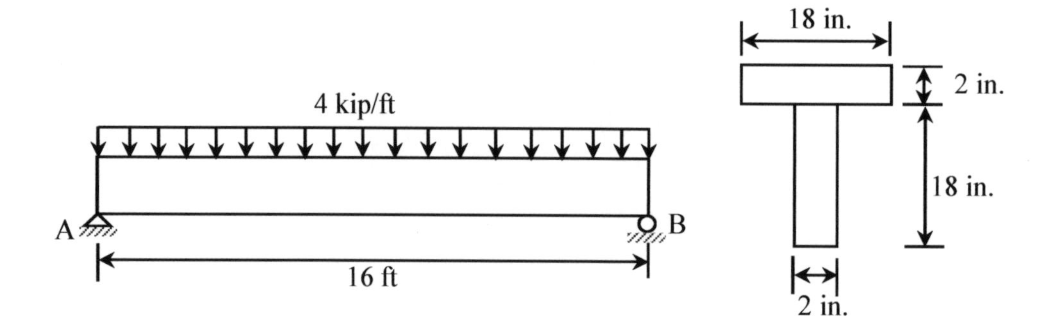

Solution:

Maximum shear force, $V_{max} = \frac{wL}{2} = \frac{\left(4\frac{\text{kip}}{\text{ft}}\right)(16\text{ ft})}{2} = 32 \text{ kip}$

The maximum shear stress occurs at the centroid. Let us determine the centroid first considering the web being the 1st element and the flange being the 2nd element.

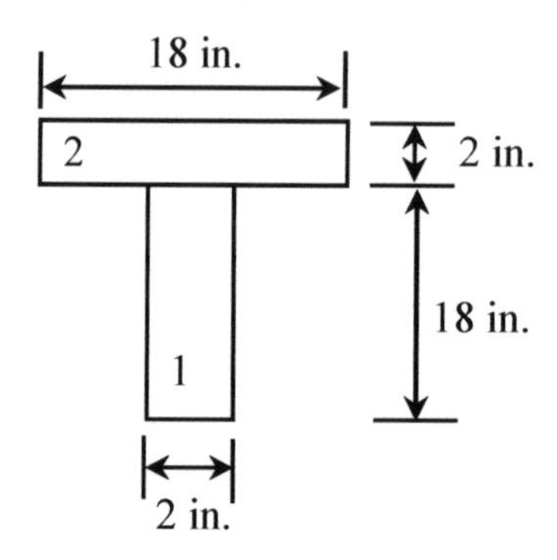

$$\bar{y} = \frac{y_1A_1 + y_2A_2}{A_1 + A_2} = \frac{9\text{in.}(2\text{in.x}18\text{in.}) + 19\text{in.}(18\text{in.x}2\text{in.})}{2\text{in.x}18\text{in.} + 18\text{in. x}2\text{in.}} = 14 \text{ in.}$$

$$I_x = \frac{b_1h_1^3}{12} + A_1(\bar{y} - y_1)^2 + \frac{b_2h_2^3}{12} + A_2(\bar{y} - y_2)^2$$

$$= \frac{2\text{in.}(18\text{in.})^3}{12} + (18\text{in.} \times 2\text{in.})(14\text{in.} - 9\text{in.})^2 + \frac{18\text{in.}(2\text{in.})^3}{12} + (18\text{in.} \times 2\text{in.})(14\text{in.} - 19\text{in.})^2$$

$$= \left(972\text{in.}^4 + 900\text{in.}^4\right) + \left(12\text{in.}^4 + 900\text{in.}^4\right)$$

$$= 2{,}784 \text{ in.}^4$$

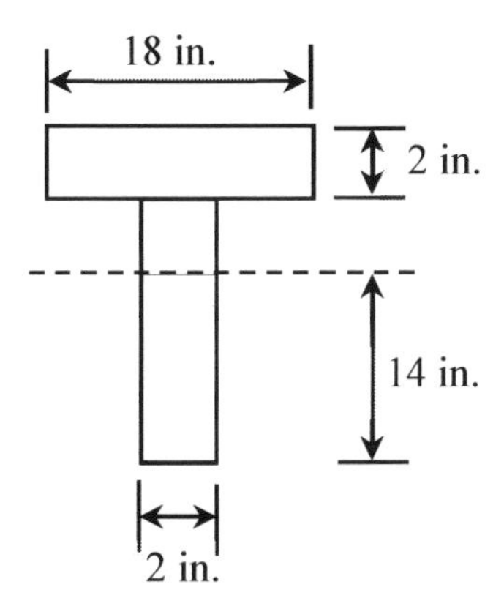

Area below the concerned point, $A' = 2 \text{ x } 14 \text{ in.}^2$
Centroid of A' from neutral axis, $\bar{y}' = 7$ in.
Thickness at the concerned point, $b = 2$ in.

Maximum shear stress, $\tau_{max} = \dfrac{VQ}{Ib} = \dfrac{V(A\bar{y})}{Ib} = \dfrac{32 \text{ kip}(2 \text{ x}14 \text{ in.}^2)\text{x}7 \text{ in.}}{(2{,}784 \text{ in.}^4)\ (2 \text{ in.})} = 1.126 \text{ ksi} = \underline{1{,}126 \text{psi}}$

In the NCEES exam, you may not be asked to solve this type of big problems. They may provide the centroid and moment of inertia so that this problem can be solved in 6 minutes. The author listed this problem here to revise the whole procedure.

4.4.2 Transverse Shear Flow

Maximum shear stress at the cross-section of a beam at a point is considered the maximum shear stress at the top or bottom sides of the beam. The shear force per unit length of the beam can be determined as:

$$q = \frac{VQ}{Ib}(b)$$

$$q = \frac{VQ}{I}$$

This shear force value is required to determine the amount of force applied on nail or glue in beam section.

Example 4.21
The following three lumber sections (10 in. x 4 in.) is to be nailed at certain distance to make a beam section. That beam will be subjected to 0.5 kip/ft load with a span of 20 ft. The nail has a diameter of 7/8 in. and spaced 12-in. center to center. Determine the shear stress in the nail.

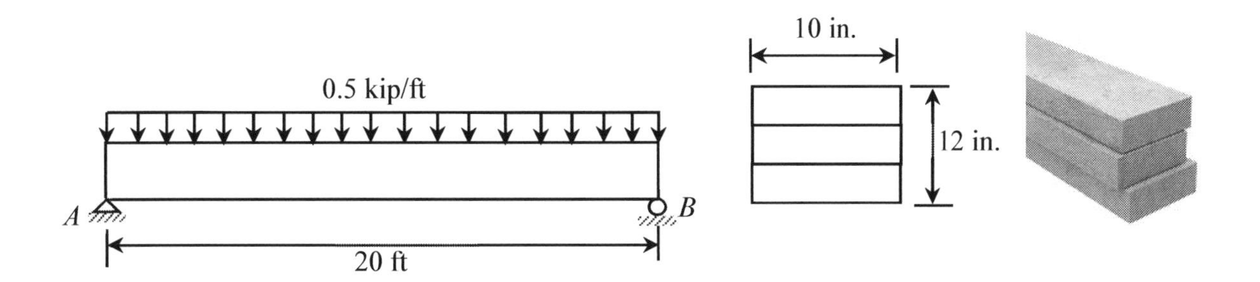

Solution:

Maximum shear force, $V_{max} = \frac{wL}{2} = \frac{0.5\frac{\text{kip}}{\text{ft}}(20\,\text{ft})}{2} = 5\ \text{kip}$

The shear flow at 2-in. from the neutral axis (at the layer interface) is to be determined first. This is because, the nail shear stress occurs at the layer interface. A' = 4 in. x 10 in. (the top member).

$$q = \frac{VQ}{I} = \frac{(5\,\text{kip})(4\,\text{in. x } 10\,\text{in.})(4\,\text{in.})}{\frac{10\,\text{in.}(12\,\text{in.})^3}{12}} = 0.555\,\frac{\text{kip}}{\text{in.}}$$

$$\text{Nail spacing} = \frac{\text{Force in the nail}}{\text{Shear Flow}}$$

Force in the nail = Nail spacing x shear flow = 12 in. x 0.555 kip/in. = 6.67 kip
Area = π (7/8 in.)^2/4 = 0.60 in.^{2}
Stress = Force in the nail / Area = 6.67 kip / 0.6 in.^{2} = 11.12 ksi

4.5 Axial

This topic is based on Article 1.6 of the PE Civil Handbook.

4.5.1 Axial Deformation by Mechanical Loading

Based on PE Civil Handbook, Article 1.6.2.6 Uniaxial Loading and Deformation, when the load acts along the longitudinal center-line of a member, it is termed as the uniaxial loading. This chapter is all about uniaxial loading and its effect on the structural member. To understand it, let us assume a load of P is applied on a uniaxial body of original cross-sectional area of A, original length of L as shown below.

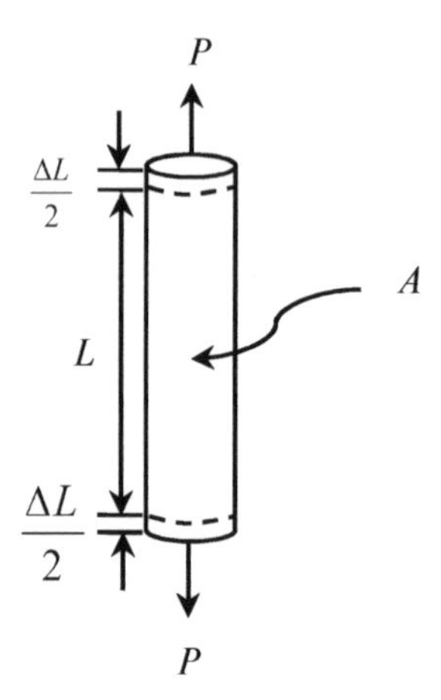

The applied axial stress on the member can be written as, $\sigma = \frac{P}{A}$

After applying a tensile force of P, there will be axial deformation (elongation for tension and contraction for compression). Let us assume there will be elongation of δ on both sides of the member. The total elongation is ΔL. The resulting axial strain can be written as –

Strain, $\varepsilon = \dfrac{\delta}{L}$

If the material is within the linear elastic region (proportional limit), from the Hooke's law,

Modulus of elasticity or Young's modulus, $E = \dfrac{\sigma}{\varepsilon} = \dfrac{P/A}{\delta/L} = \dfrac{PL}{A\delta}$

Rearranging the above equation, $\delta = \dfrac{PL}{AE}$. Therefore, the deformation or change in length can be calculated as: $\delta = \dfrac{PL}{AE}$.

Example 4.22

A steel bar has a length of 2.5 m and cross-section of 200 mm x 100 mm. The modulus of elasticity of this material is 210 GPa. Determine the increase in length after applying a tensile force of 150 kN.

Solution:

Length, $L = 2.5$ m
Cross-section, $A = 0.2$ m x 0.1 m
Modulus of elasticity, $E = 210 \times 10^9$ Pa
Tensile force, $P = 150{,}000$ N

Change in length, $\delta = \dfrac{PL}{AE}$

$$= \frac{150{,}000 \text{ N}(2.5 \text{ m})}{(0.2 \text{ x } 0.1 \text{ m}^2)\left(210\text{x}10^9 \dfrac{\text{N}}{\text{m}^2}\right)} = 0.000089 \text{ m} \quad = \underline{0.089 \text{ mm}}$$

Example 4.23

A steel rod is 0.02 m in diameter, and 2.5 m in length. The modulus of elasticity of this material is 210 GPa. Determine the final length of the rod after applying a tensile force of 150 kN.

Solution:

Length, $L = 2.5$ m

Cross-section, $A = \dfrac{\pi}{4}D^2 = \dfrac{\pi}{4}(0.02\text{ m})^2$

Modulus of elasticity, $E = 210 \times 10^9$ Pa
Tensile force, $P = 150{,}000$ N

Change in length, $\delta = \dfrac{PL}{AE} \quad = \dfrac{150{,}000 \text{ N}(2.5 \text{ m})}{\dfrac{\pi}{4}(0.02 \text{ m})^2\left(210 \times 10^9 \dfrac{\text{N}}{\text{m}^2}\right)}$

$= 0.00568$ m $\quad \approx 5.7$ mm

Final Length $L_{final} = L_{initial} + \delta = 2{,}500 \text{ mm} + 5.7 \text{ mm} = \underline{2{,}505.7 \text{ mm}}$

Example 4.24
A bar is 4 m long and has a Poisson's Ratio of 0.3. The modulus of elasticity of the material is 210 GPa. If a stress of 200 kPa is applied uniaxialy on it what will be the change in length?

Solution:

Length, $L = 4.0$ m
Modulus of elasticity, $E = 210 \times 10^9$ Pa
Applied stress, $\sigma = 200 \times 10^3$ Pa

Change in length, $\delta = \dfrac{PL}{AE}$

$$= \left(\frac{P}{A}\right)\left(\frac{L}{E}\right) = (\sigma)\left(\frac{L}{E}\right) = 200\times10^3\ \text{Pa}\left(\frac{4\ \text{m}}{210\times10^9\ \text{Pa}}\right)$$

$$= 3.8\times10^{-6}\ \text{m} \quad = \underline{0.0038\ \text{mm}}$$

Example 4.25
The column is constructed from high-strength concrete and four A-36 steel reinforcing rods. If it is subjected to an axial force of 800 kN, determine the required diameter of each rod so that one-fourth of the load is carried by the steel and three-fourths by the concrete. $E_{st} = 200$ GPa, $E_c = 25$ GPa.

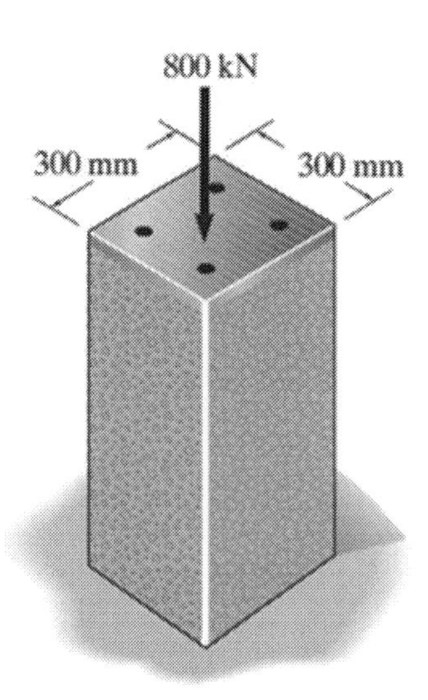

Solution:

Force in steel, P_{st} = ¼ of 800 kN = 200 kN
Force in concrete, P_{con} = ¾ of 800 kN = 600 kN
As a compatibility condition, Strain in Concrtete = Strain in Steel

$$\delta_{con} = \delta_{st}$$

$$\frac{P_{con}L}{\left(0.3\times0.3\text{m}^2 - A_{st}\right)\left(25\times10^9\ \text{Pa}\right)} = \frac{P_{st}L}{A_{st}\left(200\times10^9\ \text{Pa}\right)}$$

$$A_{st} = \frac{0.09P_{st}}{8P_{con} + P_{st}}$$

$$4\left[\frac{\pi d^2}{4}\right] = \frac{0.09(200)}{8(600) + 200}$$

$d = 0.0339$ m = $\underline{33.9\ \text{mm}}$

4.5.2 Axial Deformation by Thermal Loading

The length of a material increases or decreases with increase or decrease in temperature, respectively. The change in length due to change in temperature is called thermal deformation. Article 1.6.3 Thermal Deformations states:

$$\delta_t = \alpha L(T - T_o)$$

δ_t = deformation caused by a change in temperature
α = temperature coefficient of expansion
L = length of member
T = final temperature
T_o = initial temperature

Example 4.26

A 5 m steel rod has a coefficient of thermal expansion and contraction of 6 x10^{-6} per °F. If the temperature of the body is decreased by 50 °F, determine the thermal strain.

Solution:

Coefficient of thermal expansion and contraction, α = 6 x10^{-6} per °F
Decrease in temperature, ΔT = 50 °F
Length, L = 5.0 m
Thermal strain = $\alpha(\Delta T)$ = 6 x10^{-6} per °F (50 °F) = $\underline{3 \text{ x}10^{-4}}$

Example 4.27

A 10 m steel rod is snugly supported by two rigid supports at the ends as shown in figure below. The coefficient of thermal expansion and contraction of the rod is 6 x10^{-6} per °F and the elastic modulus is 210 GPa. If the temperature of the body is increased by 50 °F, determine the thermal stress developed at the supports.

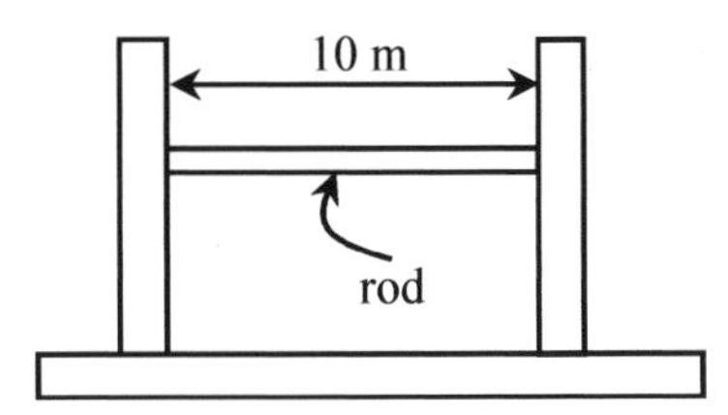

Solution:

Coefficient of thermal expansion and contraction, α = 6 x10^{-6} per °F
Decrease in temperature, ΔT = 50 °F
Elastic modulus, E = 210 GPa
Thermal strain, $\varepsilon = \alpha(\Delta T)$ = 6 x10^{-6} per °F (50 °F) = 3x10^{-4}

$$\text{Thermal stress, } \sigma = E\varepsilon = 210 \text{ GPa}\left(3x10^{-4}\right) = 630\text{x}10^{-4} \text{ GPa} = \underline{63 \text{ MPa}}$$

Note: for thermal expansion and contraction both ends moves away or in equally for thermal expansion and contraction respectively. If the total change in length is L, the ends will move by $L/2$.

4.6 Combined Stresses

4.6.1 Pressure Vessel

A pressure vessel is a container designed to hold gases or liquids at a pressure substantially different from the ambient pressure. Many pressure vessels are made of steel. To manufacture a cylindrical or spherical pressure vessel, rolled and possibly forged parts would have to be welded together. Some mechanical properties of steel, achieved by rolling or forging, could be adversely affected by welding, unless special precautions are taken. In addition to adequate mechanical strength, current standards dictate the use of steel with a high impact resistance, especially for vessels used in low temperatures. In applications where carbon steel would suffer corrosion, special corrosion resistant material should also be used. In mechanics of materials, pressure vessel is classified as thin-walled or thick walled considering the stress-strain variation in the wall. If the ratio of the wall thickness and the inner radius is equal or less than 0.1 or (10%) $\left(\frac{t}{r_i} \le \frac{1}{10}\right)$, then the stress-strain difference between the inner wall and outer wall is so small that it can be considered uniform. This type of pressure vessel is known as thin-walled. Thin-walled pressure vessel is studied in introductory mechanics courses. The thick-walled pressure vessel is commonly covered in advanced (or senior level) mechanics courses.

4.6.2 Cylindrical Thin-Walled Pressure Vessel

In a cylindrical thin-walled pressure vessel two types of stresses are developed; the first one being along the longitudinal direction and the second one being along the tangential direction as shown in figure below. Consider a cylindrical pressure vessel with inner radius r_i, outer radius r_o and wall thickness t subjected to an internal gage pressure P_i.

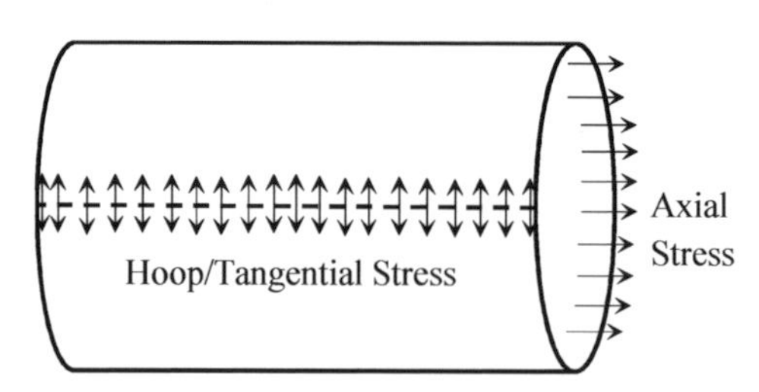

For vessels with end caps, the axial stress (σ_a) is: $\sigma_a = P_i\left(\frac{r_i^2}{r_o^2 - r_i^2}\right) \approx \frac{P_i r}{2t}$

For internal pressure, the stress at the inside wall along the tangential direction is:

$$\sigma_t = P_i\left(\frac{r_o^2 + r_i^2}{r_o^2 - r_i^2}\right) \approx \frac{P_i r}{t}$$

For external pressure, the stresses at the outside wall is: $\sigma_t = -P_o\left(\frac{r_o^2 + r_i^2}{r_o^2 - r_i^2}\right) \approx -\frac{P_o r}{2t}$

σ_t = tangential (hoop) stress

P_i = internal pressure; P_o = external pressure

r_i = inside radius; r_o = outside radius

t = wall thickness

$r = \frac{r_i + r_o}{2}$ = Average radius

4.6.3 Spherical Thin-Walled Pressure Vessel

In a spherical thin-walled pressure vessel one type of stresses are developed which is similar to the axial stress in cylindrical thin-walled pressure vessel. The stress in a spherical thin-walled pressure vessel is:

$$\sigma = \frac{P_i r}{2t}$$

Example 4.28
A cylindrical vessel has an inner diameter of 2 ft and a wall thickness of 1 in. After applying a pressure of 100 psi, a crack was developed longitudinally at the vessel wall. Determine the failure/cracking stress of the thin walled pressure vessel.

Solution:

Longitudinal crack developed means it was failed in hoop stress.

Inner radius, $r_i = 12\text{in.}$

Outer radius, $r_o = 12.0\text{ in.} + 1.0\text{ in.} = 13\text{ in.}$

Average radius, $r = \frac{r_i + r_o}{2} = \frac{12\text{in.} + 13\text{in.}}{2} = 12.5\text{ in.}$

$\frac{t}{r_i} = \frac{1\text{ in}}{12\text{ in}} < \frac{1}{10}$

Therefore, it is a thin-walled pressure vessel.

Hoop stress, $\sigma_t = \frac{p_i r}{t} = \frac{100\text{ psi}(12.5\text{ in.})}{1.0\text{ in.}} = \underline{1{,}250\text{ psi}}$

Example 4.29
A spherical vessel has an inner diameter of 12 in. and a wall thickness of 0.5 in. After applying an internal pressure of 100 psi, determine the stress in the wall of the pressure vessel.

Solution:

Longitudinal crack developed means it was failed in hoop stress.

Inner radius, $r_i = 6\text{ in.}$

Outer radius, $r_o = 6\text{ in.} + 0.5\text{ in.} = 6.5\text{ in.}$

Average radius, $r = \frac{r_i + r_o}{2} = \frac{6\text{in.} + 6.5\text{in.}}{2} = 6.25\text{ in.}$

$\frac{t}{r_i} = \frac{0.5\text{ in.}}{6\text{ in.}} = \frac{1}{12} < \frac{1}{10}$; so it is a thin-walled pressure vessel.

Hoop stress, $\sigma = \frac{P_i r}{2t} = \frac{100\text{ psi}(6.25\text{ in.})}{2(0.5\text{in.})} = \underline{625\text{ psi}}$

4.6.4 Combined Stress in Beam

It is well known that beams undergo shear forces, moment and occasionally axial forces. It has been discussed separately how these three forces cause stress in the beam section. It has also been discussed that these forces cause stresses in axial direction of the beam.

a) The axial stress (σ_n) produced by normal force is uniform all over the section.
b) The axial stress (σ_b) produced by bending is tensile or compressive at the top point, the opposite at the bottom point and zero at the neutral axis.
c) The stress (τ) produced by the shear force is the maximum at the neural axis and zero at the top and the bottom fibers.
d) Torsion in beam is very rare. If it presents, it produces the shear stress the maximum at the outer fiber.

In this section, the bending stress is expressed as σ_b to differentiate from normal stress (σ_n). The combined axial stress is the arithmetic sum of bending stress and normal stress, i.e.,

$$\sigma_{axial} = \sigma_n + \sigma_b$$

The shear stress (τ) is not combined with the axial stress as the shear stress acts transverse to the beam. To elaborate the above statements, let assume a beam as shown in figure below which has internal shear force, moment and normal force at a section, *a-a*.

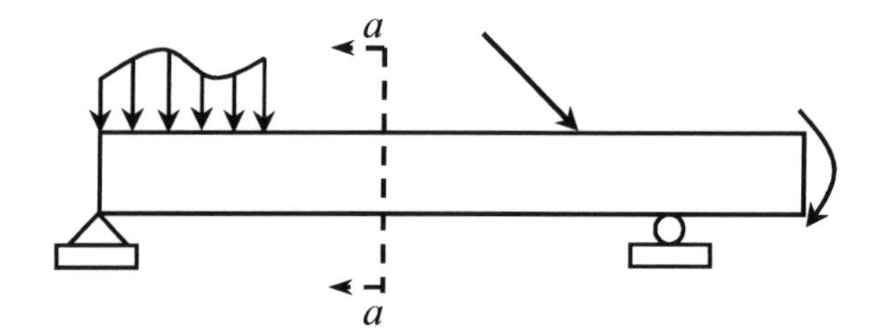

The bending stress, normal stress, and shear stress diagrams can be drawn as shown in figure below.

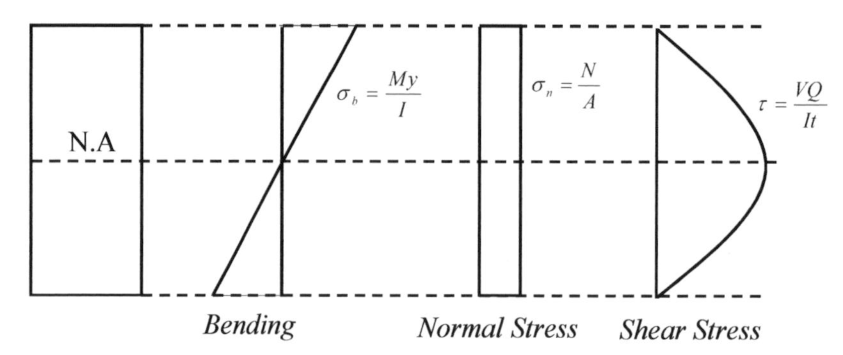

Bending stress, normal stress and shear stress diagrams in a section of a beam

When these stresses are combined, only bending and normal stresses are combined; shear stresses are dealt with separately. The following examples expect to clarify the above discussion.

Example 4.30

Determine the maximum axial stress and the maximum shear stress of the following beam as shown in figure below immediate to the left of *C*.

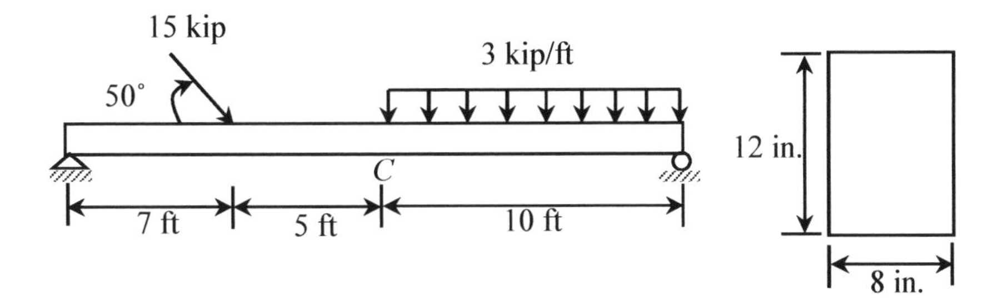

Solution:

To determine the stresses at C, it is required to determine the internal reactions at C. Let us find out those. Consider the whole structure as shown in figure below:

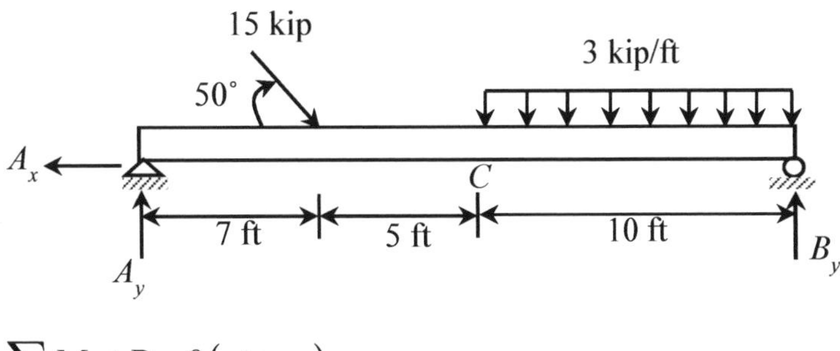

$$\sum M \text{ at } B = 0(\circlearrowright + ve)$$

$$-(3\text{kip/ft})(10\text{ft})(5\text{ft}) - 15\sin 50(15\text{ft}) + 22A_y = 0$$

$$A_y = 14.65\text{kip}$$

$$\sum F_x = 0 \quad (\rightarrow +ve)$$

$$15\cos 50 - A_x = 0$$

$$A_x = 9.64\,\text{kip}$$

Cut at C and consider the left part shown in figure below:

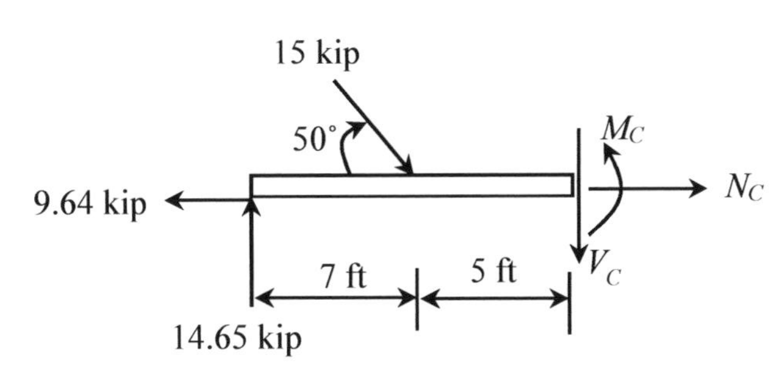

$$\sum M \text{ at } C = 0(\circlearrowright + ve)$$

$$-M_C + 14.65 \text{ kip } (12 \text{ ft}) - 15 \sin 50 \text{ } (5 \text{ ft}) = 0$$

$$Mc = 118.3\,\text{kip.ft}$$

$$\sum F_x = 0 \quad (\rightarrow +ve)$$

$$Nc - 9.64\,kip + 15\cos 50 = 0$$

$$Nc = 0$$

$$\sum F_y = 0(\uparrow +ve)$$

$$-Vc + 14.65\,\text{kip} - 15\sin 50 = 0$$

$Vc = 3.16\,\text{kip}$

Normal stress $\sigma_n = 0$ as there is no normal force at C.

Maximum shear stress $\tau_{\max} = \dfrac{VQ}{It} = 1.5\dfrac{V}{A} = 1.5\dfrac{3.16\,\text{kip}}{(12\text{x }8)\,\text{in.}^2} = 0.049\ \text{ksi} = 49\ \text{psi}$

Maximum bending stress $\sigma_{b,\max} = \dfrac{Mc}{I} = \dfrac{(118.3(12)\,\text{kip.in.})(6\,\text{in.})}{\dfrac{8\,\text{in.}(12\,\text{in.})^3}{12}} = 7.4\ \text{ksi}$

As there is no normal stress, so the maximum bending stress is the maximum axial stress.

Answers:

$\tau_{\max} = 49\ \text{psi}$

$\sigma_{axial} = 7.4\ \text{ksi}$

Example 4.31

Determine the maximum axial stress and the maximum shear stress of the following beam as shown in figure below immediate to the left of C.

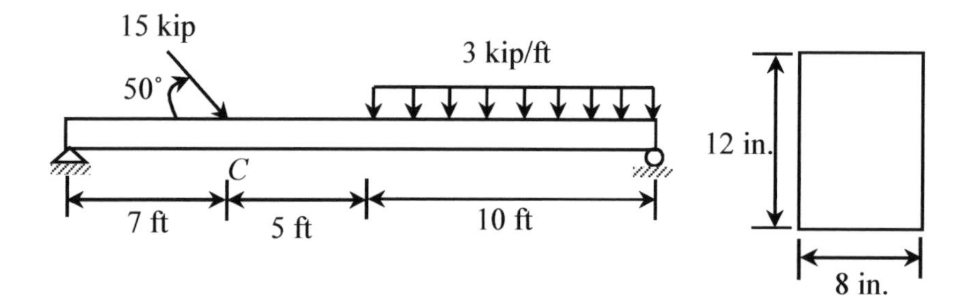

Solution:

To determine the stresses at C, it is required to determine the internal reactions at C. Let us find out those. Consider the whole structure shown in figure below:

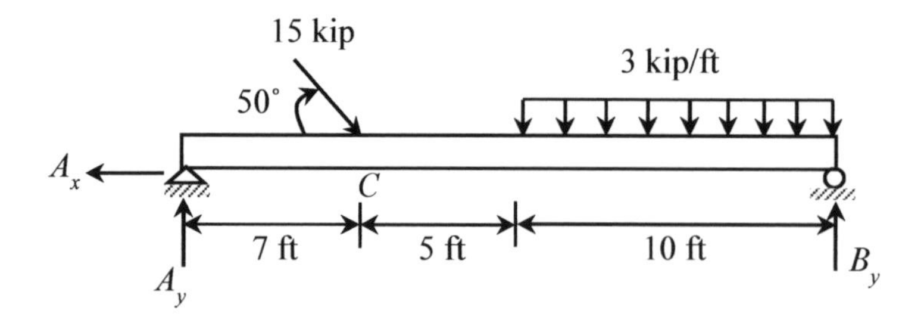

$\sum M \text{ at } B = 0 (\circlearrowleft +ve)$

$$-(3\,\text{kip/ft})(10\,\text{ft})(5\,\text{ft}) - 15\sin 50(15\,\text{ft}) + 22A_y = 0$$

$$A_y = 14.65\,\text{kip}$$

$\sum F_x = 0 \ (\rightarrow +ve)$

$$15\cos 50 - A_x = 0$$

$$A_x = 9.64\,\text{kip}$$

Cut at C and consider the left part shown in figure below:

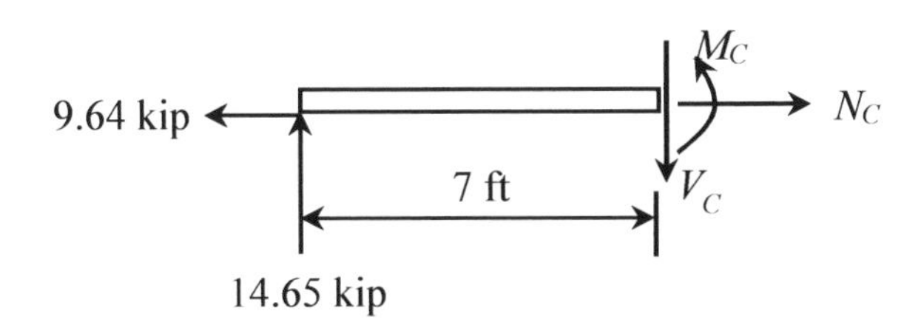

$$\sum M \text{ at } C = 0(\circlearrowright + ve)$$

$$-Mc + 14.65\,\text{kip}(12\,\text{ft}) = 0$$

$$Mc = 102.55\,\text{kip.ft}$$

$$\sum F_x = 0 \quad (\rightarrow +ve)$$

$$Nc - 9.64\,\text{kip} = 0$$

$$Nc = 9.64\,\text{kip}$$

$$\sum F_y = 0(\uparrow +ve)$$

$$-Vc + 14.65\,\text{kip} = 0$$

$$Vc = 14.65\,\text{kip}$$

Maximum shear stress $\tau_{\max} = \dfrac{VQ}{It} = 1.5\dfrac{V}{A} = 1.5\dfrac{14.65\text{ kip}}{(12\text{x } 8)\text{in.}^2} = 0.229\text{ ksi} = 229\text{ psi}$

Maximum bending stress $\sigma_{b,\max} = \dfrac{Mc}{I} = \dfrac{(102.55(12)\text{kip.in.})(6\,\text{in.})}{\dfrac{8\,\text{in.}(12\,\text{in.})^3}{12}} = 6.4\text{ ksi}$

Maximum normal stress $\sigma_n = \dfrac{N}{A} = \dfrac{9.64}{12x8} = 0.1\text{ ksi}$

The combined axial stresses are shown in figure below.

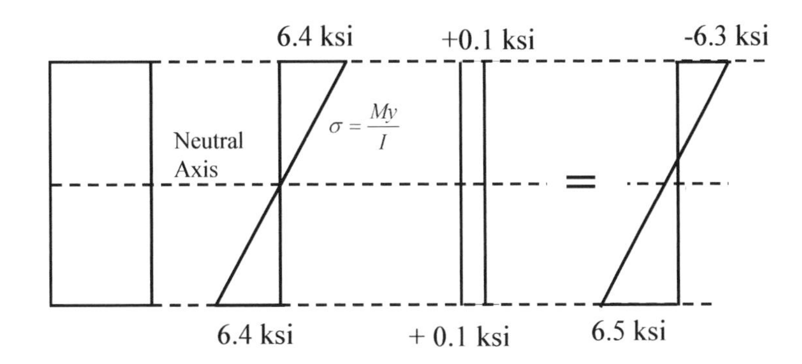

4.6.5 Combined Stress in Column

In column or in compression block, if the load is not applied at the centroid of the column or block section, moment develops. If the load is applied in a symmetric line then one-directional moment develops as–

$$M = Pe$$

where P is the applied load and e is the eccentricity of the load application. The total compression axial stress, assuming compressive stress be positive, at any point of the base can be calculated as –

$$\sigma_{Total} = \sigma_N \pm \frac{Mc}{I}$$

σ_N = normal compressive stress $= \frac{P}{A}$

M = Produced moment

c = Point of concern from the centroid of the section

I = Moment of inertia of the section about the axis about which moment develops

If the load is not applied in any of the symmetric line, then biaxial moment develops and the total compression axial stress, assuming compressive stress be positive, at any point can be calculated as –

$$\sigma_{Total} = \sigma_N \pm \frac{M_x c_x}{I_x} \pm \frac{M_y c_y}{I_y}$$

σ_N = normal compressive stress $= \frac{P}{A}$

$M_x = Pe_x$ = Produced moment about the x-axis

e_x = Eccentricity of the load with respect the x-axis

$M_y = Pe_y$ = Produced moment about the y-axis

e_y = Eccentricity of the load with respect the y-axis

I_x = Moment of inertia of the section about the x-axis

I_y = Moment of inertia of the section about the y-axis

c_x = concerned point from the x-axis

c_y = concerned point from the y-axis

Example 4.32

A compression block is supporting a compression load of 24 kip acting on the x-axis with 3 ft eccentricity as shown in figure below. The base dimension of the block is 10 ft x 2 ft, and the height is 6 ft. Determine the total axial stress at the other corners, A, B and C due to this eccentric loading.

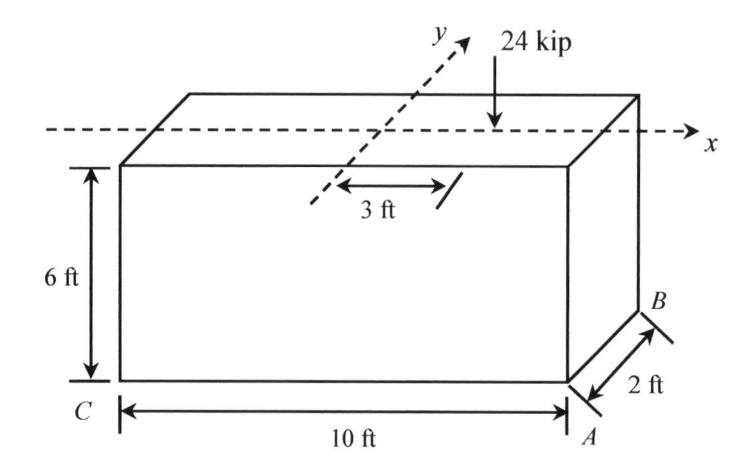

Solution:

The load is eccentric about the y-axis and it will create a moment of –

$M = Pe$ = 24 kip (3 ft) = 72 kip.ft

At corners, A and B, this moment will cause compressive axial stress. At corner C, this moment will cause tensile axial stress. Let assume the compressive stress be positive.

$$\sigma_{Total} = \sigma_N \pm \frac{Mc}{I} = \frac{24\,\text{kip}}{(2\,\text{ft x} 10\,\text{ft})} \pm \frac{72\,\text{kip.ft}(5\,\text{ft})}{\frac{2\,\text{ft}(10\,\text{ft})^3}{12}} = 1.2 \text{ ksf} \pm 2.16 \text{ ksf}$$

$$\sigma_{A \text{ and } B} = 1.2 \text{ ksf} + 2.16 \text{ ksf} = 3.36 \text{ ksf}$$

$$\sigma_C = 1.2 \text{ ksf} - 2.16 \text{ ksf} = -0.96 \text{ ksf} \text{ (tensile stress of } \underline{0.96 \text{ ksf}})$$

Example 4.33

A compression block is supporting a corner load of 24 kip. The base dimension of the block is 10 ft x 2 ft, and the height is 6 ft as shown in figure below. Determine the total axial stress at the other corners *A*, *B* and *C* due to this eccentric loading.

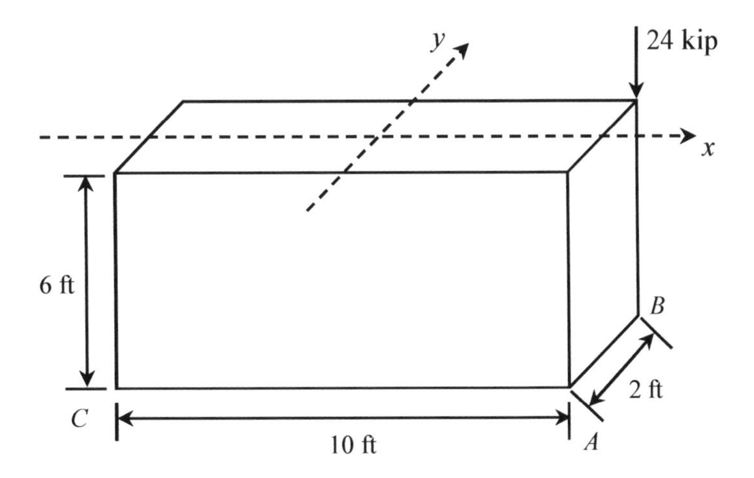

Solution:

M_x = moment with respect to the *x*-axis = 24 kip (1 ft) = 24 kip.ft
c_x = point of concern from the *x*-axis = 1 ft

I_x = moment of inertia with respect to the *x*-axis $= \frac{bh^3}{12} = \frac{10\,\text{ft}(2\,\text{ft})^3}{12} = 6.67 \text{ ft}^4$

M_y = 24 kip (5 ft) = 120 kip.ft
c_y = 5 ft

I_y = moment of inertia with respect to *y*-axis $= \frac{bh^3}{12} = \frac{2\,\text{ft}(10\,\text{ft})^3}{12} = 166.67 \text{ ft}^4$

Let assume the compressive stress be positive.

$$\sigma_{Total} = \sigma_N \pm \frac{M_x c_x}{I_x} \pm \frac{M_y c_y}{I_y} = \frac{24\,\text{kip}}{(10\,\text{ft})(2\,\text{ft})} \pm \frac{24\,\text{kip.ft}(1\,\text{ft})}{6.67 \text{ ft}^4} \pm \frac{(120\,\text{kip.ft})(5\,\text{ft})}{166.67\,\text{ft}^4}$$
$$= 1.2\,\text{ksf} \pm 3.6\,\text{ksf} \pm 3.6\,\text{ksf}$$

$$\sigma_A = \sigma_N - \frac{M_x c_x}{I_x} + \frac{M_y c_y}{I_y}$$
$$= 1.2 \text{ ksf} - 3.6 \text{ ksf} + 3.6 \text{ ksf}$$
$$= \underline{1.2 \text{ ksf } (\textit{compression})}$$

$$\sigma_B = \sigma_N + \frac{M_x c_x}{I_x} + \frac{M_y c_y}{I_y}$$
$$= 1.2 \text{ ksf} + 3.6 \text{ ksf} + 3.6 \text{ ksf}$$
$$= \underline{8.4 \text{ ksf} \left(\textit{compression} \right)}$$

$$\sigma_C = \sigma_N - \frac{M_x c_x}{I_x} - \frac{M_y c_y}{I_y}$$
$$= 1.2 \text{ ksf} - 3.6 \text{ ksf} - 3.6 \text{ ksf}$$
$$= \underline{-6.0 \text{ ksf} \left(6.0 \text{ksf, } \textit{tension} \right)}$$

4.6.6 Transformation of Stress

For the special case of a *two-dimensional* stress state, the equations for principal stress reduce to:

$$\sigma_a, \sigma_b = \frac{\sigma_x + \sigma_y}{2} \pm \sqrt{\left(\frac{\sigma_x - \sigma_y}{2} \right)^2 + \left(\tau_{xy} \right)^2}$$

$$\sigma_c = 0$$

The two nonzero values calculated from this equation are temporarily labeled σa and σb and the third value σc is always zero in this case. Depending on their values, the three roots are then labeled according to the convention:

- *algebraically largest* = σ_1
- *algebraically smallest* = σ_3
- *other* = σ_2.

A typical 2D stress element is shown below with all indicated components shown in their positive sense.

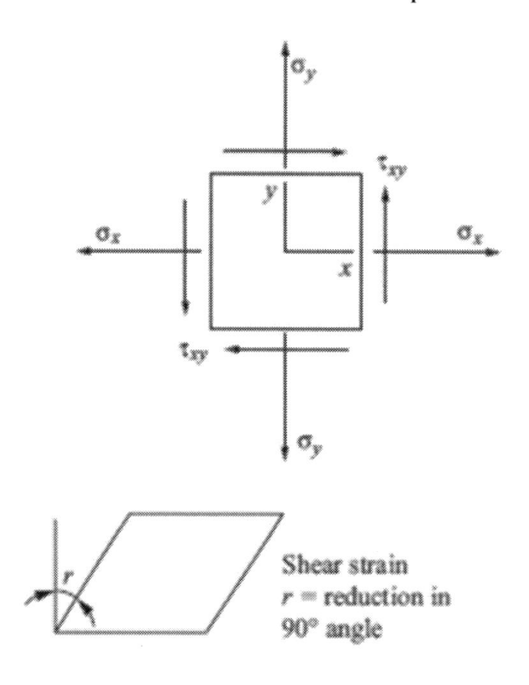

To construct a Mohr's circle, use the following sign conventions:

1. Tensile normal stress components are plotted on the horizontal axis and are considered positive. Compressive normal stress components are negative.
2. For constructing Mohr's circle only, shearing stresses are plotted above the normal stress axis when the pair of shearing stresses, acting on opposite and parallel faces of an element, forms a clockwise couple. Shearing stresses are plotted below the normal axis when the shear stresses form a counterclockwise couple.

The circle drawn with the center on the normal stress (horizontal) axis with center, *C*, and radius, *R*, where

$$R = \sqrt{\left(\frac{\sigma_x - \sigma_y}{2}\right)^2 + \left(\tau_{xy}\right)^2}$$

$$C = \frac{\sigma_x + \sigma_y}{2}$$

The two nonzero principal stresses are then:

$$\sigma_a = C + R$$
$$\sigma_b = C - R$$

The maximum *in-plane* shear stress is $\tau_{in} = R$. However, the maximum shear stress considering three dimensions is always.

$$\tau_{\max} = \frac{\sigma_a - \sigma_b}{2}$$

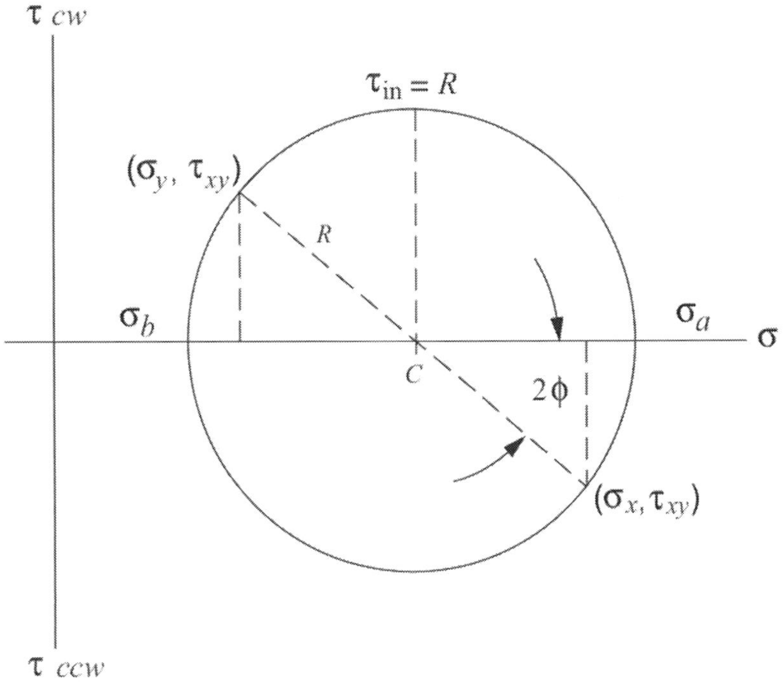

Example 4.34

The state of stress at a point in a structural member can be shown in figure below. Determine the following using the Mohr Circle:

a) The state of stress at the point on another element oriented 30° clockwise from the position shown.
b) The principal stresses
c) The orientation of principal stresses
d) The maximum in-plane shear stress
e) The orientation of the maximum in-plane shear stress

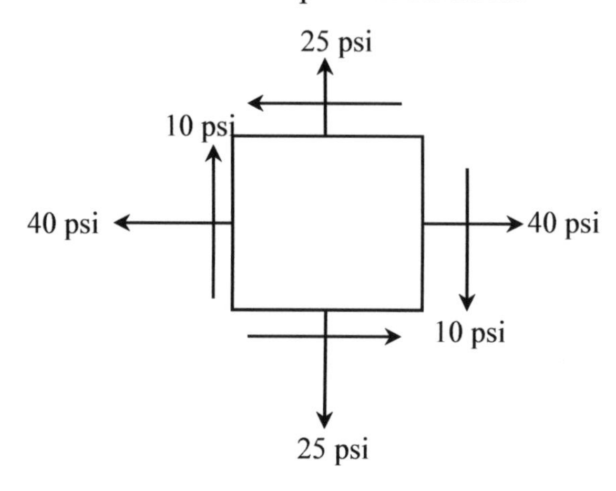

Solution:

$\sigma_x = 40$ psi (Away from the element is positive)
$\sigma_y = 25$ psi (Away from the element is positive)
$\tau_{xy} = -10$ psi (Upward in the right side of the element is positive)

Center, $C = \sigma_{avg} = \dfrac{\sigma_x + \sigma_y}{2} = \dfrac{40\text{ psi} + 25\text{ psi}}{2} = 32.5\text{ psi}$

Radius, $R = \sqrt{\left(\dfrac{\sigma_x - \sigma_y}{2}\right)^2 + \tau_{xy}^2} = \sqrt{\left(\dfrac{40\text{ psi} - 25\text{ psi}}{2}\right)^2 + (-10\text{ psi})^2} = 12.5\text{ psi}$

$\dfrac{\sigma_x - \sigma_y}{2} = \dfrac{40\text{ psi} - 25\text{ psi}}{2} = 7.5\text{ psi}$

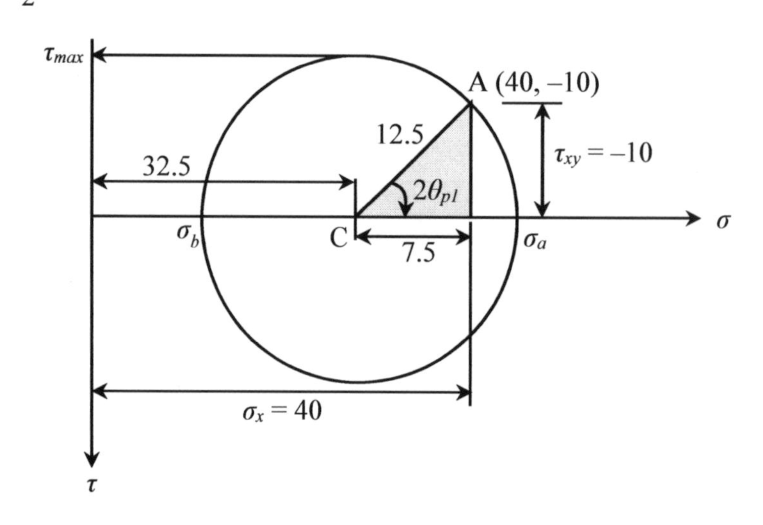

$$2\theta_{p1} = \tan^{-1}\left(\frac{-10\,\text{psi}}{7.5\,\text{psi}}\right) = -53.1^o$$

$$\theta_{p1} = \frac{-53.1^o}{2} = -26.56^o \text{ (or clock–wise } 26.56^\circ)$$

a) The state of stress at the point on another element oriented 30° clockwise is shown below.

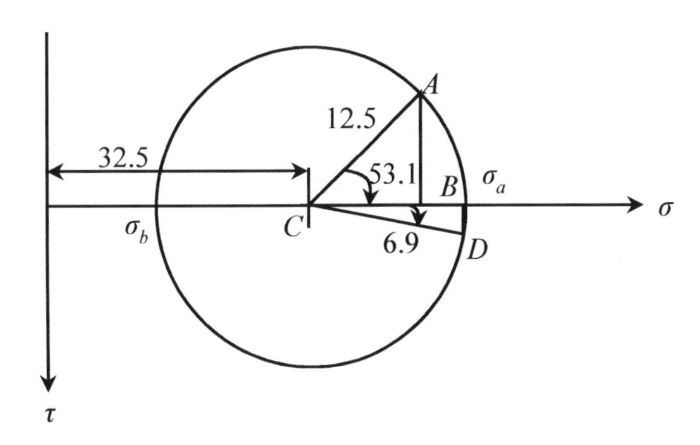

Let, the state of stress oriented 30° clockwise can be represented by the point D.

Therefore, <ACD = 60°

As shown above that <ACB = 53.1°

So, <BCD = 6.9°

From the triangle, ΔBCD

BC ⊥ BD and CD = radius = 12.5 psi

$$\frac{BD}{CD} = \sin 6.9^\circ$$

$$BD = CD\sin 6.9^\circ = 12.5\ \sin 6.9^\circ = 1.5\text{ psi}$$

Therefore, τ_{xy} at – 30° is 1.5 psi.

Again,

$$CB = CD\cos 6.9^\circ = 12.5\ \cos 6.9^\circ = 12.4\text{ psi}$$

Therefore, σ_x at – 30° is 32.5 psi + 12.4 psi = 44.9 psi.

$(\sigma_x, \tau_{xy}) \equiv (44.9, 1.5)$ psi

b) The principal stresses

$$\sigma_a = C + R = 32.5\,\text{psi} + 12.5\,\text{psi} = 45\text{ psi}$$

$$\sigma_b = C - R = 32.5\,\text{psi} - 12.5\,\text{psi} = 20\,\text{psi}$$

c) The orientation of principal stresses

$$2\theta_{p1} = \tan^{-1}\left(\frac{-10}{7.5}\right) = -53.1^o$$

$$\theta_{p1} = \frac{-53.1^o}{2} = -26.56^o \text{ (or clock–wise } 26.56^\circ)$$

$$\theta_{p2} = \theta_{p1} + 90 = -26.56^o + 90^o = 63.44^o \text{ (counter-clockwise)}$$

$\theta_{p1} = -26.56^o$ (or clock–wise 26.56°)

$\theta_{p2} = 63.44^o$ (counter-clockwise)

d) The maximum in-plane shear stress, $\tau_{max} = R = 12.5$ psi
e) The orientation of the maximum in-plane shear stress

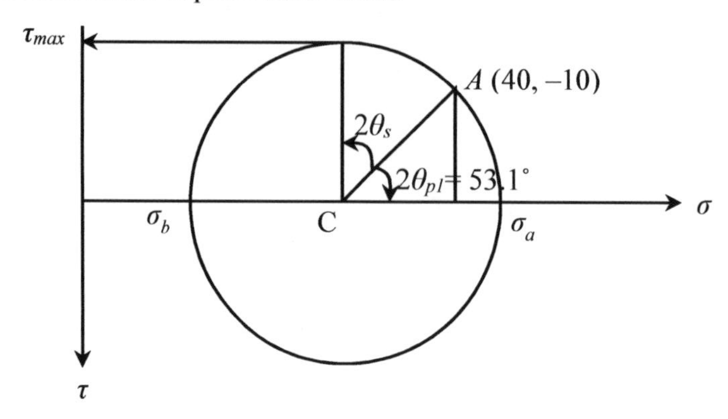

From figure:

$$2\theta_{p1} + 2\theta_s = 90^o$$

$$2\theta_s = 90^o - 53.1^o = 36.9^o$$

$\theta_s = 18.45°$ (counter–clock–wise 18.45°)

$\theta_{s2} = \theta_{s1} + 90 = 18.45^o + 90^o = 108.45^o$ (counter–clock–wise 108.45°)

Example 4.35

An element is subjected to the following plane stress condition as shown in figure below. Determine the principal stresses and the maximum in-plane shear stress.

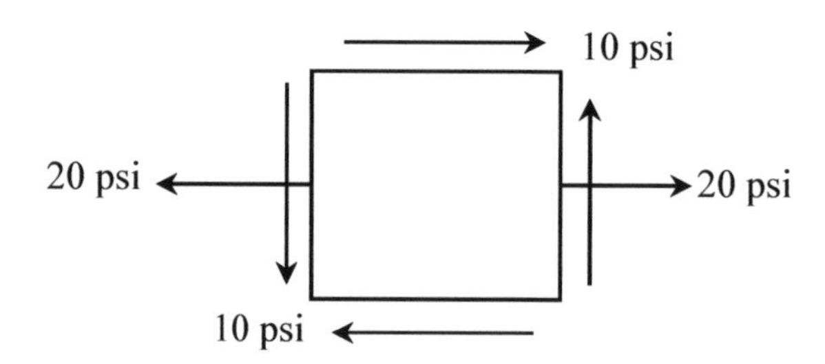

Solution:

$\sigma_x = 20$ psi (Away from the element is positive); $\sigma_y = 0$; $\tau_{xy} = 10$ psi

$$\text{Radius, } R = \sqrt{\left(\frac{\sigma_x - \sigma_y}{2}\right)^2 + \tau_{xy}^2} = \sqrt{\left(\frac{20\,\text{psi} - 0\,\text{psi}}{2}\right)^2 + 10\,\text{psi}^2} = 14.14 \text{ psi}$$

$$C = \sigma_{avg} = \frac{\sigma_x + \sigma_y}{2} = \frac{20\,\text{psi} + 0\,\text{psi}}{2} = 10 \text{ psi}$$

$\sigma_{1/2} = \sigma_{avg} \pm R =$ 10 psi ± 14.14 psi = <u>24. 14 psi, –4.14 psi</u>

$\tau_{max} = R =$ <u>14.14 psi</u>

4.7 Deflection

This topic is based on Article 1.6 of the PE Civil Handbook. The possible deflection for different structures under different loads types are given below. Therefore, the design philosophy for deflection is that the maximum possible deflection, due to the applied loads on a member must be equal or less than the allowable. If not, choose larger section which satisfies the allowable deflection limit.

Example 4.36
What is the maximum deflection of the beam in figure below? $E = 29 \text{ x}10^3$ ksi, $I = 200$ in^4. Assume the beam is in linear–elastic limit.

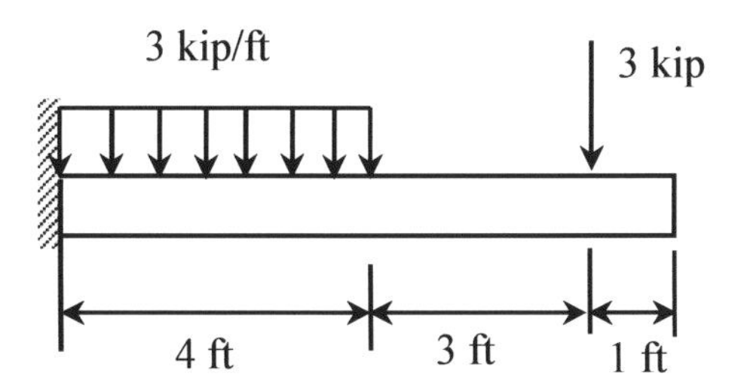

Solution:

Article 1.6 of the PE Civil Handbook:
The maximum deflection occurs at the end of the beam. As the beam is in linear–elastic region, superposition principle applies. Deflection (v_1) by the uniformly distributed load –

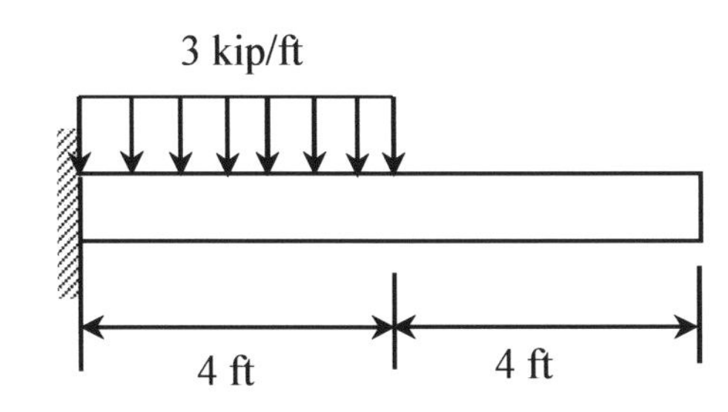

$$v_1 = \frac{7wL^4}{384EI} = \frac{3\text{ kip/ft}\left(\frac{1}{12}\right)(8\times12\text{ in.})^4}{384(29\times10^3\text{ ksi})(200\text{ in.}^4)} = 0.0095\text{ in.}\,(\downarrow)$$

Deflection (v_2) by the point load –

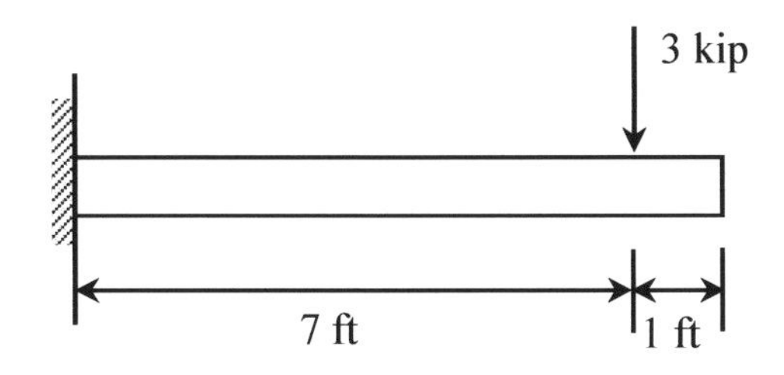

$$v_2 = \frac{Pa^2}{6EI}(3L-a) = \frac{3\text{ kip}(7\times12\text{ in.})^2}{6(29\times10^3\text{ ksi})(200\text{ in.}^4)}(3\times8\times12\text{ in.}-7\times12\text{ in.}) = 0.124\text{ in.}\,(\downarrow)$$

The combined deflection at the end $v = v_1 + v_2 = 0.0095\text{in.} + 0.124\text{in.} = \underline{0.134\text{in.}(\downarrow)}$

4.8 Beams

The author believes that the topics required for the beam analysis are already covered in bending and shear.

4.9 Columns

This topic is based on Article 1.6 of the PE Civil Handbook. There is no sharp definitions of short column and long column. The understanding is that short column tends to fail in compressive yielding. On the other hand, if a column is tall, it fails by lateral displacement at the middle (called, buckling). In compressive yielding failure, material is utilized perfectly and before failure, shows visible deformation. On the other hand, bucking failure is sudden and material property is not perfectly utilized.

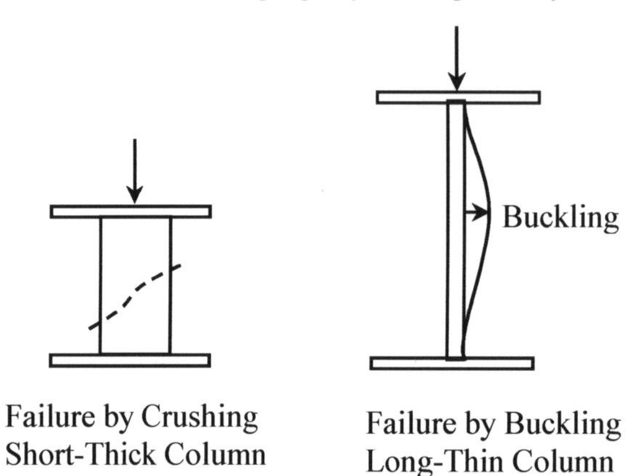

Depending on shape and length of the column, Leonhard Euler developed an equation to determine the critical/maximum load below which no buckling is to be occurred. That load is called Euler Critical buckling load. It is determined as:

$$P_{cr} = \frac{\pi^2 EI}{(Kl)^2}$$

P_{cr} = Euler Buckling load
E = Modulus of elasticity or Young's Modulus
I = Minimum moment of inertia
K = Effective length factor to account for end supports
L = unbraced length of the column

The reason of considering the minimum moment of inertia is that the column is susceptible to fail along the weaker direction. Then, Euler critical buckling stress (σ_{cr}) can be calculated as –

$$\sigma_{cr} = \frac{Axial\ Load}{Cross\text{-}sectional\ Area} = \frac{P_{cr}}{A} = \frac{\frac{\pi^2 EI}{(Kl)^2}}{A} = \frac{\pi^2 E}{\frac{(Kl)^2 A}{I}} = \frac{\pi^2 E}{\left(\frac{Kl}{r}\right)^2}$$

A = cross-sectional area of the column

r = minimum radius of gyration, $\sqrt{\frac{I}{A}}$

$\frac{Kl}{r}$ = slenderness ratio for the column

Assumptions made in Euler's theory:

- The column is initially perfectly straight, axially loaded and uniform.
- The column material is perfectly elastic, homogeneous and isotropic and obeys Hooke's Law.
- The length of the column is very large compared to the lateral dimensions.
- The direct stress is very small compared with the bending stress.
- The self-weight of the column is neglected.
- The column will fail by buckling only.

Theoretical effective-length factors for columns include:

Pinned-pinned, $K = 1.0$
Fixed-fixed, $K = 0.5$
Fixed-pinned, $K = 0.7$
Fixed-free, $K = 2.0$

Explanations

Condition (a) Fixed-Fixed with Side-Sway Inhibited. Both ends are fixed supported with side-sway inhibited. Side-sway inhibited meaning no lateral translation of the column is possible. This is possible if joints are rigid to make it fixed supported and bracing is provided to resist the side-sway as shown below.

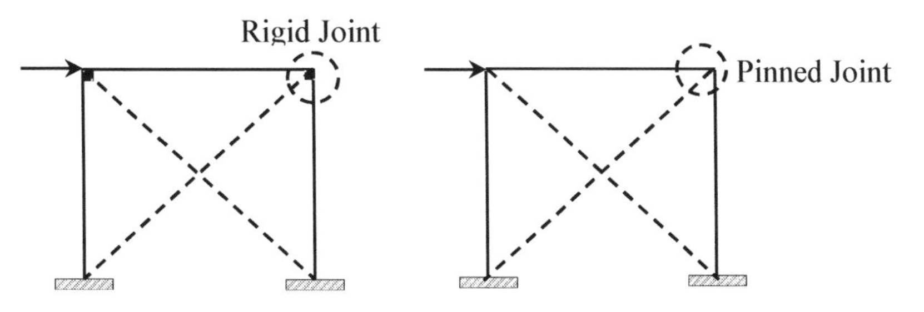

Condition (a) Fixed-Fixed with Side-Sway Inhibited.

Condition (b) Fixed-Pinned with Side-Sway Inhibited.

Condition (b) Fixed-Pinned with Side-Sway Inhibited. One end is fixed and the other end is pinned supported with side-sway inhibited as shown in the above figure.

Condition (c) Pinned-Pinned with Side-Sway inhibited. Both ends are pinned supported with side-sway inhibited as shown in the above figure. This is the typical case for braced frame. If the support types and sway information are not available use this case.

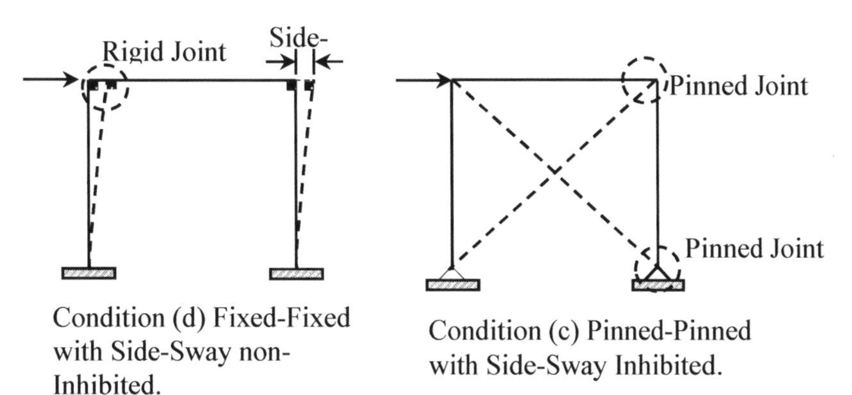

Condition (d) Fixed-Fixed with Side-Sway non-Inhibited.

Condition (c) Pinned-Pinned with Side-Sway Inhibited.

Condition (d) Fixed-Fixed with Side-Sway non-inhibited. Both ends are fixed joints with side-sway not inhibited as shown below. If no bracing is provided side-sway exists.

Condition (e) Fixed-Free with Side-Sway non-inhibited. One end is fixed supported and the other end is free with side-sway not inhibited. If no bracing is provided side-sway exists and the pinned joint can sway freely and can be termed as free. An isolated column fixed at base also falls in this category.

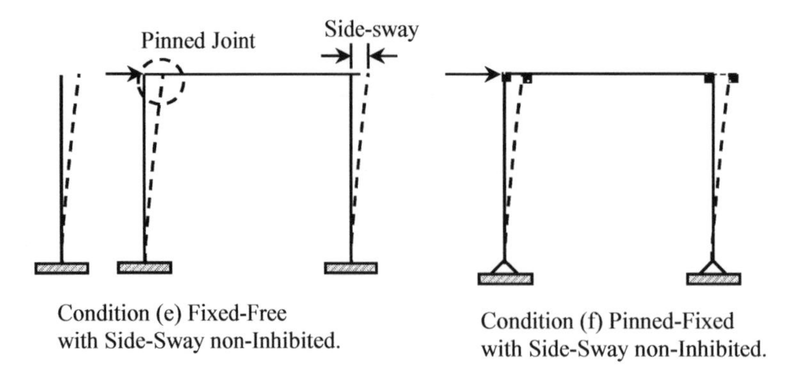

Condition (e) Fixed-Free with Side-Sway non-Inhibited.

Condition (f) Pinned-Fixed with Side-Sway non-Inhibited.

Condition (f) Pinned-Fixed with Side-Sway non-inhibited. Both ends are pinned supported with side-sway not inhibited. If no bracing is provided side-sway exists.

Items to remember:

a) In real structure, joints are usually pinned connected unless rigid connection (moment frame) is intentionally built with customized feature.
b) Only bracing can resist the side-sway.
c) Fixed joint and rigid joint are very often interchangeably used; they both mean the same thing.

The above discussion very often used the term bracing and rigid/fixed joint. Therefore, the authors feel it is important to introduce a concept which will be helpful in your future courses. There are two types of framing systems (beam-column connections): braced frame and moment. In general, a braced frame consists of diagonal members used to resist lateral loads as shown below.

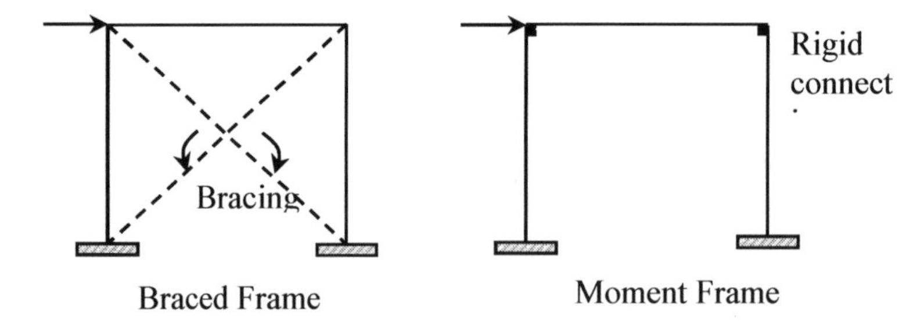

Braced Frame

Moment Frame

Moment-resisting connections involves constructing very rigid beam-to-column connections that permit moment transfer across the joint. Monolithically-poured reinforced concrete structures inherently have moment-resisting joints, but steel and timber frames do not. A typical moment-resisting beam-to-column steel-framed connection involves transferring horizontal loads through the beam flanges directly to the column flanges by using angles and column web stiffener plates as shown below. The analysis of the connection is complex. It is very labor-intensive and expensive to construct and is not as good as other methods of stabilization.

Example 4.37

Calculate the Euler critical buckling stress of a 12 m column with both ends fixed ($K = 0.5$). The modulus of elasticity of the column is 210 GPa and the radius of gyration of the section about the weakest axis is 0.01 m. Assume the column follows the Euler Buckling Stress assumptions.

Solution:

Modulus of elasticity, $E = 210$ GPa

Length of column, $l = 12$ m

Effective length factor, $K = 0.5$
Radius of gyration about the weakest axis, $r_{min} = 0.01$ m

Euler critical buckling stress, $\sigma_{cr} = \dfrac{\pi^2 E}{\left(\dfrac{Kl}{r}\right)^2} = \dfrac{\pi^2(210\times10^9\ \text{Pa})}{\left(\dfrac{0.5(12)\,\text{m}}{0.01\,\text{m}}\right)^2} = 5.76\times10^6\ \text{Pa} = \underline{5.76\ \text{MPa}}$

Example 4.38
The steel post ($E = 200$ GPa) shown in figure below is cantilevered at its base and supports a weight at its upper end ($K = 2.0$). Considering that buckling can occur about either plane, determine the maximum allowable weight it can support. The post length is $L = 4$ m, the other cross-sectional dimensions are $a = 120$ mm and $b = 250$ mm, and the uniform wall thickness is 15 mm.

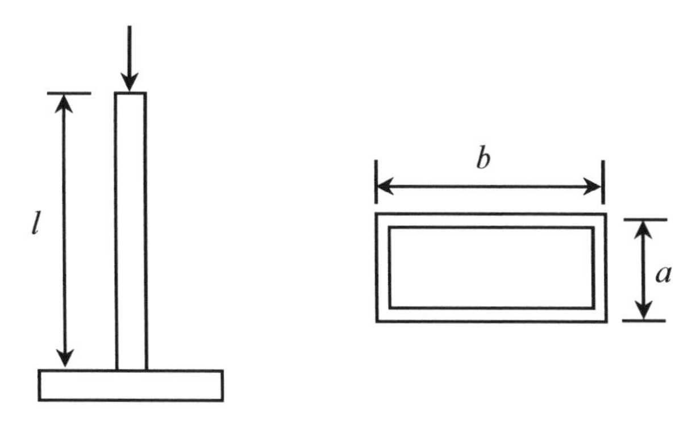

Solution:

Modulus of elasticity, $E = 200$ GPa
Length of column, $L = 4$ m
Effective length factor, $K = 2.0$

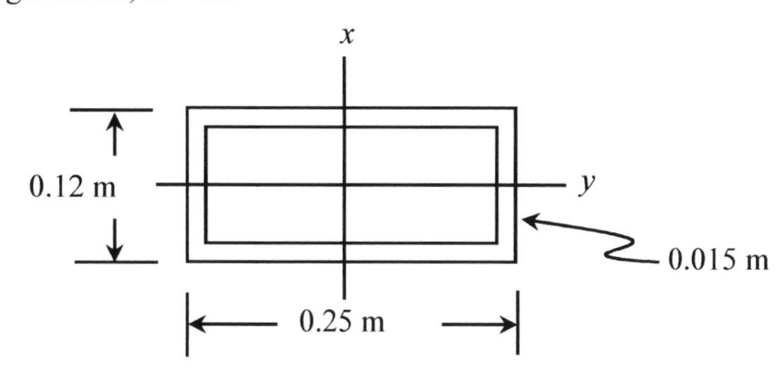

The buckling, and therefore the maximum allowable load, will be governed by the plane with the lower moment of inertia.

$$I_y = \frac{1}{12}\left[(0.25\,\text{m})(0.12\,\text{m})^3 - (0.25\,\text{m} - 0.03\,\text{m})(0.12\,\text{m} - 0.03\,\text{m})^3\right] = 2.26\times10^{-5}\ \text{m}^4$$

$$I_x = \frac{1}{12}\left[(0.12\,\text{m})(0.25\,\text{m})^3 - (0.12\,\text{m} - 0.03\,\text{m})(0.25\,\text{m} - 0.03\,\text{m})^3\right] = 7.64\times10^{-5}\ \text{m}^4$$

I_y is minimum and the buckling will occur about this axis. The column can be modeled as a beam that is fixed-free.

$$P_{cr} = \frac{\pi^2 EI}{(Kl)^2} = \frac{\pi^2(200\times10^9\ \text{Pa})(2.26\times10^{-5}\ \text{m}^4)}{(2\times4\,\text{m})^2}$$

$$P_{cr} = \underline{6.98\times10^5\ \text{N}}$$

4.10 Slabs

It is not clearly mentioned what type of problem may be from the slab. One-way slab is designed using a 1-ft strip and considering it a beam. Two-way slab requires much computation and should not be covered in the PE Civil Breadth Exam.

Example 4.39
A slab is 15 ft by 20 ft and has a thickness of 7.0 inch. The concrete weighs 150 pcf. The dead load of the slab (psf) is most nearly:

Solution: Dead Load = 150 lb/ft^3 x (7.0/12 ft) = 87.5 psf

4.11 Footings

Spread footings (along with mat-slab, slab-on-grade, pad, rubble trench, and earth bag) are a type of shallow foundation that transfers a building's weight to the earth very near the surface.

Example 4.40
A footing designed to resist a moment in addition to an axial column load is called a:

A. Combined footing
B. Eccentric footing
C. Spread footing
D. Strap footing

Solution:

A footing designed to resist a moment in addition to an axial column load is called an Eccentric footing.

Example 4.41
A 15-inch by 15-inch reinforced-concrete column has a dead load of 150 kip and live load of 120 kip. The allowable bearing pressure of underneath soil is 4,000 psf. The bottom of the foundation is located 4-ft below the final grade. Reinforced concrete and the soil weigh 150 pcf and 120 pcf respectively. Assuming a 21-inch deep footing, the appropriate size of the square foundation is most nearly:

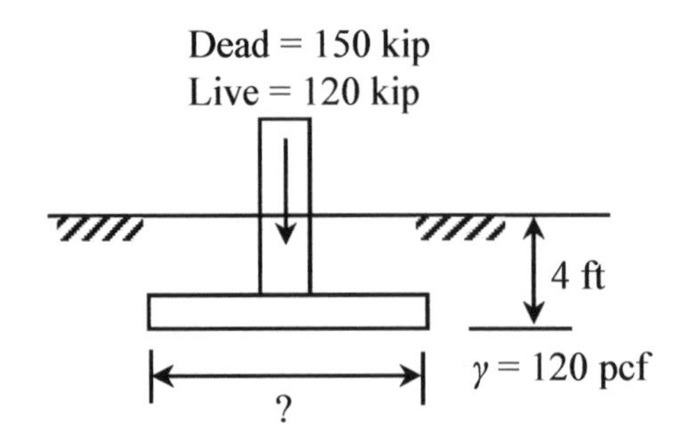

A. 8 ft square
B. 7 ft square
C. 9 ft square
D. 10 ft square

Solution: Effective bearing pressure by soil = 4,000 psf – (21/12 ft)(150 pcf) – (27/12 ft)(120 pcf) = 3,513 psf

$$\text{Area required} = \frac{\text{Load}}{\text{Effective Bearing Pressure}} = \frac{150\,\text{kip} + 120\,\text{kip}}{3.513\,\text{psf}} = 76.85\,\text{ft}^2$$

Use, 9-ft square with total area of 81 ft^2

4.12 Retaining Walls

The lateral earth pressure is discussed in Chapter 3. The following example will clarify the design concept of retaining wall (most commonly gravity retaining wall). Gravity walls hold in earth by the weight of the wall material. They could be a stack of large rocks, or more formal like pavers. Two types of analysis is performed: a) the overturning moment by the lateral force must be resisted by the resistive moment by the gravity force (weight) of the wall and the soil on it, b) the friction force underneath the wall must resist the lateral force on the wall.

Example 4.42

A semigravity retaining wall consisting of plain concrete (weight = 145 lb/ft^3) is shown in figure below. The bank of supported earth is assumed to weigh 110 lb/ft^3, to have a ϕ of 30°, and to have a coefficient of friction against sliding on soil of 0.5. Determine the safety factors against overturning and sliding. Passive pressure can be neglected for overturning resistance and soil above the footing toe may be eroded easily. Use the Rankine expression for calculating the horizontal pressures.

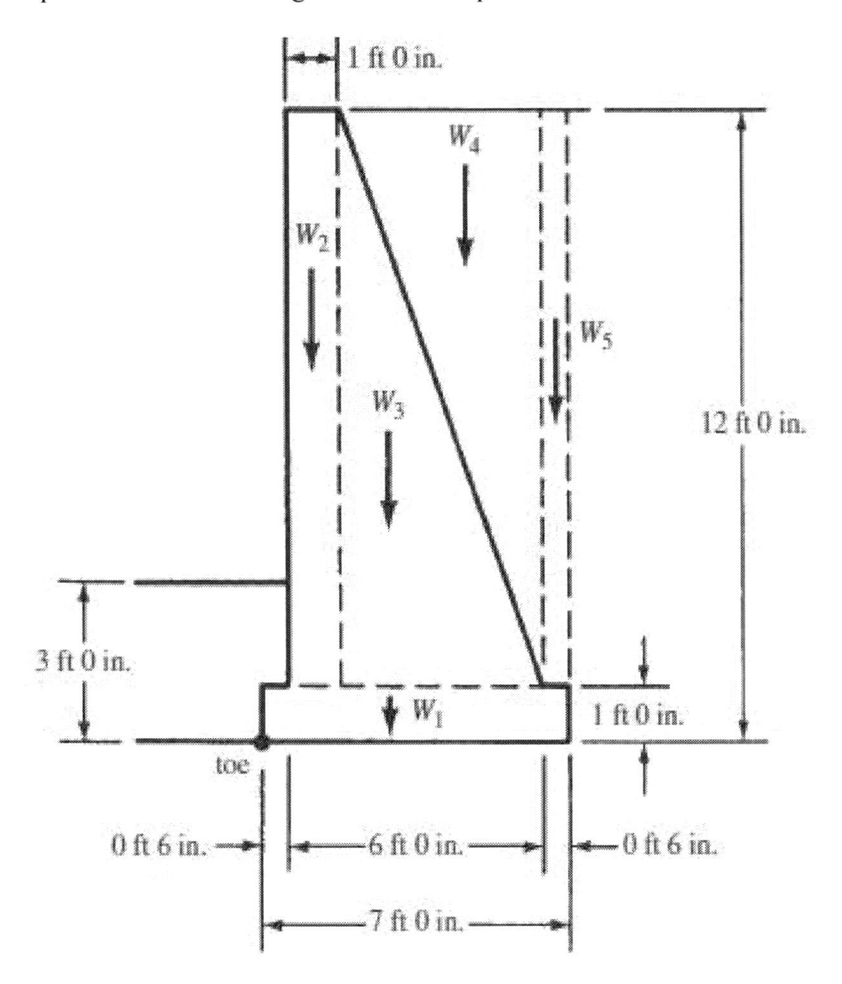

Solution:

Active earth pressure coefficient, $K_a = \dfrac{1-\sin\phi'}{1+\sin\phi'} = \dfrac{1-\sin 30}{1+\sin 30} = 0.333$

Passive earth pressure coefficient, $K_p = \dfrac{1+\sin\phi'}{1-\sin\phi'} = \dfrac{1+\sin 30}{1-\sin 30} = 3.0$

Active lateral force $P_a = \dfrac{1}{2}K_a\gamma z^2 = \dfrac{1}{2}(0.333)\left(110\dfrac{\text{lb}}{\text{ft}^3}\right)(12\,\text{ft})^2 = 2{,}637\,\text{lb}$

Passive lateral force $P_p = \dfrac{1}{2}K_p\gamma z^2 = \dfrac{1}{2}(3.0)\left(110\dfrac{\text{lb}}{\text{ft}^3}\right)(1.0\,\text{ft})^2 = 165$ lb [As mentioned, soil above the footing toe may be eroded easily and we considered only 1.0 ft.]

Overturning Moment = Force x Lever Arm = 2,637 lb x (1/3 of 12 ft) = 10,548 lb.ft
Resistive Moment by gravity (Passive pressure is neglected for overturning resistance):

Force		Moment Arm		Moment
$W_1 = (7)(1)(145\ \text{pcf})$	=	1,015 lb × 3.5 ft	=	3,552 ft-lb
$W_2 = (1)(11)(145\ \text{pcf})$	=	1,595 lb × 1.0 ft	=	1,595 ft-lb
$W_3 = (\frac{1}{2})(5)(11)(145\ \text{pcf})$	=	3,988 lb × 3.17 ft	=	12,642 ft-lb
$W_4 = (\frac{1}{2})(5)(11)(110\ \text{pcf})$	=	3,025 lb × 4.83 ft	=	14,611 ft-lb
$W_5 = (0.5)(11)(110\ \text{pcf})$	=	605 lb × 6.75 ft	=	4,084 ft-lb
R_v	=	10,228 lb	M =	36,484 ft-lb

Passive pressure can be neglected for overturning resistance. Otherwise, we would add 165 lb x 1/3 of 1.0 ft = 55 lb.ft.
Safety factor against overturning = 36,484 lb.ft / 10,548 lb.ft = 3.46 safe for overturing

Resistive force by friction = μR_v = 0.50 x Weight = 0.50 x 10,228 lb = 5,114 lb
Total resistive force = Friction + Passive = 5,114 lb + 165 lb = 5,279 lb
Sliding force = Active force = 2,637 lb
Safety factor against sliding = 5,279 lb / 2,637 lb = 2.0 safe for sliding

Chapter 5
Hydraulics and Hydrology

The topics presented in this chapter are ordered as specified in the NCEES PE Civil Exam specifications. This chapter, i.e., Chapter 5 is also primarily based on Chapter 6 of the PE Civil Handbook.

5.1 Open-Channel Flow

Open-Channel Flow (i.e. canals, culverts, drainage ditches, streams, non-pressurized pipes) involves atmospheric pressure and gravity to sustain flow through the channel. Variations in channel roughness, size, slope, path, etc. all impact the flow calculations. The continuity equation is something we need to use very often here and there. It states the conservation of flow between two cross-sections (1 and 2) of a continuous conduit as follows:

$$Q = A_1 v_1 = A_2 v_2$$

Q = flow rate, ft^3/sec
A = cross sectional area of the flow, ft^2
v = mean velocity of the flow, ft/sec

PE Civil Handbook, Article 6.4 Open-Channel Flow discusses this topic. This continuity equation is mostly used for closed conduit and can be used for open-channel as well.

Example 5.1
An incompressible fluid is flowing through a 4-ft diameter pipe with a velocity of 10 ft/s. If the pipe is connected to a 3-ft diameter pipe, the increase in velocity (ft/s) is most nearly:

Solution:

Velocity through 4-ft. diameter pipe, $v_1 = 10\ \frac{\text{ft}}{\text{sec}}$

Area of 4-ft diameter pipe, $A_1 = \frac{\pi D_1^{\ 2}}{4} = \frac{\pi(4)^2}{4} = 4\pi$

Area of 3-ft diameter pipe, $A_2 = \frac{\pi D_2^{\ 2}}{4} = \frac{\pi(3)^2}{4} = 2.25\pi$

Continuity Equation: $A_1 v_1 = A_2 v_2$

Therefore, $v_2 = \frac{A_1 v_1}{A_2} = \frac{(4\pi)\left(10\frac{\text{ft}}{\text{sec}}\right)}{(2.25\pi)} = 17.8\ \frac{\text{ft}}{\text{sec}}$

Increase in velocity = 17.8 ft/sec – 10 ft/sec = 7.8 ft/sec

Example 5.2
Oil flows into the pipe at A with an average velocity of 0.2 m/s and exits through B with an average velocity of 0.15 m/s. Determine the maximum velocity of the oil as it emerges from C.

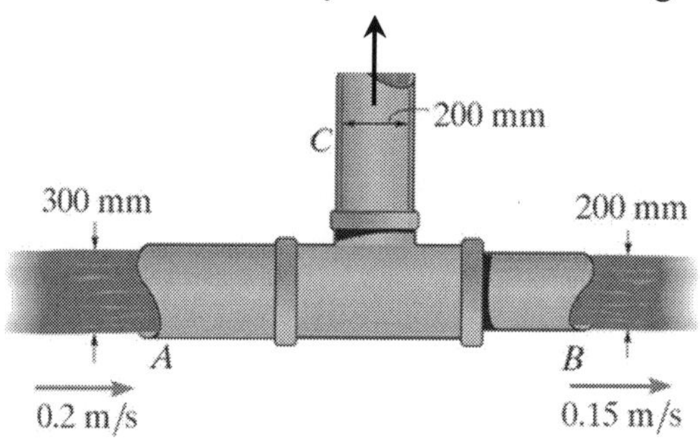

Solution:

$$A_A v_A = A_B v_B + A_C v_C$$

$$\frac{\pi(0.3\,\text{m})^2}{4}\left(0.2\frac{\text{m}}{\text{sec}}\right) = \frac{\pi(0.2\,\text{m})^2}{4}\left(0.15\frac{\text{m}}{\text{sec}}\right) + \frac{\pi(0.2\,\text{m})^2}{4}(v_C)$$

v_C = 0.3 m/s

5.1.1 Specific Energy

The specific energy of a liquid in an open channel is the total mechanical energy (expressed as a head) relative to the bottom of the channel. The specific energy reaches a minimum value at some intermediate point, called the critical point, characterized by the critical depth and critical velocity. The minimum specific energy is also called the critical energy. Article 6.4 of the PE Ref. Civil Handbook expresses the Specific Energy as:

$$E = \alpha\frac{v^2}{2g} + y = \frac{\alpha Q^2}{2gA^2} + y$$

E = specific energy
Q = discharge (ft^3/sec)
v = velocity (ft/sec)
y = depth of flow (ft)
A = cross-sectional area of flow (ft2)
α = kinetic energy correction factor, usually 1.0
z = elevation (ft)

Example 5.3
Water flows with an average speed of 6 ft/s in a rectangular channel having a width of 5 ft. Water is considered to be incompressible and the flow is steady. If the depth of the water is 2 ft, determine the specific energy.

Solution:

Flow, $Q = Av = (5 \text{ ft x } 2 \text{ ft}) \text{ x } (6 \text{ ft/sec}) = 60 \text{ ft}^3\text{/sec}$

$$\text{Specific Energy, } E = \frac{\alpha Q^2}{2gA^2} + y = \frac{(1.0)\left(60\frac{\text{ft}^3}{\text{sec}}\right)^2}{2\left(32.2\frac{\text{ft}}{\text{sec}^2}\right)(5\,\text{ft} \times 2\,\text{ft})^2} + 2\,\text{ft} = \underline{2.56\,\text{ft}}$$

5.1.2 Conservation of Energy

Energy is conserved for a fluid in an open channel flow. The energy calculated at one location in the flow will be equal to the energy calculated at any other location in the same flow, unless there is head losses due to friction.

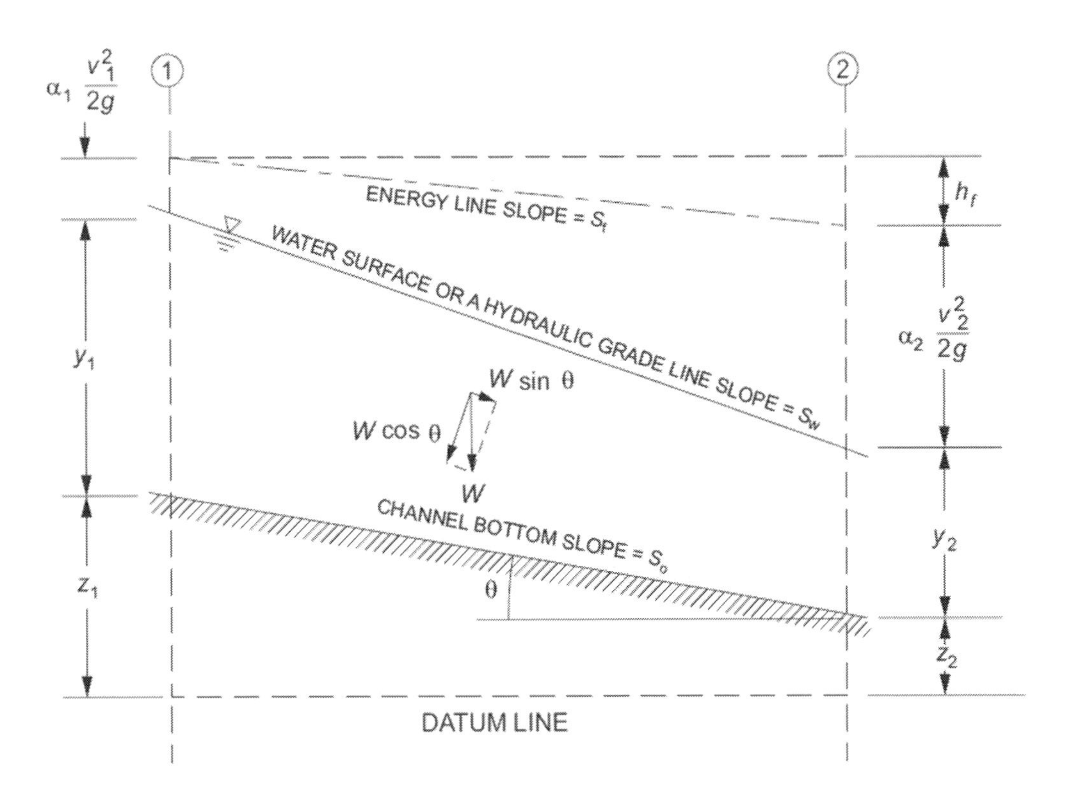

$$z_1 + y_1 + \frac{\alpha_1 v_1^2}{2g} = z_2 + y_2 + \frac{\alpha_2 v_2^2}{2g} + h_f$$

z_1, z_2 = elevations of the channel bottom (ft)
y_1, y_2 = depths of flow (ft)
v_1, v_2 = velocities (ft/sec)
α_1, α_2 = kinetic energy coefficients
h_f = frictional loss

5.1.3 Critical Depth

Critical depth is defined as the depth of flow where energy is at a minimum for a particular discharge. Critical flow occurs when the flow velocity in a channel equals the wave velocity generated by a disturbance or obstruction. Critical flow is unstable and often sets up standing waves between super and subcritical flow. When the actual water depth is below critical depth it is called supercritical as it is in a higher energy state. Likewise actual depth above critical depth is called subcritical as it is in a lower energy state.

$$\frac{v^2}{2g} = \frac{y}{2}$$

v = flow velocity (ft/sec)
y = depth of flow (ft)
g = acceleration due to gravity (ft/sec^2)

For Rectangular Channels:

$$Q_c = \left(\frac{A^3 g}{T} \right)^{1/2}$$

Q_c = critical flow in a channel at minimum specific energy (ft^3/sec)
g = acceleration due to gravity (ft/sec^2)
T = width of the water surface at top (ft)
A = area of channel flow (ft^2)

$$y_c = \left(\frac{q^2}{g} \right)^{1/3}$$

y_c = critical depth (ft)
q = unit discharge (cfs/ft) = Q/B
B = channel width (ft)
g = acceleration due to gravity (ft/sec^2)

Example 5.4
Water flows with an average speed of 6 ft/s in a rectangular channel having a width of 5 ft. Water is considered to be incompressible and the flow is steady. If the depth of the water is 2 ft, determine the critical depth.

Solution:

Flow, $Q = Av$ = (5 ft x 2 ft) x (6 ft/sec) = 60 ft^3/sec

$$\text{Critical depth, } y_c = \left(\frac{q^2}{g}\right)^{1/3} = \left(\frac{\left(\frac{Q}{B}\right)^2}{g}\right)^{1/3} = \left(\left(\frac{60\frac{\text{ft}^3}{\text{sec}}}{5\,\text{ft}}\right)^2 \div 32.2\frac{\text{ft}}{\text{sec}^2}\right)^{1/3} = \underline{1.648\,\text{ft}}$$

5.1.4 Froude Number

The Froude number, *Fr*, is a dimensionless value that describes different flow regimes of open channel flow. The Froude number is a ratio of inertial and gravitational forces.

- Gravity (numerator) - moves water downhill
- Inertia (denominator) - reflects its willingness to do so.

Froude Number = ratio of inertial forces to gravity forces: $Fr = \dfrac{V}{\sqrt{gy_h}} = \sqrt{\dfrac{Q^2T}{gA^3}}$

y_h = hydraulic depth = A / T
T = width of the water surface at top (ft)

Fr = 1, critical flow
Fr > 1, supercritical flow (fast rapid flow)
Fr < 1, subcritical flow (slow / tranquil flow)

- Subcritical occurs when the actual water depth is greater than critical depth. Subcritical flow is dominated by gravitational forces and behaves in a slow or stable way. It is defined as having a Froude number less than one.
- Supercritical flow is dominated by inertial forces and behaves as rapid or unstable flow. Supercritical flow transitions to subcritical through a hydraulic jump which represents a high energy loss with erosive potential. When the actual depth is less than critical depth it is classified as supercritical. Supercritical flow has a Froude number greater than one.
- Critical flow is the transition or control flow that possesses the minimum possible energy for that flowrate. Critical flow has a Froude number equal to one.

The Froude number is a measurement of bulk flow characteristics such as waves, sand bedforms, flow/depth interactions at a cross section or between boulders. The denominator represents the speed of a small wave on the water surface relative to the speed of the water, called wave celerity. At critical flow, celerity equals flow velocity. Any disturbance to the surface will remain stationary. In subcritical flow, the flow is controlled from a downstream point and information is transmitted upstream. This condition leads to backwater effects. Supercritical flow is controlled upstream and disturbances are transmitted downstream.

Example 5.5
Water is flowing in a formed, unfinished concrete rectangular channel of 3.5 m wide at a velocity of 1.777 m/s. The channel longitudinal slope is 0.1 percent. For a depth of 2.0 m, calculate the normal discharge and the Froude number of the flow.

Solution:

Cross-sectional area, $A = 3.50 \times 2.0 = 7.0\ \text{m}^2$
Velocity, $v = 1.777$ m/s
Normal discharge, $Q = Av = 7.0\ \text{m}^2 (1.777\ \text{m/s}) = \underline{12.44\ \text{m}^3/\text{sec}}$

Hydraulic depth, $y_h = A / T = 7.0\ \text{m}^2 / = 3.50\ \text{m} = 2.0\ \text{m}$

$$\text{Froude number, } Fr = \frac{v}{\sqrt{g y_h}} = \frac{1.777\dfrac{\text{m}}{\text{sec}}}{\sqrt{\left(9.81\dfrac{\text{m}}{\text{sec}^2}\right)(2.0\,\text{m})}} = \underline{0.40}$$

Example 5.6

A rectangular channel transports water at 8 m^3/s. Water is considered to be incompressible and the flow is steady. The channel width is 3 m and the water depth is 2 m. Is the flow subcritical or supercritical?

Solution:

$$\text{Velocity of the flow, } v = \frac{Q}{A} = \frac{8\dfrac{\text{m}^3}{\text{sec}}}{(3\text{m}\times 2\text{m})} = 1.333\,\frac{\text{m}}{\text{sec}}$$

$$\text{Froude number, } Fr = \frac{v}{\sqrt{g y_h}} = \frac{1.333\dfrac{\text{m}}{\text{sec}}}{\sqrt{\left(9.81\dfrac{\text{m}}{\text{sec}^2}\right)(2.0\,\text{m})}} = 0.301$$

As Fr is less than 1.0, <u>the flow is subcritical.</u>

$$\text{Critical depth, } y_c = \left(\frac{q^2}{g}\right)^{1/3} = \left(\frac{\left(\dfrac{Q}{B}\right)^2}{g}\right)^{1/3} = \left(\left(\frac{8\dfrac{\text{m}^3}{\text{sec}}}{3\,\text{m}}\right)^2 \div 9.81\frac{\text{m}}{\text{sec}^2}\right)^{1/3} = 0.898\,\text{m}$$

As the flow depth is greater than the critical depth, <u>the flow is subcritical.</u>

Example 5.7

A rectangular channel having a width of 3 m is required to transport 40 m^3/s of water. Water is considered to be incompressible and the flow is steady. Determine the critical depth and critical velocity of the flow.

Solution

$$\text{Critical depth, } y_c = \left(\frac{q^2}{g}\right)^{1/3} = \left(\frac{\left(\dfrac{Q}{B}\right)^2}{g}\right)^{1/3} = \left(\left(\frac{40\dfrac{\text{m}^3}{\text{sec}}}{3\,\text{m}}\right)^2 \div 9.81\frac{\text{m}}{\text{sec}^2}\right)^{1/3} = 2.6267\,\text{m}$$

At Critical flow, Froude number = 1.0

$$Fr = \frac{v_c}{\sqrt{g y_c}} = 1.0$$

$$\frac{v_c}{\sqrt{\left(9.81\dfrac{\text{m}}{\text{sec}^2}\right)(2.6267\,\text{m})}} = 1.0$$

Therefore, v_c = <u>5.08 m/sec</u>

5.1.5 Specific Energy Diagram

From Article 6.4 of the PE Civil Handbook:

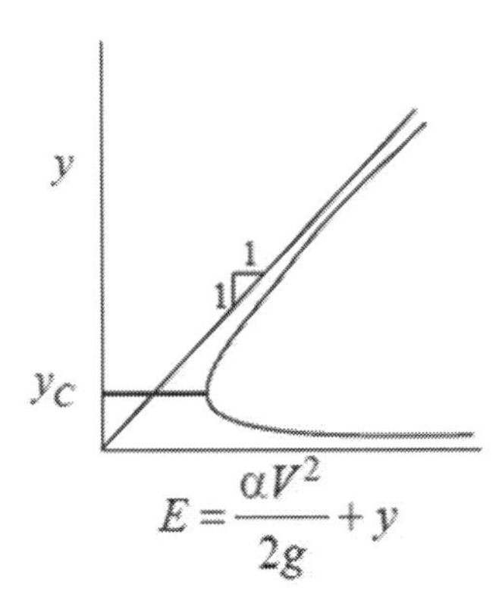

Alternate depths: depths with the same specific energy

y_1 = flow depth at supercritical flow

y_2 = flow depth at subcritical flow

$$y_2 = \frac{y_1}{2}\left[\sqrt{1+8Fr_1^2} - 1\right]$$

Uniform flow is a flow condition where depth and velocity do not change along a channel.

Example 5.8

Water flows at 18 m^3/s over the 4-m-wide spillway of the dam. Water is considered to be incompressible and the flow is steady. If the depth of the water at the bottom apron is 0.5 m, determine the depth y_2 of the water after the hydraulic jump.

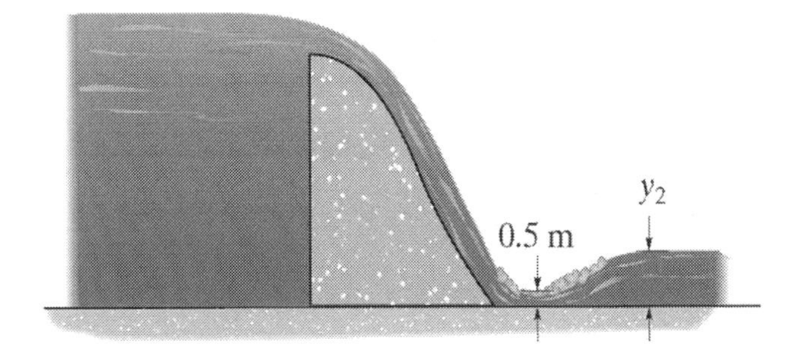

Solution:

The velocity of the flow at section (1) of depth y_1 = 0.5 m is

Flow velocity at Section-1 (0.5 m high), $v_1 = \frac{Q}{A_1} = \frac{18\,\frac{\text{m}^3}{\text{sec}}}{(4\,\text{m} \times 0.5\,\text{m})} = 9.0\,\frac{\text{m}}{\text{sec}}$

Froude number at Section-1 (0.5 m high), $(Fr)_1 = \frac{v_1}{\sqrt{gy_1}} = \frac{9.0\,\frac{\text{m}}{\text{sec}}}{\sqrt{\left(9.81\,\frac{\text{m}}{\text{sec}^2}\right)(0.5\,\text{m})}} = 4.06$

Since $(Fr)_1$ is greater than 1.0, the flow at Section-1 is supercritical, which means a hydraulic jump may occur.

$$y_2 = \frac{y_1}{2}\left[\sqrt{1+8Fr_1^2}-1\right] = \frac{0.5\,\text{m}}{2}\left[\sqrt{1+8(4.06)^2}-1\right] = \underline{2.63\,\text{m}}$$

5.1.6 Manning's Equation

The Manning's equation is an empirical equation that applies to uniform flow in open channels and is a function of the channel velocity, flow area and channel slope. Under the assumption of uniform flow conditions the bottom slope is the same as the slope of the energy grade line and the water surface slope.

From Article 6.4 of the PE Civil Handbook: $Q = \dfrac{1.486}{n} A R_H^{2/3} S^{1/2}$

$$v = \frac{1.486}{n} R_H^{2/3} S^{1/2}$$

Q = discharge or flow rate (ft^3/sec)
v = flow velocity (ft/sec)
n = Manning's roughness coefficient
A = cross-sectional area of flow (ft^2)
R_H = hydraulic radius (ft) = P/A
P = wetted perimeter (ft)
S = slope (ft/ft)

The term, $K = \dfrac{1.486}{n} A R_H^{2/3}$ is known as conveyance. Therefore, $K = \dfrac{Q}{\sqrt{S}}$

Article 6.4 of the PE Civil Handbook presents the approximate values of Manning's roughness coefficient. A small part is shown as follows:

Material		**Manning *n***
Closed Conduit or Built-up Channel	Metal:	
	Brass	0.01
	Copper	0.011
	Steel – welded	0.012
	Steel – riveted	0.016
	Cast iron – coated	0.013
	Wrought iron – galvanized	0.016
	Corrugated metal (storm drain)	0.024
	Nonmetal:	
	Glass	0.01
	Cement	0.011
	Cement mortar	0.013
	Concrete culvert	0.013
	Concrete-lined channel/pipe	0.015
	Wood	0.012
	Clay	0.013
	Brickwork	0.013
	Brickwork with cement mortar	0.015
	Masonry/rubble masonry	0.025
	Sanitary sewer coated with slime	0.013
	Asphalt	0.013
	Plastic	0.013

Example 5.9
The trapezoidal channel shown below has a Manning's roughness of 0.017.

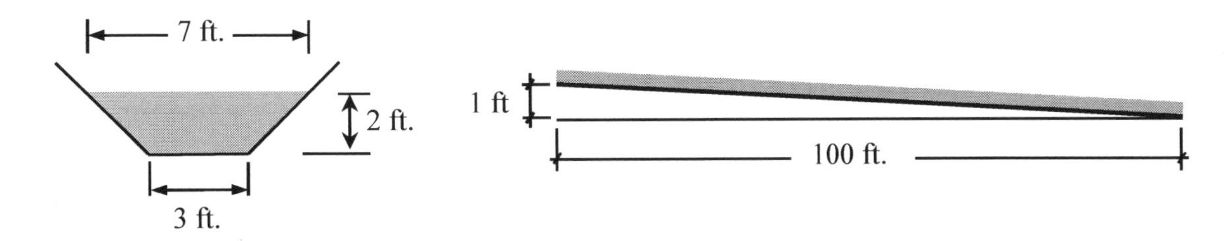

From the section and profile of the channel, the normal discharge (ft³/sec) is most nearly:

Solution:

$$\text{Wetted area, } A = \left(\frac{7\,\text{ft} + 3\,\text{ft}}{2}\right)(2\,\text{ft}) = 10\,\text{ft}^2$$

$$\text{Wetted perimeter, } P = 3\,\text{ft} + 2\sqrt{(2\,\text{ft})^2 + (2\,\text{ft})^2} = 8.66\,\text{ft}$$

$$\text{Hydraulic radius, } R_H = \frac{A}{P} = \frac{10\,\text{ft}^2}{8.66\,\text{ft}} = 1.16\,\text{ft}$$

$$\text{Longitudinal slope, } S = \frac{1\,\text{ft}}{100\,\text{ft}} = 0.01$$

$$Q = \frac{1.486}{n} A R_H^{2/3} S^{1/2} = \left(\frac{1.486}{0.017}\right)(10\,\text{ft}^2)(1.16\,\text{ft})^{2/3}(0.01)^{1/2} = \underline{96.2\ \frac{\text{ft}^3}{\text{sec}}}$$

Example 5.10
The sides and bottom of the channel shown below are made of formed and unfinished concrete with Manning's roughness of 0.017. Calculate the minimum slope on which the channel must be laid to carry 50 ft³/sec of water with a depth of 2 ft.

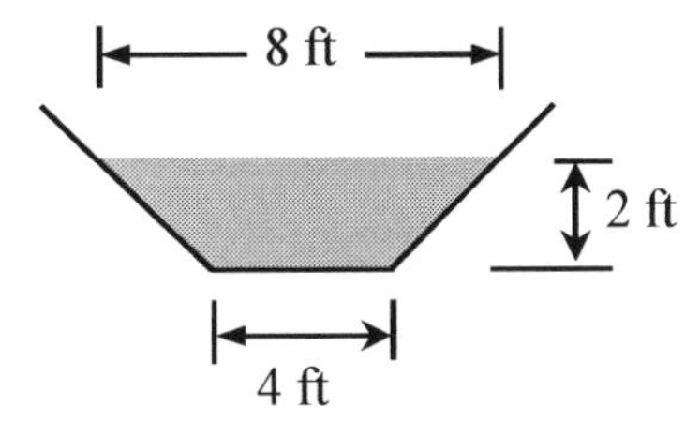

Solution:

$$Q = \left(\frac{1.486}{n}\right) A R_H^{2/3} S^{1/2}$$

$$S = \left(\frac{Qn}{1.486\, A R_H^{2/3}}\right)$$

$$A = (4\,\text{ft} \times 2\,\text{ft}) + \frac{1}{2}(2\,\text{ft} \times 2\,\text{ft}) \times 2 = 12\,\text{ft}^2$$

$$P = 4\,\text{ft} + 2\sqrt{(2\,\text{ft})^2 + (2\,\text{ft})^2} = 9.66\,\text{ft}$$

$$R_H = \frac{A}{P} = \frac{12\,\text{ft}^2}{9.66\,\text{ft}} = 1.24\,\text{ft}$$

$$\text{Therefore, } S = \left[\frac{\left(50\frac{\text{ft}^3}{\text{sec}}\right)(0.017)}{(1.486)\left(12\,\text{ft}^2\right)(1.24\,\text{ft})^{2/3}} \right]^2 = \underline{0.0017}$$

Therefore, the channel must drop at least 1.7 ft per 1,000 ft of length.

5.1.7 Chezy Equation

Chezy Equation is similar to Manning's Equation with Manning's roughness (n) replaced by Chezy's resistance coefficient (C). Article 6.4 of the PE Ref. Civil Handbook states:

$$v = C\sqrt{R_H S}$$

$$Q = CA\sqrt{R_H S}$$

where

v = velocity in channel (ft/sec)
Q = flow in channel (ft^3/sec)
C = Chezy's resistance coefficient
R_H = hydraulic radius (ft)
S = slope of hydraulic surface (ft/ft)

$C = \frac{1}{n} R_H^{1/6}$ where n = Manning's roughness coefficient

5.2 Stormwater Collection and Drainage

A storm drainage system is intended to remove excess rain and ground water (i.e. runoff) from surfaces such as streets, parking lots, sidewalks, roofs, etc. Excess rain is that which is not captured by natural landscape such as grass areas, trees, plants, etc. Storm drains are typically connected to gutters and stormwater inlets. There are two main types of stormwater drain inlets:

a) side – located adjacent to curbs, relying on the ability (size and orientation) of the opening to capture flow.
b) grated – typically located in large, relatively flat areas. Inlet is usually depressed at the invert of the channel to improve capture capacity.

Most inlets have grids to prevent objects (i.e. people, vehicles, large objects, or debris) from falling into the storm drain. The grids (or grate bars) are spaced to allow water, sediment, and small objects to enter drain. Catch basins (similar in function to a house sewer trap) traps large debris, sediment, and objects. The catch basin is located below the outlet where water from the top of the reservoir overflows into the storm sewer. By capturing large sediments and debris before they enter the storm drainage piping, catch basins act as the first (and oftentimes the only) step in stormwater pretreatment. Typically, stormwater picks up oil, heavy metals, pesticides, etc. as it flows down streets, sidewalks, and other impervious surfaces before discharging into rivers, lakes, or reservoirs – untreated. Storm drains may discharge into man-made excavations known as:

- Detention Pond – an area where excess stormwater is stored or held temporarily and then slowly drained when water levels in the receiving channel recede. A detention basin typically drains after the peak of the storm flow has passed, sometimes while it is still raining.

- Retention Pond – an area where excess stormwater is stored on a more permanent basis. Stormwater often remains in a retention basin indefinitely, only losing volume to evaporation and absorption into the soil. Retention ponds are also used to recharge underground water aquifers.

5.3 Storm Characteristics

The PE Ref. Civil Handbook does not specify the topics for storm characteristics. The author believes that the following sections include the topics required for the Breadth exam.

5.4 Runoff Analysis

Article 6.5 of the PE Ref. Civil Handbook states, General Probability $p = \frac{n_i}{N}$

p = probability of occurrence of a flood flow of class i (variate i)
n_i = number of items in the i-th class
N = total number of items in a series

The probability of single occurrence in a given storm year is given as, $P(x \geq x_T) = p = \frac{1}{T}$

Where, x = magnitude of event
x_T = design level event
T = storm/flood return period (years)

The Rational formula is widely used to size storm sewers, culverts, stormwater inlets, and storm sewer pipes. The simplified flood frequency equation is given as, $x_T = \bar{x} + K_T s$

x_T = estimated event magnitude
$\bar{x}$ = sample mean (observed data)
T = storm/flood return period (years)
K_T = frequency factor (Normal, Extreme Value, Exponential/Pearson)
s = standard deviation of the sample

Table. Frequency Factor for Normal Distribution (A small part is shown here. See the Handbook)

Exceedance Probability	**Return Period**	***K***	**Exceedance Probability**	**Return Period**	***K***
0.0001	10,000	3.719	0.450	2.22	0.126
0.0005	2,000	3.291	0.500	2.00	0.000
0.001	1,000	3.090	0.550	1.82	–0.126
0.002	500	2.88	0.600	1.67	–0.253
0.003	333	2.76	0.650	1.54	–0.385
0.004	250	2.65	0.700	1.43	–0.524
0.005	200	2.576	0.750	1.33	–0.674
0.010	100	2.326	0.800	1.25	–0.842
0.025	40	1.960	0.850	1.18	–1.036
0.050	20	1.645	0.900	1.11	–1.282
0.100	10	1.282	0.950	1.053	–1.645
0.150	6.67	1.036	0.975	1.026	–1.960
0.200	5.00	0.842	0.990	1.010	–2.326
0.250	4.00	0.674	0.995	1.005	–2.576

Example 5.11

A 200-acre drainage area consists of four different watershed areas as shown in Table. The mean annual rainfall intensity in the area is 2.0 in./hr, and the standard deviation of the rainfall data is 0.7163 in./hr. Assume the rainfall is normally distributed and the Rational method is applicable. The estimated rainfall at a 20-year time interval is most nearly:

Solution:

Estimated rainfall intensity, $x_T = \overline{x} + K_T s$

x = sample mean (observed data) = 2.0 in./hr

T = storm/flood return period (years) = 20 years

s = standard deviation of the sample = 0.7163 in./hr

For return period of 20 years, frequency factor K_T = 1.645 as follows from the handbook.

Frequency Factor for Normal Distribution

Exceedance Probability	Return Period	*K*	Exceedance Probability	Return Period	*K*
0.010	100	2.326	0.800	1.25	–0.842
0.025	40	1.960	0.850	1.18	–1.036
0.050	20	1.645	0.900	1.11	–1.282
0.100	10	1.282	0.950	1.053	–1.645

Estimated rainfall, $x_T = \overline{x} + K_T s$ = 2.0 in./hr + 1.645 x 0.7163 in./hr = 3.178 in./hr

Rational method states, peak discharge, $Q = CIA$

Q = peak discharge (ft^3/sec)

C = runoff coefficient

I = rainfall intensity from an intensity-duration frequency curve for a duration of t_c (in./hr)

A = watershed area (acres)

t_c = time of concentration, which is the time required for the runoff to travel from the hydraulically most distant point of the watershed to the point of interest (min)

Multiple watersheds may require summation of times to determine an overall time for the system. Unit conversion from acre-in./hr to ft^3/sec is most often approximated to 1.0.

$$C_w = \frac{C_1A_1 + C_2A_2 + C_3A_3 + \ldots C_nA_n}{A_1 + A_2 + A_3 + \ldots A_n}$$

where C_w = weighted/composite runoff coefficient for whole drainage area

Table. Runoff Coefficients for Rational Formula (A small part is shown here. See the handbook)

Type of Drainage Area	Runoff Coefficient, *C**
Business:	
Downtown areas	0.70–0.95
Neighborhood areas	0.50–0.70
Residential:	
Single-family areas	0.30–0.50
Multi-units, detached	0.40–0.60
Multi-units, attached	0.60–0.75
Suburban	0.25–0.40
Apartment dwelling areas	0.50–0.70
Industrial:	
Light areas	0.50–0.80
Heavy areas	0.60–0.90
Parks, cemeteries	0.10–0.25
Playgrounds	0.20–0.40
Railroad yards areas	0.20–0.40
Unimproved areas	0.10–0.30
Lawns:	
Sandy soil, flat, 2%	0.05–0.10
Sandy soil, average, 2–7%	0.10–0.15
Sandy soil, steep, 7%	0.15–0.20
Heavy soil, flat, 2%	0.13–0.17
Heavy soil, average, 2–7%	0.18–0.22
Heavy soil, steep, 7%	0.25–0.35

Example 5.12

A major channel collects storm water from three regions as shown below. Water from Regions 1 and 2 meet at *A* and then flow 2,250-ft to reach *B*. Water from Region 3 flows to point *B* directly. Water from point *B* travel 4,500 ft to reach the point *C* from where the major channel collects the water. The water travel paths and their flow velocities for each travel path are mentioned as well.

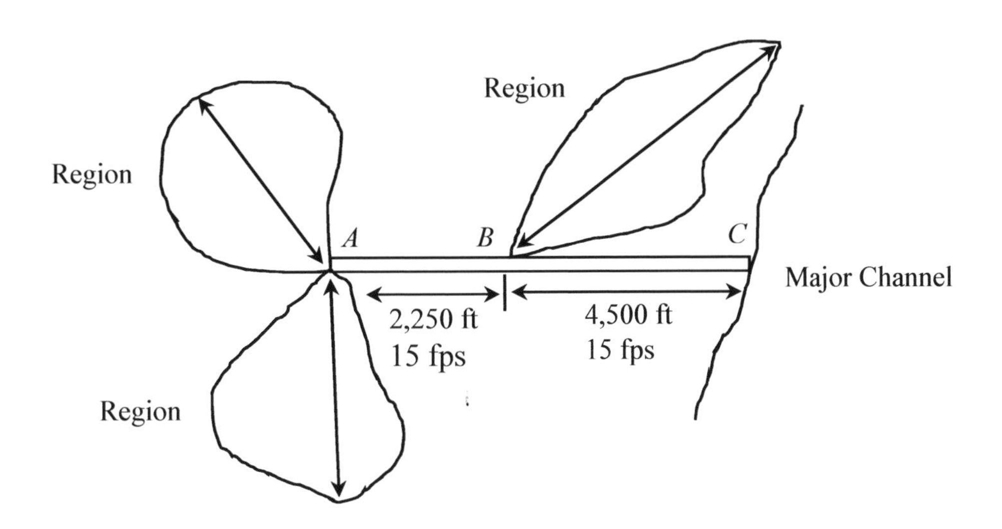

	Longest Path, ft	Flow Velocity, fps
Region 1	3,000	4
Region 2	3,600	6
Region 3	4,800	8
AB	2,250	15
BC	4,500	15

The time of concentration (min) for the major channel is most nearly:

Solution:

Time of travel in Region 1 = 3,000 ft / 4 fps = 750 sec
Time of travel in Region 2 = 3,600 ft / 6 fps = 600 sec (Region 1 is bigger, 750 sec)
Time to travel 2,250-ft of channel, *AB* = 2,250 ft / 15 fps = 150 sec
Time from Regions 1 and 2 to come to *B* = 750 sec + 150 sec = 900 sec
Time of travel in Region 3 = 4,800 ft / 8 fps = 600 sec (smaller compared to 900 sec)
Time to travel 4,500-ft of channel, *BC* = 4,500 ft / 15 fps = 300 sec
Time of concentration = 900 sec + 300 sec = 1,200 sec = 20 min

Example 5.13
A 200-acre drainage area consists of four different watershed areas as shown in Table. The mean annual rainfall intensity in the area is 2.0 in./hr, the estimated rainfall at a 20-year time interval is 3.178 in./hr and the standard deviation of the rainfall data is 0.7163 in./hr. Assume the rainfall is normally distributed, a 20-year time interval and Rational method is applicable.

Segment	**Land Type**	**Segment Area**
1	Lawns (Heavy soil, average slope 2–7%)	35%
2	Playgrounds	15%
3	Asphaltic Street	40%
4	Drives and walks	10%

The peak flow (cfs) based on the maximum runoff coefficients is most nearly:

Solution:

Estimated rainfall, $I = 3.178$ in./hr
For C, let us take the maximum value as the problem asked.

Segment	**Land Type**	**Area (Acre)**	***C* (max) from Handbook Table**
1	Lawns (Heavy soil, average slope 2–7%)	200 x 0.35 = 70	0.22
2	Playgrounds	200 x 0.15 = 30	0.40
3	Asphaltic Street	200 x 0.40 = 80	0.95
4	Drives and walks	200 x 0.10 = 20	0.85

$$C = \frac{C_1A_1 + C_2A_2 + C_3A_3 + C_4A_4}{A_1 + A_2 + A_3 + A_4} = \frac{0.22(70) + 0.40(30) + 0.95(80) + 0.85(20)}{200} = 0.602$$

$Q = CIA$ = (0.602) (3.178 in./hr) (200 acre) = 383 cfs ≈ 380 cfs

NRCS (SCS) Rainfall Runoff Method states, Runoff depth (in.), $Q=\frac{(P-0.2S)^2}{P+0.8S}$

$$S=\frac{1{,}000}{CN}-10$$

$$CN=\frac{1{,}000}{S+10}$$

Q = runoff depth (in.)
P = precipitation (in.)
S = maximum basin retention (in.)
CN = curve number
I_a = initial abstraction (in.) ≈ 0.2S

Loss (in.) = P – Q = $\frac{(S+I_a)-\frac{I_a^2}{P}}{1-\frac{I_a}{P}+\frac{S}{P}}$

As P becomes increasingly large, Loss (in.) = $S + I_a$

Peak Discharge Method, $q_p = q_u A_m Q$

q_p = peak flow (ft3/sec)
q_u = unit peak flow (ft3/sec/mi2/in.)
A_m = basin area (mi2)
Q = runoff depth (in.)

$$q_u = 10^{C_o + C_1 \log t_c + C_2 (\log t_c)^2}$$

C_0, C_1, C_2 = TR-55 coefficients
t_c = time of concentration (min)
I_a = initial abstraction (in.)

SCS Hydrologic Soils Group Type Classifications

Group A: Deep sand, deep loess, aggregated silts
Group B: Shallow loess, sandy loam
Group C: Clay loams, shallow sandy loam, soils low in organic content, and soils usually high in clay
Group D: Soils that swell significantly when wet, heavy plastic clays, and certain saline soils

Table. Minimum Infiltration Rates for the Various Soil Groups

Group	**Minimum Infiltration Rate (in./hr)**
A	0.30 – 0.45
B	0.15 – 0.30
C	0.0 – 0.05

Table. Ratios for SCS Dimensionless Unit Hydrograph and Mass Curve (a small part, see the handbook)

Time Ratios, t/T_p	**Discharge Ratios, q/q_p**	**Mass Curve Ratios, Q_a/Q**
0	0.000	0.000
0.1	0.030	0.001
0.2	0.100	0.006
0.3	0.190	0.012
0.4	0.310	0.035
0.5	0.470	0.065
0.6	0.660	0.107

Table. Runoff Curve Numbers for Urban Areas (Average Watershed Condition, $I_a = 0.2\ S_R$) (a small part is shown here, see the handbook for the full table)

Land Use Description	**Curve Numbers for Hydrologic Soil Group**			
	A	**B**	**C**	**D**
Fully developed urban areas (vegetation established)				
Lawns, open spaces, parks, golf courses, cemeteries, etc.				
Good condition; grass cover on 75% or more of the area	39	61	74	80
Fair condition; grass cover on 50 to 75% or more of the area	49	69	79	84
Poor condition; grass cover on 50% or less of the area	68	79	86	89
Paved parking lots, roofs, driveways, etc. (excl. right-of-way)				
Streets and roads	98	98	98	98
Paved with curbs and storm sewers (excl. right-of-way)	98	98	98	98
Gravel (incl. right-of-way)	76	85	89	91
Dirt (incl. right-of-way)	72	82	87	89
Paved with open ditches (incl. right-of-way)	83	89	92	93
Average % impervious				
Commercial and business areas 85	89	92	94	95

Table. Coefficients for SCS Peak Discharge Method (a small part is shown here, see the handbook)

Rainfall Type	I_a/P	C_0	C_1	C_2
I	0.10	2.30550	−0.51429	−0.11750
	0.20	2.23537	−0.50387	−0.08929
	0.25	2.18219	−0.48488	−0.06589
	0.30	2.10624	−0.45695	−0.02835
	0.35	2.00303	−0.40769	−0.01983
	0.40	1.87733	−0.32274	0.05754
	0.45	1.76312	−0.15644	0.00453
	0.50	1.67889	−0.06930	0.0
IA	0.10	2.03250	−0.31583	−0.13748
	0.20	1.91978	−0.28215	−0.07020
	0.25	1.83842	−0.25543	−0.02597
	0.30	1.72657	−0.19826	0.02633
	0.50	1.63417	−0.09100	0.0

Example 5.14

A 350 acres watershed has most likely soils that swell significantly when wet, heavy plastic clays, and certain saline soils. The primary land is newly graded area. The 30-year storm has an estimated gross rainfall of 2.8 in. Using the NRCS (SCS) method, the net runoff (in.) from this watershed is most nearly:

Solution:

Soils that swell significantly when wet, heavy plastic clays, and certain saline soils is Hydrologic Soil Group D. From the Table, CN = 94 for newly graded area of Group D.

The maximum basin retention (in.), $S = \frac{1{,}000}{CN} - 10 = \frac{1{,}000}{94} - 10 = 0.638$

Given, P = precipitation = 2.8 in.

The net runoff, $Q = \frac{(P - 0.2S)^2}{P + 0.8S} = \frac{(2.8\text{in.} - 0.2 \times 0.638\text{in.})^2}{(2.8\text{in.} + 0.8 \times 0.638\text{in.})} = \underline{0.8\text{in.}}$

Example 5.15

The estimated precipitation of a 256-acre area is 15.1 in. considering the return period of 10 years. The maximum basin retention (S) is 7.85 in. Assume the rainfall data is normally distributed and the rainfall falls under the category of Type II by the NRCS. The average curve number of the soil in the area is 56 and the time of concentration of the flow is 100 min. The peak flow (ft³/sec) using the NRCS (SCS) rainfall runoff method is most nearly:

Solution:

Precipitation, P = 15.1 in.

The maximum basin retention (in.), S = 7.85

The net runoff, $Q = \frac{(P - 0.2S)^2}{P + 0.8S} = \frac{(15.1\text{in.} - 0.2 \times 7.85\text{in.})^2}{(15.1\text{in.} + 0.8 \times 7.85\text{in.})} = 8.56\text{in.}$

Initial abstraction, $I_a = 0.2S = 0.2$ (7.85 in.) = 1.57 in.

I_a / P = 1.57 in. / 15.1 in. = 0.10

For Type II, from the handbook table: $C_o = 2.55323$, $C_1 = -0.61512$ and $C_2 = -0.16403$

Coefficients for SCS Peak Discharge Method

Rainfall Type	I_a/P	C_0	C_1	C_2
II	0.10	2.55323	-0.61512	-0.16403

Now, $q_u = 10^{C_o + C_1 \log t_c + C_2 (\log t_c)^2}$

$= 10^{2.55323 + (-0.61512)\log(100\text{min}) + (-0.16403)(\log(100\text{min}))^2}$

$= 4.64 \frac{\text{ft}^3}{\text{sec.mi}^2\text{.in.}}$

Area, A_m = 256 acre = 256 x 43,560 ft² = 256 x 43,560 ft²/(5,280 ft/mi)² = 0.40 mi²

Using Peak Discharge Method, peak flow, $q_p = q_u A_m Q$

$= \left(4.64 \frac{\text{ft}^3}{\text{sec.mi}^2\text{.in.}}\right)(0.40\text{mi}^2)(8.56\text{in.}) = \underline{15.9\ (\text{ft}^3/\text{sec})}$

5.5 Detention and Retention Ponds

From Article 6.5 of the PE Civil Handbook:
Rational Method

$V_{in} = i\Sigma ACt$

$V_{out} = Q_o t$

where

Q_0 = outflow rate (cfs)
A = drainage area (acres)
C = rational method runoff coefficient
t = time (min)
i = average rainfall intensity (in./hr)

Storage volume required:

$V_s = V_{in} - V_{out}$

Routing Equation, $\frac{1}{2}(I_1 + I_2)\Delta t + \left(S_1 - \frac{1}{2}O_1\Delta t\right) = \left(S_2 + \frac{1}{2}O_2\Delta t\right)$

where

I = inflow (volume/time)
O = outflow (volume/time)
S = storage (volume/time)
Δt = time interval (time)

Modified Puls Routing Method, $(I_1 + I_2) + \left(\frac{2S_1}{\Delta t} - O_1\right) = \left(\frac{2S_2}{\Delta t} + O_2\right)$

Example 5.16

A natural lake does not have any chemical reactions; it has initially contained 1,500 tons of water. Three months period 800 tons of water has flowed into the lake. The 100 tons of water has been from rain into the lake. The 300 tons of water flow out of the lake, 100 tons of water pumped for irrigation purpose and 50 tons of water have lost from the lake evaporation. What is the amount of water (tons) in the lake at the end of the period?

Solution:

Initial mass of water =1,500 tons
Water flow into the lake = 800 tons
Out of water from Lake = 300 (Flow) + 50 (Evaporation) = 350 tons
Generation of water in Lake =100 (Rainwater) tons
Consumption of water in Lake = 100 (Pumped) tons
Accumulation of water, W= In of water – Out of water + Generation of water – Consumption of water
The general balance equation, W = 800 – 350 + 100 – 100 = 450 tons
Final mass of water in Lake= Initial mass of water + W = 1,500+450 = 1,950 tons

Example 5.17

For the month of April, the average inflow in an area is 5.0 cfs by surface flow and the outflow is 4.5 cfs by surface drainage. The precipitation recorded for the month is 4.0 in. The estimated evaporation (in.) is 6.2 in. Assume impervious bottom and sides of the land. The land has a surface area (ft^2) of most nearly:

Solution:

Water In = Water Out + Water Storage
Surface Inflow + Precipitation = Surface Outflow + Evaporation + Storage
5.0 cfs water + 4.0 in. water = 4.5 cfs water + 6.2 in. water + 0
5 x (3,600 x 24 x 30) ft^3 + (4 /12) ft (A ft^2) = 4.5 x (3,600 x 24 x 30) ft^3 + (6.2 /12) ft (A ft^2)
12,960,000 + 0.3333A = 11,664,000 + 0.5167A
0.183A = 12,960,000 – 11,664,000
0.183A = 1,296,000
A = 7,082,000 ft^2

Example 5.18

The rainfall over time on a 150-acre area is shown below. Assume a total of 1.1 in. of rainfall is infiltrated during the first 30 min. Assume the area has negligible surface storage capacity. If the rest of the water flow to a retention pond with vertical sides and the water is retained there. The depth of water in the pond is allowed to have a maximum height of 55 ft. The volume of surface water (ft^3) the pond is required to store is most nearly:

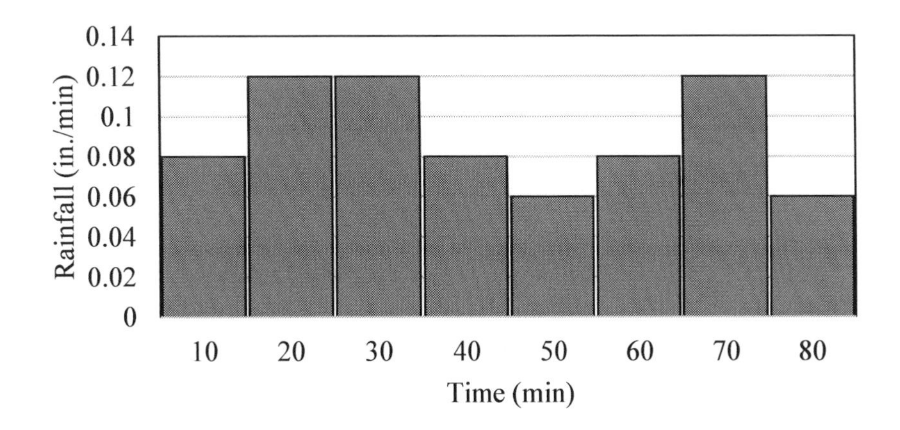

Solution:

Total rainfall = Area under the curve
= 3 col. of 0.08 in./min + 3 col. of 0.12 in./min +2 col. of 0.06 in./min
= [3 x 0.08 in./min + 3 x 0.12 in./min + 2 x 0.06 in./min] x 10 min = 7.2 in.
Infiltration = 1.1 in.
Total surface water available = Rainfall – Infiltration = 7.2 in. – 1.1 in. = 6.1 in.
Total volume of surface water = 6.1 in. x 150 acre = (6.1 /12 ft) x (150 x 43,560 ft^3)
= 39,857,400 ft^3

5.6 Pressure Conduit

From Article 6.3 of the PE Civil Handbook, Velocity (ft/sec or m/s), $V = k_1 C R_H^{0.63} S^{0.54}$

Discharge (ft^3/sec or m^3/s), $Q = VA = = k_1 C A R_H^{0.63} S^{0.54}$
C = roughness coefficient
k_1 = 0.849 for SI units
k_1 = 1.318 for USCS units
R_H = hydraulic radius (ft or m)
S = slope of energy grade line (ft/ft or m/m) = h_f / L

For Circular Pipe Flow, $Q = 0.432CD^{2.63}S^{0.54}$ (USCS units)

$$Q = 0.432CD^{2.63}\left(\frac{h_f}{L}\right)^{0.54}$$ Where D = pipe diameter (ft)

For circular Pipe Head Loss (as feet), $h_f = \frac{4.73L}{C^{1.852}D^{4.87}}Q^{1.852}$

h_f = head loss (ft)
L = pipe length of head loss (ft)
D = pipe diameter (ft)
Q = flow (cfs)
C = Hazen-Williams coefficient

For Circular Pipe Head Loss (as pressure), $P = \frac{4.52Q^{1.85}}{C^{1.85}D^{4.87}}$

P = pressure loss (psi per foot of pipe)
Q = flow (gpm)
D = pipe diameter (in.)
C = Hazen-Williams coefficient

Article 6.3 of the PE Civil Handbook list some values of Hazen-Williams Coefficient C

Pipe Material	***C***
Ductile iron	140
Concrete (regardless of age)	130
Cast iron:	
New	130
5 yr old	120
20 yr old	100
Welded steel, new	120
Wood stave (regardless of age)	120
Vitrified clay	110
Riveted steel, new	110
Brick sewers	100
Asbestos-cement	140
Plastic	150
Galvanized iron (concrete-lined)	120

From Article 6.3 of the PE Civil Handbook, Darcy-Weisbach Equation (Head Loss),

$$h_f = f_a\frac{L_a}{D_a}\frac{v_a^2}{2g} = f_b\frac{L_b}{D_b}\frac{v_b^2}{2g}$$

$$\frac{\pi D^2}{4}v = \frac{\pi D_A^2}{4}v_A + \frac{\pi D_B^2}{4}v_B$$

h_f = head loss (ft)
$f = f(Re, \varepsilon/D)$, friction factor from Moody, Darcy, or Stanton diagram
D = diameter of the pipe (ft)
L = length of which the pressure drop occurs (ft)
v = velocity (ft/sec)
g = acceleration due to gravity (ft/sec^2)

From Article 6.3 of the PE Civil Handbook, Minor Losses in Pipe Fittings, Contractions, and Expansions, head losses also occur as the fluid flows through pipe fittings (i.e., elbows, valves, couplings, etc.) and sudden pipe contractions and expansions.

$$\frac{P_1}{\gamma}+z_1+\frac{v_1^2}{2g}=\frac{P_2}{\gamma}+z_2+\frac{v_2^2}{2g}+h_f+h_{f,fitting}$$

$$\frac{P_1}{\rho g}+z_1+\frac{v_1^2}{2g}=\frac{P_2}{\rho g}+z_2+\frac{v_2^2}{2g}+h_f+h_{f,fitting}$$

$$h_{f,fitting}=C\frac{v^2}{2g}$$

Specific fittings have characteristic values of C, which will be provided in the problem statement. A generally accepted nominal value for head loss in well-streamlined gradual contractions is:

$$h_{f,fitting}=0.04\frac{v^2}{2g}$$

From Article 6.3 of the PE Civil Handbook, The *head loss* at either an *entrance* or *exit* of a pipe from or to a reservoir is also given by the *hf*, fitting equation. Values for *C* for various cases are shown as follows:

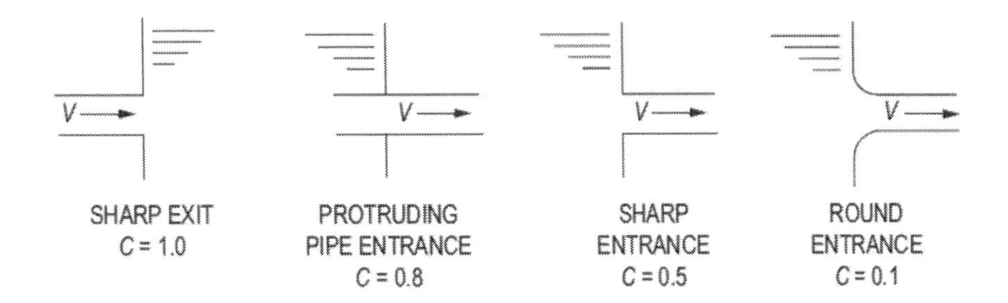

From Article 6.3 of the PE Civil Handbook, Minor Head Loss Coefficients

Component	Loss Coefficient
Globe valve, fully open	10.0
Swing check valve, fully open	2.5
Gate valve, fully open	0.2
Short-radius elbow	0.9
Medium-radius elbow	0.8
Long-radius elbow	0.6
45° elbow	0.4
Closed return bend	2.2
Standard tee – flow through run	0.6
Standard tee – flow through branch	1.8
Exit	1.0

Example 5.19

Sewage, assumed to be water at 20 °C, is pumped from the wet well using a pump and a 50-mm-diameter pipe. The friction factor is $f = 0.026$. The (gage) vapor pressure for water at 20 °C is –98.7 kPa and has a density of 998.3 kg/m^3. Water is considered to be incompressible. The cavitation will occur at the juncture, where water is about to enter the pump since the pressure here is the smallest. Thus, $p_B = -98.7$ kPa.

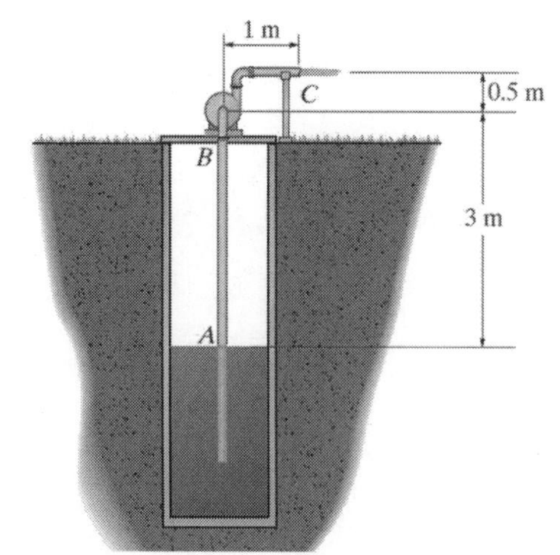

Determine the maximum discharge from the pump without causing cavitation.

Solution:

Head loss from A to B, $h_{L,AB} = f\frac{L_{AB}}{D}\frac{v^2}{2g} = (0.026)\left(\frac{3\text{m}}{0.05\text{m}}\right)\frac{v^2}{2\left(9.81\frac{\text{m}}{\text{s}^2}\right)} = 0.07951v^2$

Applying energy equation from A to B with the datum at A,

$$\frac{P_A}{\gamma} + \frac{v_A^2}{2g} + z_A + h_{f,pump} = \frac{P_B}{\gamma} + \frac{v_2^2}{2g} + z_B + h_{turb} + h_L$$

$$0+0+0+0 = \frac{-98.7\frac{\text{N}}{\text{m}^2}}{\left(998.3\frac{\text{kg}}{\text{m}^3}\right)\left(9.81\frac{\text{m}}{\text{sec}^2}\right)} + \frac{v^2}{2\left(9.81\frac{\text{m}}{\text{sec}^2}\right)} + 3\text{m} + 0 + 0.07951\,v^2$$

Solving, $v = 7.4$ m/s

Discharge, $Q = vA = 7.4$ m/s x π x (0.025 m)^2 = <u>0.015 m^3/s</u>

From Article 6.3 of the PE Civil Handbook, Pipe Bends, Enlargements, and Contractions, the force exerted by a flowing fluid on a bend, enlargement, or contraction in a pipeline may be computed using the impulse-momentum principle.

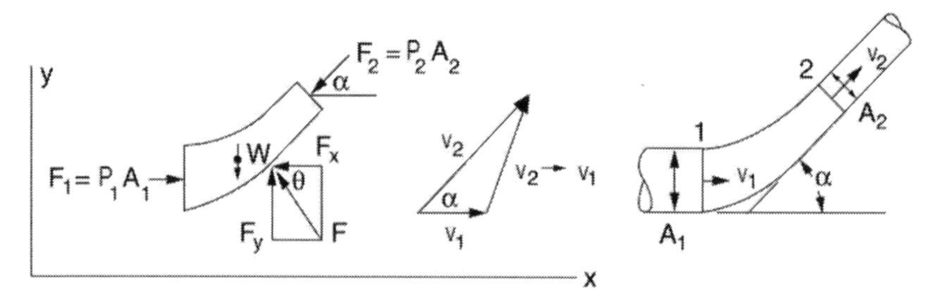

$$P_1A_1 - P_2A_2\cos\alpha - F_x = Q\rho\left(v_2\cos\alpha - v_1\right)$$

$$F_y - W - P_2A_2\sin\alpha - = Q\rho\left(v_2\sin\alpha - 0\right)$$

If the pressures P_1 and P_2 are zero, then:

$$-F_x = \rho Q\left(v_2\cos\alpha - v_1\right) \text{ or } F_x = -\rho Q\left(v_2\cos\alpha - v_1\right)$$

$$F_y = \rho Q\left(v_2\sin\alpha - 0\right)$$

F = force exerted by the bend on the fluid (force exerted by fluid on the bend is equal in magnitude and opposite in sign), F_x and F_y are the x-component and y-component of the force

$$F = \sqrt{(F_x)^2 + (F_y)^2} \text{ and } \theta = \tan^{-1}\left(\frac{F_y}{F_x}\right)$$

P = internal pressure in the pipe line
A = cross-sectional area of the pipe line
W = weight of the fluid
v = velocity of the fluid flow
α = angle the pipe bend makes with the horizontal
ρ = density of the fluid
Q = fluid volumetric flow rate

Example 5.20
The fluid stream shown in figure below is a 1.75-in-diameter jet of water at 60 °F with a velocity of 25 ft/s. The velocity leaving the block is also 25 ft/s. Water has a density of 62.4 pcf or 1.94 slug/ft³. Compute the forces in the vertical and horizontal directions on the block.

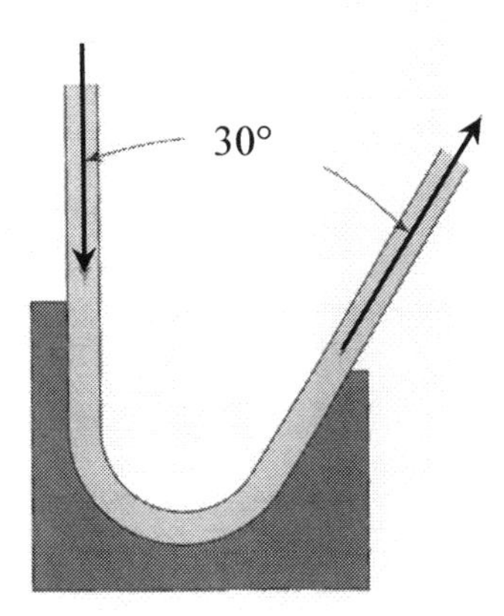

Solution:

$$Q = Av = \frac{\pi(1.75\,\text{in.})^2}{4} \times \frac{\text{ft}^2}{144\,\text{in.}^2} \times 25\frac{\text{ft}}{\text{sec}} = 0.418\frac{\text{ft}^3}{\text{sec}}$$

$$F_x = -\rho Q(v_2 \cos\alpha - v_1) = -\rho Q(v_2 \cos 60° - 0)$$

$$= -\left(1.94\frac{\text{slug}}{\text{ft}^3}\right)\left(0.418\frac{\text{ft}^3}{\text{sec}}\right)\left(25\frac{\text{ft}}{\text{sec}}\right)\cos 60°$$

$$= -10.13\,\text{lb}$$

$$= \underline{10.13\,\text{lb}(\rightarrow)}$$

$$F_y = \rho Q\left(v_{2_y} - v_{1_y}\right) = \rho Q\left[v_2 \sin 60° - (-v_1)\right] = \rho Q\left[v_2 \sin 60° + v_1\right]$$

$$= \left(1.94\frac{\text{slug}}{\text{ft}^3}\right)\left(0.418\frac{\text{ft}^3}{\text{sec}}\right)\left[25\frac{\text{ft}}{\text{sec}}\sin 60° + 25\frac{\text{ft}}{\text{sec}}\right]$$

$$= \underline{37.79\,\text{lb}(\uparrow)}$$

Example 5.21

Compute the horizontal and vertical forces exerted on the vane shown in Figure below due to a flow of water at 50 °C. The velocity is constant at 15 m/s. Use the water density of 988 kg/m³.

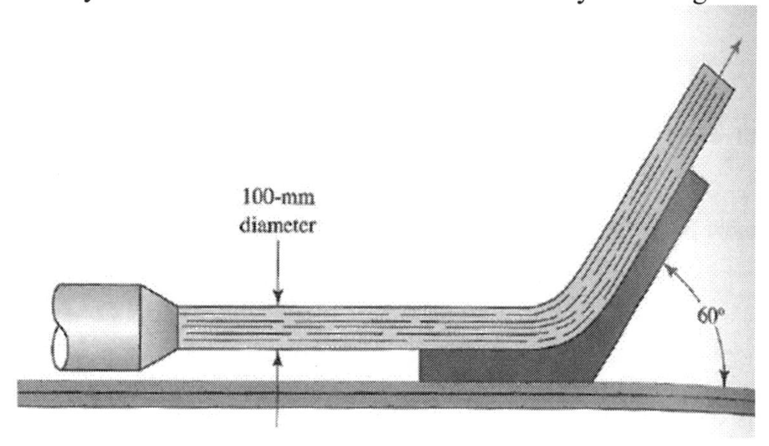

Solution:

Because the diameter is the same at A and B, velocity, $v = v_A = v_B = 15$ m/sec

$$Q = Av = \frac{\pi(0.10\text{m})^2}{4} \times 15\frac{\text{m}}{\text{sec}} = 0.118\frac{\text{m}^3}{\text{sec}}$$

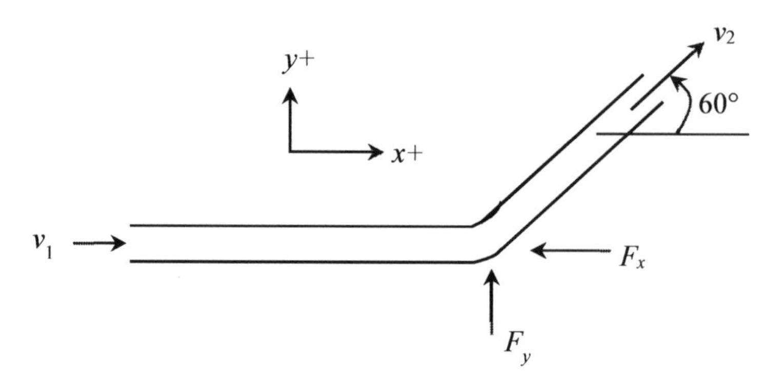

$$
\begin{aligned}
F_x &= -\rho Q\left(v_2 \cos\alpha - v_1\right) \\
&= -\rho Q v_1\left(\cos 60° - 1\right) \\
&= -\rho Q v_1\left(0.5 - 1\right) \\
&= -988\frac{\text{kg}}{\text{m}^3}\times\frac{0.118\,\text{m}^3}{\text{sec}}\times 15\frac{\text{m}}{\text{sec}}\times\left(-0.5\right) \\
&= 873\frac{\text{kg.m}}{\text{sec}^2} \\
&= 873\,\text{N}
\end{aligned}
$$

$$
F_y = \rho Q\left[v_{2_y} - v_{1_y}\right] = \rho Q\left[v_2 \sin 60° - 0\right]
$$

$$
= 988\frac{\text{kg}}{\text{m}^3}\left(0.118\frac{\text{m}^3}{\text{sec}}\right)\left(15\frac{\text{m}}{\text{sec}}\right)(\sin 60°) = \underline{1{,}512\,\text{N}}
$$

5.7 Energy and Continuity Equation

From Article 6.2 of the PE Civil Handbook:
Continuity Equation: So long as the flow Q is continuous, the *continuity equation*, as applied to one-dimensional flows, states that the flow passing two points (1 and 2) in a stream is equal at each point,

$$A_1 v_1 = A_2 v_2.$$
$$Q = Av$$
$$\dot{m} = \rho Q = \rho A v$$

Q = volumetric flow rate
$\dot{m}$ = mass flow rate
A = cross-sectional area of flow
v = average flow velocity
ρ = fluid density

For steady, one-dimensional flow, $\dot{m}$ is a constant. If the density is constant, then Q is constant.

Example 5.22
Determine the required size of standard Schedule 40 steel pipe to carry 192 m3/h of water with a maximum velocity of 6.0 m/s.

Solution:

Because Q and v are known, the required area can be found from
$Q = Av$
$A = Q/v$
First, we must convert the volume flow rate to the units of m^3/s:
$Q = 192\ m^3/h\ (1\ h/3600\ s) = 0.0533\ m^3/s$

$$
A = \frac{Q}{v} = \frac{0.0533\dfrac{\text{m}^3}{\text{sec}}}{6.0\dfrac{\text{m}}{\text{sec}}} = 0.00888\,\text{m}^2 = \underline{8.88\times 10^{-3}\,\text{m}^2}
$$

Example 5.23

Water flows along the triangular trough with an average velocity of 5 m/s and the vertical depth of 0.3 m. Use the water density of 1,000 kg/m^3. The channel has a longitudinal slope of 30°. Calculate the volumetric discharge and the mass flow rate.

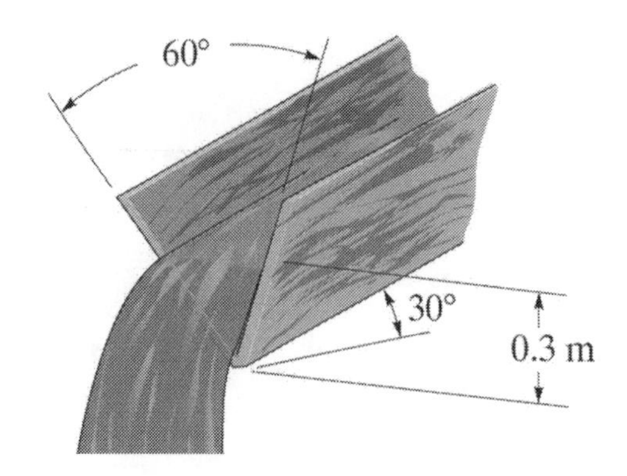

Solution:

Top width of the flow, w = 2[0.3 m (tan 30°)] = 0.3464 m

Height of the cross section perpendicular to the flow, h = (0.3 m)(cos 30°) = 0.2598 m

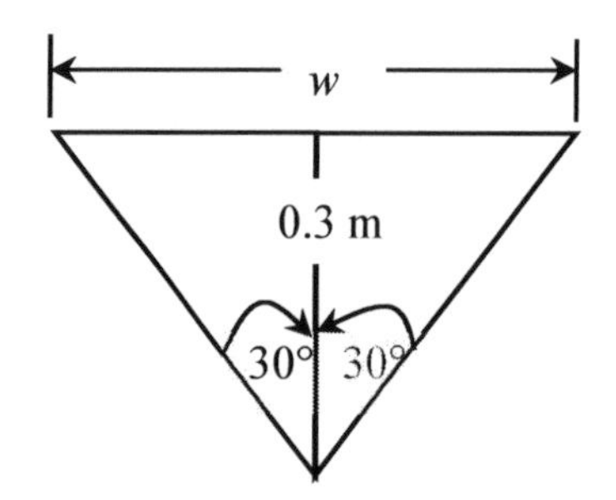

Cross-sectional area, $A = \frac{1}{2}(0.3464\,\text{m})(0.2598\,\text{m}) = 0.045\,\text{m}^2$

$$Q = Av = 0.045\,\text{m}^2 \times 5\frac{\text{m}}{\text{sec}} = 0.225\,\frac{\text{m}^3}{\text{sec}}$$

$$\dot{m} = \rho Q = \left(1{,}000\,\frac{\text{kg}}{\text{m}^3}\right)\left(0.225\,\frac{\text{m}^3}{\text{sec}}\right) = \underline{225\,\frac{\text{kg}}{\text{sec}}}$$

Example 5.24

If water flows at 150 kg/s through the double wye at B, at 50 kg/s through C, and at 150 kg/s through D, determine the average velocity of flow through the pipe at A.

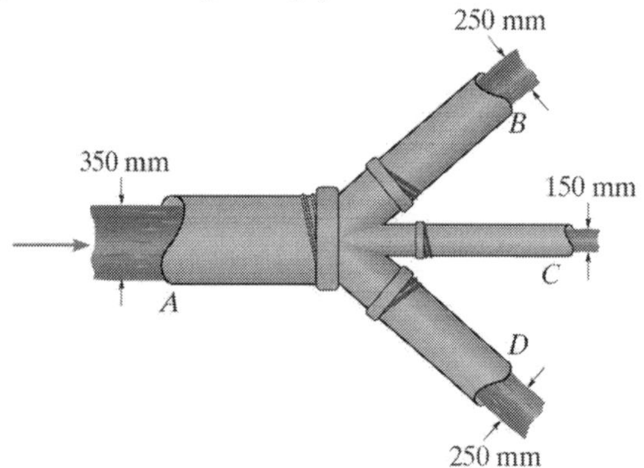

Solution:

$$\dot{m}_A = \dot{m}_B + \dot{m}_C + \dot{m}_D$$

$$\dot{m}_A = 150\,\frac{\text{kg}}{\text{s}} + 50\,\frac{\text{kg}}{\text{s}} + 150\,\frac{\text{kg}}{\text{s}}$$

Therefore, $\dot{m}_A = 350\,\frac{\text{kg}}{\text{s}}$

Now, $\dot{m}_A = \rho A_A v_A$

$$350\,\frac{\text{kg}}{\text{s}} = \left(1{,}000\frac{\text{kg}}{\text{m}^3}\right)\left(\pi\left(0.175\,\text{m}\right)^2\right)v_A$$

$v_A = \underline{3.64 \text{ m/s}}$

From Article 6.2 of the PE Civil Handbook: Energy Equation, the energy equation for steady incompressible flow with no shaft device is:

$$\frac{P_1}{\gamma} + z_1 + \frac{v_1^2}{2g} = \frac{P_2}{\gamma} + z_2 + \frac{v_2^2}{2g} + h_f$$

$$\frac{P_1}{\rho g} + z_1 + \frac{v_1^2}{2g} = \frac{P_2}{\rho g} + z_2 + \frac{v_2^2}{2g} + h_f$$

where h_f = the head loss, considered a friction effect, and all remaining terms are defined above. If the cross-sectional area and the elevation of the pipe are the same at both sections (1 and 2), then $z_1 = z_2$ and $v_1 = v_2$. The pressure drop $P_1 - P_2$ is given by the following:

$$P_1 - P_2 = \gamma h_f = \rho g h_f$$

Field Equation, the field equation is derived when the energy equation is applied to one-dimensional flows. Assuming no friction losses and that no pump or turbine exists between sections 1 and 2 in the system,

$$\frac{P_2}{\gamma} + \frac{v_2^2}{2g} + z_2 = \frac{P_1}{\gamma} + \frac{v_1^2}{2g} + z_1 \quad \text{or}$$

$$\frac{P_2}{\rho} + \frac{v_2^2}{2} + z_2 g = \frac{P_1}{\rho} + \frac{v_1^2}{2} + z_1 g$$

P_1, P_2 = pressure at sections 1 and 2
v_1, v_2 = average velocity of the fluid at the sections
z_1, z_2 = vertical distance from a datum to the sections (the potential energy)
γ = specific weight of the fluid = ρg
g = acceleration due to gravity
ρ = fluid density

Example 5.25
Water is flowing in an open channel (Figure) at a depth of 2 m and a velocity of 3 m/s. It then flows down a chute into another channel where the depth is 1 m and the velocity is 10 m/s. Assuming frictionless flow, determine the difference in elevation of the channel floors.

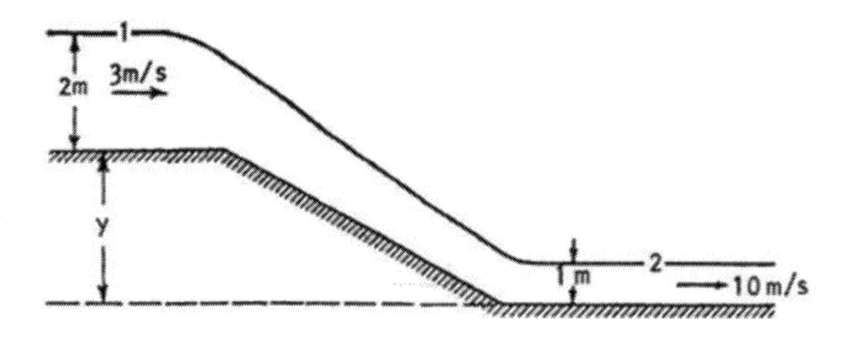

Solution:

The velocities are assumed to be uniform over the cross-sections, and the pressures hydrostatic. The points 1 and 2 may be selected on the free surface, as shown, or they could be selected at other depths.

The energy equation $\frac{P_2}{\gamma}+\frac{v_2^2}{2g}+z_2=\frac{P_1}{\gamma}+\frac{v_1^2}{2g}+z_1$

$z_1 = y + 2$
$z_2 = 1.0\text{ m}$
$v_1 = 3.0\text{ m/s}$
$v_2 = 10\text{ m/s}$
$P_1 = P_2 = 0$

Then, $\frac{0}{\gamma}+\frac{\left(10.0\frac{\text{m}}{\text{s}}\right)^2}{2\left(9.81\frac{\text{m}}{\text{s}^2}\right)}+1.0\text{m}=\frac{0}{\gamma}+\frac{\left(3.0\frac{\text{m}}{\text{s}}\right)^2}{2\left(9.81\frac{\text{m}}{\text{s}^2}\right)}+(y+2)$

Solving, $y =$ 3.64 m

From Article 6.2 of the PE Civil Handbook: Hydraulic Gradient (Grade Line), hydraulic grade line is the line connecting the sum of pressure and elevation heads at different points in conveyance systems. If a row of piezometers were placed at intervals along the pipe, the grade line would join the water levels in the piezometer water columns. From Article 6.2 of the PE Civil Handbook: Energy Line (Bernoulli Equation), the Bernoulli equation states that the sum of the pressure, velocity, and elevation heads is constant. The energy line is this sum or the total head line above a horizontal datum. The difference between the hydraulic grade line and the energy line is the $v^2/2g$ term.

$$H=z_a+\frac{P_a}{\gamma}+\frac{v_a^2}{2g}$$

H = total head (ft)
P_a/γ = pressure head (ft)
γ = specific weight of fluid (pcf)
P_a = pressure (psf)
$\frac{v_a^2}{2g}$ = velocity head (ft)
v_a = velocity (ft/sec)
g = acceleration due to gravity (32.2 ft/sec^2)
z_a = elevation (ft)

Example 5.26

Professor Islam is building a cabin on a hillside and has proposed the water system shown below. The distribution tank in the cabin maintains a pressure of 30.0 psig above the water. There is an energy Joss of 15.5 lb.ft/lb in the piping. When the pump is delivering 40 gal/min of water, compute the head delivered by the pump to the water.

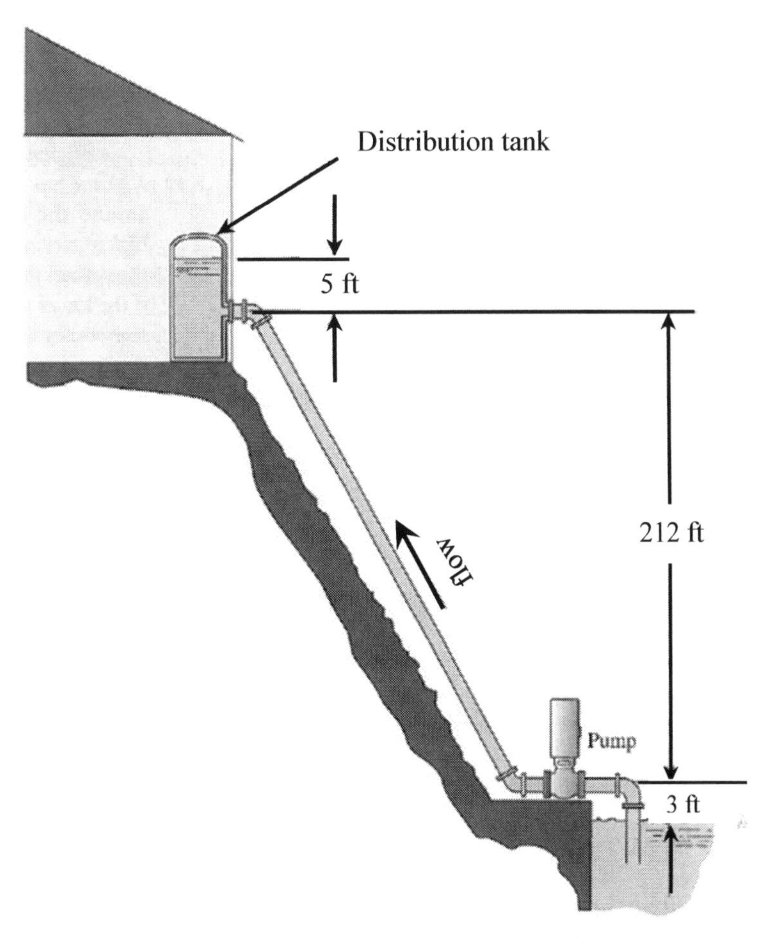

Ref. Mott and Untener, *Applied Fluid Mechanics*, 7/e, Pearson.

Solution:

$$\frac{P_1}{\gamma}+z_1+\frac{v_1^2}{2g}-h_L+h_A=\frac{P_2}{\gamma}+z_2+\frac{v_2^2}{2g}$$

Let, Point 1 be at the creek surface, i.e., $P_1 = 0, v_1 = 0$

Point 2 be at the tank surface, i.e., $v_2 = 0$

$$h_A=\frac{P_2}{\gamma}+(z_2-z_1)+h_L=\frac{30\,\text{lb}}{\text{in.}^2}\frac{\text{ft}^3}{62.4\,\text{lb}}\frac{144\,\text{in.}^2}{\text{ft}^2}+220\,\text{ft}+15.5\,\text{ft}=\underline{304.7\,\text{ft}}$$

Example 5.27

Figure below shows a system in which water flows from a tank through a pipe system having several sizes and elevations. The pressure at *A* is zero and neglect the energy loss. The velocity (fps) of the flow at *G* (exit) is most nearly:

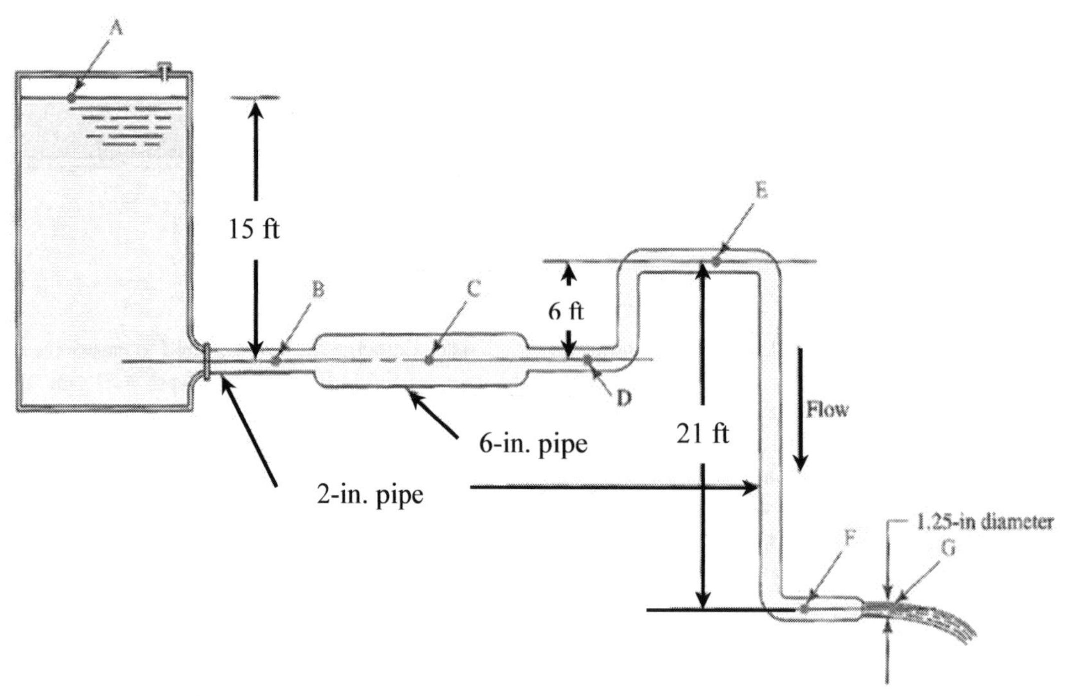

Ref. Mott and Untener, *Applied Fluid Mechanics*, 7/e, Pearson.

Solution:

$$\frac{p_A}{\gamma}+z_A+\frac{v_A^2}{g}=\frac{p_G}{\gamma}+z_G+\frac{v_G^2}{g}$$

$p_A = p_G = 0$ being the atmosphere
$v_A = 0$ the surface of the water

$$0+z_A+0=0+z_G+\frac{v_G^2}{g}$$

$$v_G=\sqrt{2g(z_A-z_G)}=\sqrt{2\left(32.2\frac{\text{ft}}{\text{sec}^2}\right)(30\,\text{ft})}=43.95\frac{\text{ft}}{\text{sec}}$$

Example 5.28
While maneuvering at the scene of a fire, a truck accidently backs over a fire hydrant and breaks it. The diameter of the water line to the hydrant is 6 in, but due to internal plumbing, the effective diameter at the water outlet is 4 in. If the flow rate of the water leaving the hydrant is 1,000 gal/min, what height will the water reach?

Solution:

Let the outlet be '1' and the maximum height of water is '2'.

$$\frac{P_1}{\gamma}+\frac{v_1^2}{2g}+z_1=\frac{P_2}{\gamma}+\frac{v_2^2}{2g}+z_2$$

$P_1 = P_2 = 0$ being the atmosphere
$v_2 = 0$ the maximum height of the water

Flow velocity at the outlet, $v_1 = \frac{Q}{A} = \frac{\left(1{,}000\frac{\text{gal}}{\text{min}} \times \frac{1\,\text{ft}^3}{7.48\,\text{gal}}\right)}{\left(\frac{\pi \times (4\,\text{in.})^2}{4} \times \frac{\text{ft}^2}{144\,\text{in.}^2}\right)} = 1{,}532\frac{\text{ft}}{\text{min}}$

Now, $\frac{0}{\gamma} + \frac{v_1^2}{2g} + 0 = \frac{0}{\gamma} + \frac{0}{2g} + z_2$

$$z_2 = \frac{v_1^2}{2g}$$

$$z_2 = \frac{\left(1{,}532\frac{\text{ft}}{\text{min}} \times \frac{1\,\text{min}}{60\,\text{sec}}\right)^2}{2 \times 32.2\frac{\text{ft}}{\text{sec}^2}} = \underline{10.1\,\text{ft}}$$

Example 5.29

Oil flows through the 50-mm-diameter vertical pipe assembly such that the pressure at A is 240 kPa and the velocity is 3 m/s. The assembly and the oil within it have a combined weight of 60 N. Take oil density to be 900 kg/m³. Determine the pressure at B.

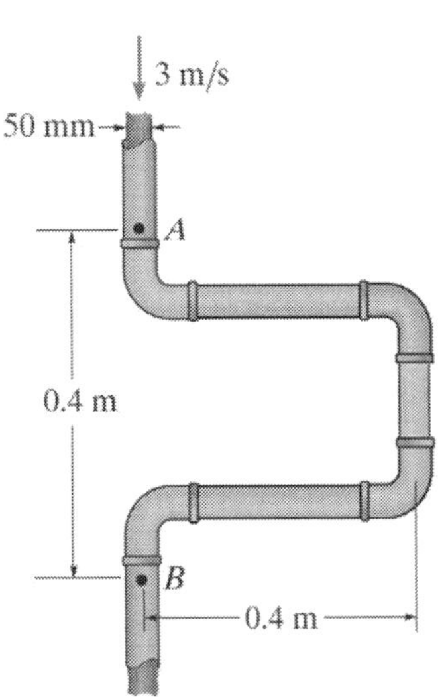

Solution:

Because the diameter is the same at A and B, velocity, $v = v_A = v_B$

$$\frac{P_A}{\rho} + \frac{v^2}{2} + z_A g = \frac{P_B}{\rho} + \frac{v^2}{2} + z_B g$$

$$\frac{240\,\text{kPa}}{900\frac{\text{kg}}{\text{m}^3}} + (0.4\,\text{m})\left(9.81\frac{\text{m}}{\text{sec}^2}\right) = \frac{P_B}{900\frac{\text{kg}}{\text{m}^3}} + 0$$

$$P_B = \underline{244\,\text{kPa}}$$

From Article 6.2 of the PE Civil Handbook:

Temperature (°F)	Specific Weight, γ (lbf/ft^3)	Mass Density, ρ (lbf-sec^2/ft^4)	Dynamic/Absolute Viscosity, μ (×10^{-5} lbf-sec/ft^2)	Kinematic Viscosity, υ (× 10^{-5} ft^2/sec)	Vapor Pressure, P_v (psi)	Surface Tension, σ (lb/ft)
32	62.42	1.940	3.746	1.931	0.09	0.00518
40	62.43	1.940	3.229	1.664	0.12	0.00514
50	62.41	1.940	2.735	1.410	0.18	0.00509
60	62.37	1.938	2.359	1.217	0.26	0.00504
70	62.30	1.936	2.050	1.059	0.36	0.00498
80	62.22	1.934	1.799	0.930	0.51	0.00492
90	62.11	1.931	1.595	0.826	0.70	0.00486
100	62.00	1.927	1.424	0.739	0.95	0.00480
110	61.86	1.923	1.284	0.667	1.24	
120	61.71	1.918	1.168	0.609	1.69	
130	61.55	1.913	1.069	0.558	2.22	
140	61.38	1.908	0.981	0.514	2.89	
150	61.20	1.902	0.905	0.476	3.72	
160	61.00	1.896	0.838	0.442	4.74	
170	60.80	1.890	0.780	0.413	5.99	
180	60.58	1.883	0.726	0.385	7.51	
190	60.36	1.876	0.678	0.362	9.34	
200	60.12	1.868	0.637	0.341	11.52	
212	59.83	1.860	0.593	0.319	14.70	

From Article 6.2 of the PE Civil Handbook:

Temperature (°C)	Specific Weight, γ (kN/m^3)	Mass Density, ρ (kg/m^3)	Dynamic/Absolute Viscosity, μ (Pa.s)	Kinematic Viscosity, υ (m^2/s)	Vapor Pressure, P_v (kPa)
0	9.805 9.807	999.8	0.001781	0.000001785	0.61
5	9.804 9.798	1000.0	0.001518	0.000001518	0.87
10	9.789 9.777	999.7 999.1	0.001307	0.000001306	1.23
15	9.764 9.730	998.2 997.0	0.001139	0.000001139	1.70
20	9.689 9.642	995.7 992.2	0.001002	0.000001003	2.34
25	9.589 9.530	988.0 983.2	0.000890	0.000000893	3.17
30	9.466 9.399	977.8 971.8	0.000798	0.000000800	4.24
40		965.3 958.4	0.000653	0.000000658	7.38
50			0.000547	0.000000553	12.33
60			0.000466	0.000000474	19.92
70			0.000404	0.000000413	31.16
80			0.000354	0.000000364	47.34
90			0.000315	0.000000326	70.10
100			0.000282	0.000000294	101.33

From Article 6.2 of the PE Civil Handbook, Reynolds Number in Open Channel for Newtonian Fluid,

$$\mathrm{Re} = \frac{vR}{\upsilon}$$

v = mean velocity of flow (ft/sec)
R = hydraulic radius (ft)

υ = kinematic viscosity (ft^2/sec)

The critical Reynolds number $(Re)_c$ is defined to be the minimum Reynolds number at which a flow will turn turbulent. Flow through an open channel is generally characterized as:

Laminar flow $Re < 500$
Transitional flow $500 < Re < 2{,}000$
Fully turbulent flow $Re \geq 2{,}000$

A chart that gives f versus Re for various values of ε/D, known as a Moody, Darcy, or Stanton friction factor diagram, is available in this section. where f = friction factor.

Reynolds number (Newtonian fluid) for Circular Pipes, $\mathrm{Re} = \dfrac{vD\rho}{\mu} = \dfrac{vD}{\upsilon}$

Reynolds number (Power law fluid) for Circular Pipes, $\mathrm{Re}' = \dfrac{v^{(2-n)} D^n \rho}{K\left(\dfrac{3n+1}{4n}\right)^n 8^{(n-1)}}$

v = fluid velocity
ρ = mass density
D = diameter of the pipe, dimension of the fluid streamline, or characteristic length
μ = dynamic viscosity
υ = kinematic viscosity
K = consistency index
n = power law index

Flow through a closed nonpressurized pipe is generally characterized as:

Laminar flow $Re < 2{,}100$
Transitional flow $2{,}100 < Re < 10{,}000$
Fully turbulent flow $Re \geq 10{,}000$

Flow through a closed pressurized pipe is generally characterized as:

Laminar flow $Re < 2{,}000$
Transitional flow $2{,}000 < Re < 4{,}000$
Fully turbulent flow $Re \geq 4{,}000$

The velocity distribution for laminar flow in circular tubes or between planes is –

$$v(r) = v_{\max}\left[1 - \left(\frac{r}{R}\right)^2\right]$$

r = the distance (m) from the centerline
R = the radius (m) of the tube or half the distance between the parallel planes
v = the local velocity (m/s) at r
v_{max} = the velocity (m/s) at the centerline of the duct
$v_{\max} = 1.18\bar{v}$, for fully turbulent flow
$v_{\max} = 2\bar{v}$, for circular tubes in laminar flow and
$v_{\max} = 1.5\bar{v}$, for parallel planes in laminar flow
where: $\bar{v}$the average velocity (m/s) in the duct

The shear stress distribution can be presented as: $\dfrac{\tau}{\tau_w} = \dfrac{r}{R}$

where: τ and τ_w are the shear stresses at radii r and R respectively.

FLOW IN CLOSED CONDUITS

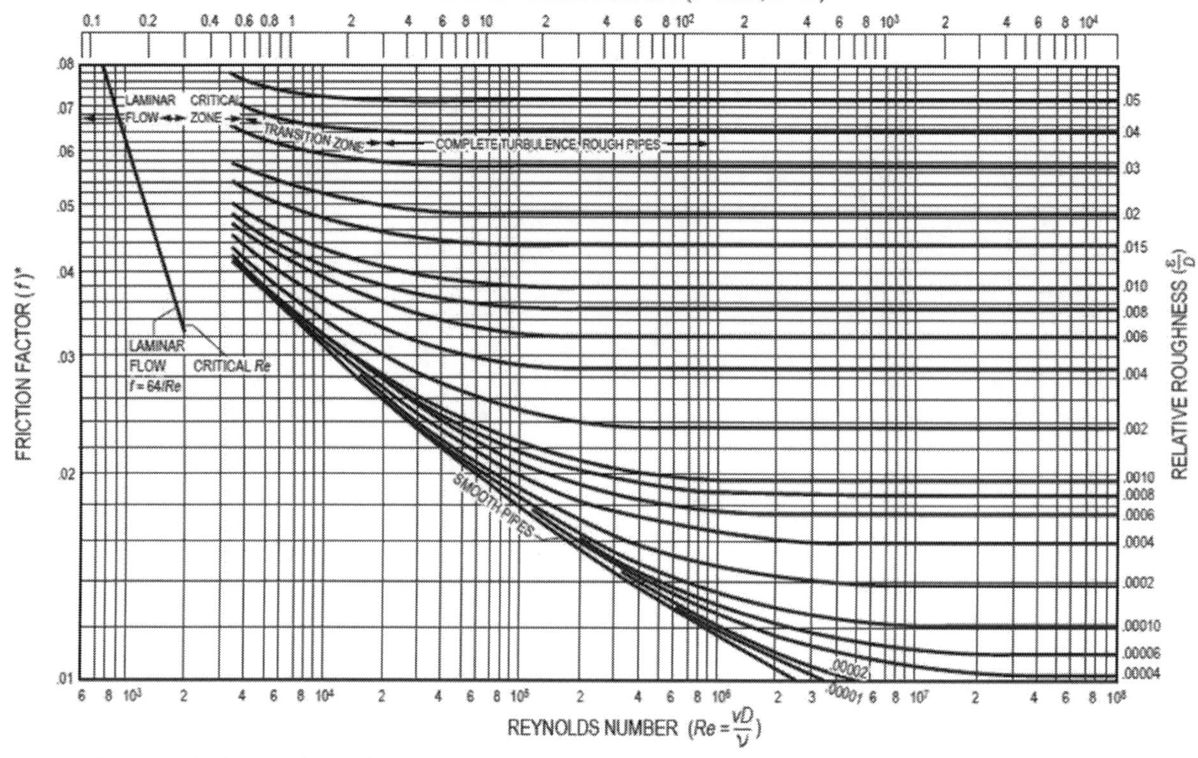

* The Fanning Friction is this factor divided by 4.

	ε (ft)	ε (mm)
GLASS, DRAWN BRASS, COPPER, LEAD	SMOOTH	SMOOTH
COMMERCIAL STEEL, WROUGHT IRON	0.0001–0.0003	0.03–0.09
ASPHALTED CAST IRON	0.0002–0.0006	0.06–0.18
GALVANIZED IRON	0.0002–0.0008	0.06–0.24
CAST IRON	0.0006–0.003	0.18–0.91
CONCRETE	0.001–0.01	0.30–3.0
RIVETED STEEL	0.003–0.03	0.91–9.1
CORRUGATED METAL PIPE	0.1–0.2	30–61
LARGE TUNNEL, CONCRETE OR STEEL LINED	0.002–0.004	0.61–1.2
BLASTED ROCK TUNNEL	1.0–2.0	300–610

Figure. Moody, Darcy, or Stanton Friction Factor Diagram

The Darcy-Weisbach equation is $h_f = f\frac{L}{D}\frac{v^2}{2g}$

$f = f(Re, \varepsilon/D)$, the Moody, Darcy, or Stanton friction factor
D = diameter of the pipe
L = length over which the pressure drop occurs
ε = roughness factor for the pipe, and other symbols as defined previously

Example 5.30

A 2-ft diameter circular tube has a laminar flow with the maximum velocity of 5 m/s. The velocity (m/s) of the flow close to the periphery and at the centerline of the tube is most nearly:

Solution:

Radius, $R = 1$ ft

Close to the periphery: Point of concern, $r \approx 1$ ft

$$v(r) = v_{max}\left[1-\left(\frac{r}{R}\right)^2\right] = 5\frac{\text{m}}{\text{s}}\left[1-\left(\frac{1\,\text{ft}}{1\,\text{ft}}\right)^2\right] = \underline{0\text{ m/s}}$$

At the centerline: Point of concern, $r = 0$ ft

$$v(r) = v_{max}\left[1-\left(\frac{r}{R}\right)^2\right] = 5\frac{\text{m}}{\text{s}}\left[1-\left(\frac{0\,\text{ft}}{1\,\text{ft}}\right)^2\right] = \underline{5\text{ m/s}}$$

Example 5.31

Water at 70 °F is pumped at the rate of 90 gal/min from a river using a 1.5-in.-diameter hose. The pipe is 120 ft long, and $\varepsilon = 0.05(10^{-3})$ ft. The water density is 1.937 slug/ft^3 and kinetic viscosity is $10.4\text{x}10^{-6}$ ft^2/sec. If the pump must supply a pressure of 30 psi to the water in the hose at C before it enters the sprinkler, determine the head loss.

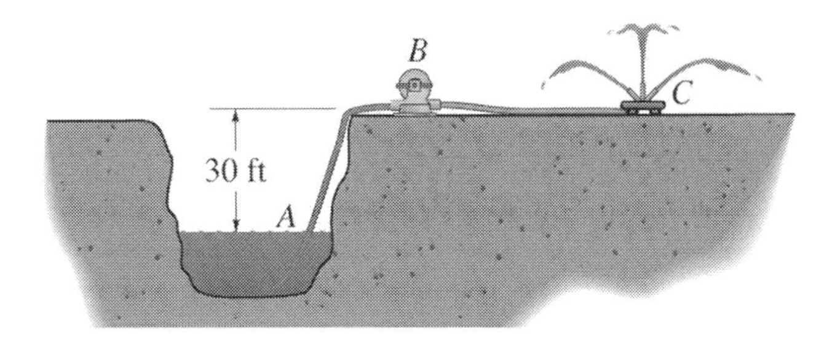

Solution:

$$\text{Velocity, } v = \frac{Q}{A} = \frac{\left(90\frac{\text{gal}}{\text{min}}\right)\left(\frac{1\,\text{min}}{60\,\text{sec}}\right)\left(0.134\frac{\text{ft}^3}{\text{gal}}\right)}{\pi\left(\frac{0.75\,\text{ft}}{12}\right)^2} = 16.38\frac{\text{ft}}{\text{sec}}$$

$$\text{Reynolds number, Re} = \frac{vD}{\upsilon} = \frac{\left(16.38\frac{\text{ft}}{\text{sec}}\right)\left(\frac{1.5\,\text{ft}}{12}\right)}{10.4\times10^{-6}\frac{\text{ft}^2}{\text{sec}}} \approx 2\times10^5$$

Relative roughness, $\varepsilon/D = 0.05(10^{-3})$ ft / (1.5/12 ft) = 0.0004

For $\varepsilon/D = 0.0004$ and Re = 2 x 10^5, from Moody diagram, $f \approx 0.0185$

$$\text{Head loss, } h_f = f\frac{L}{D}\frac{v^2}{2g} = (0.0185)\left(\frac{120\,\text{ft}}{\frac{0.15}{12}\text{ft}}\right)\left(\frac{\left(16.38\frac{\text{ft}}{\text{sec}}\right)^2}{2\left(32.2\frac{\text{ft}}{\text{sec}^2}\right)}\right) = \underline{74\,\text{ft}}$$

Again to remind you that the actual exam questions are shorter. However, you need to understand the entire analytical procedure. Also, for chart reading questions, there should be pretty-good gap in the answer options so that human-reading error does not lead a wrong answer.

Example 5.32

Oil flows through the 50-mm-diameter pipe at 0.009 m^3/s. Oil density is 900 kg/m^3. Oil is considered to be incompressible. If the friction factor is $f = 0.026$, determine the dead loss that occurs over the 80-m length.

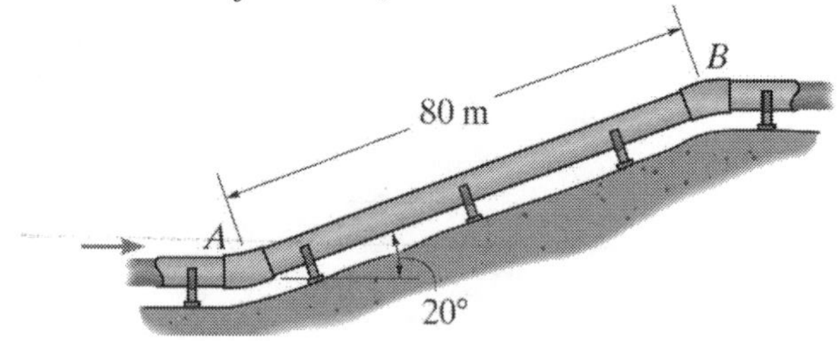

Solution:

$$\text{Mean velocity, } v = \frac{Q}{A} = \frac{0.009\frac{\text{m}^3}{\text{sec}}}{\pi(0.025\text{m})^2} = 4.584\frac{\text{m}}{\text{sec}}$$

$$\text{Head loss, } h_f = f\frac{L}{D}\frac{v^2}{2g} = 0.026\left(\frac{80\text{m}}{0.05\text{m}}\right)\frac{\left(4.584\frac{\text{m}}{\text{sec}}\right)^2}{2\left(9.81\frac{\text{m}}{\text{sec}^2}\right)} = \underline{44.55\text{m}}$$

Example 5.33

The section AB of the 100-mm-diameter galvanized iron pipe has a mass of 15 kg. Glycerin is discharged from the pipe at 3 liter/s. Glycerin is considered to be incompressible, has a density of 1,260 kg/m^3 and kinematic viscosity of $1.19\text{x}10^{-3}$ m^2/sec. Determine the head loss.

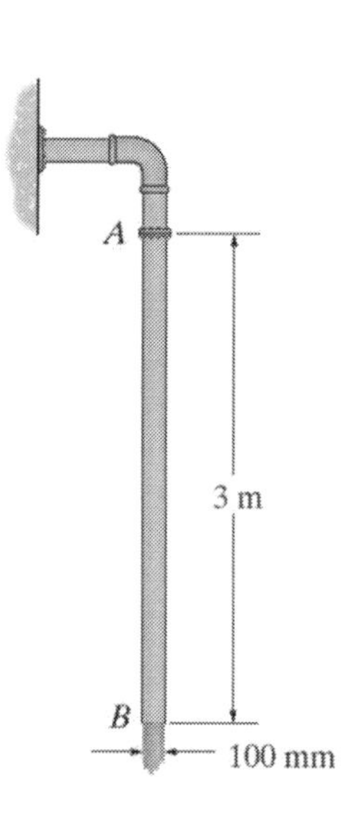

Solution:

Pipe has a constant diameter – the velocity is constant.

$$\text{Velocity, } v = \frac{Q}{A} = \frac{3\frac{\text{L}}{\text{sec}}\times10^{-3}\frac{\text{m}^3}{\text{L}}}{\pi(0.05\text{m})^2} = 0.3820\frac{\text{m}}{\text{sec}}$$

$$\text{Reynolds number, } \text{Re} = \frac{vD}{\upsilon} = \frac{\left(0.382\frac{\text{m}}{\text{sec}}\right)(0.1\text{m})}{1.19\times10^{-3}\frac{\text{m}^2}{\text{sec}}} = 32$$

(less than 2,100, laminar flow)

Since the flow is laminar, the friction factor is, $f = \frac{64}{\text{Re}} = \frac{64}{32} = 2.0$

$$\text{Head loss, } h_f = f\frac{L}{D}\frac{v^2}{2g} = 2.0\left(\frac{3\text{m}}{0.1\text{m}}\right)\frac{\left(0.382\frac{\text{m}}{\text{sec}}\right)^2}{2\left(9.81\frac{\text{m}}{\text{sec}^2}\right)} = \underline{0.4448\text{m}}$$

Example 5.34

Figure below shows a system for delivering liquid fertilizer. The nozzle on the end of the hose requires 140 kPa of pressure and 3.23 m/s of velocity to operate effectively. The hose is smooth plastic with an internal diameter of 25 mm. The fertilizer liquid has a specific gravity of 1.10 and a dynamic viscosity of $2.0\text{x}10^{-3}$

Pa·s. Neglect the energy losses on the suction side of the pump. The flow rate is 95 L/min and the friction factor of the pipe is 0.021. The length of the hose is 85 m. Calculate the pressure at the outlet of the pump.

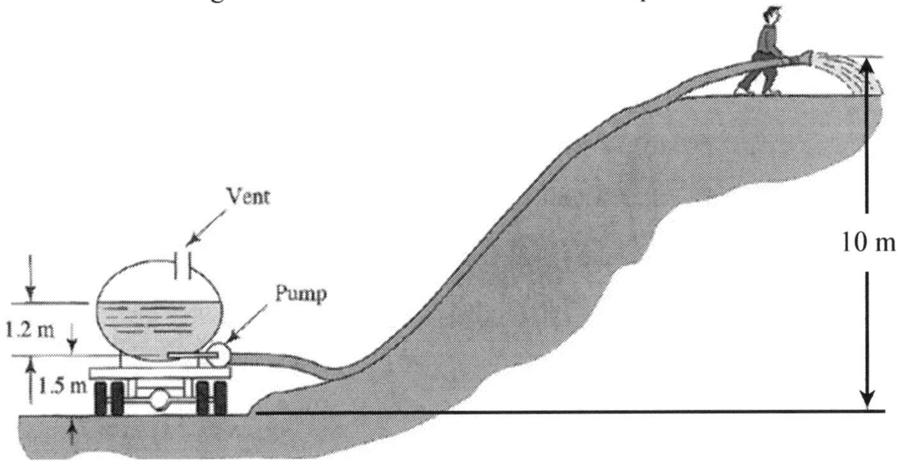

Solution:

Point 1 in hose at nozzle, i.e., P_1 = 140 kPa.
Point 2 in hose at pump outlet, i.e., P_2 = ?
Velocities at Point 1 and Point 2 are the same for having the same diameter, i.e., $v_2 = v_1$

$$\text{Head loss, } h_L = f\frac{L}{D}\frac{v^2}{2g} = (0.021)\frac{85\,\text{m}}{0.025\,\text{m}}\frac{\left(3.23\dfrac{\text{m}}{\text{sec}}\right)^2}{2\left(9.81\dfrac{\text{m}}{\text{sec}^2}\right)} = 37.86\,\text{m}$$

$$\frac{P_2}{\gamma} + z_2 + \frac{v_2^2}{2g} - h_L = \frac{P_1}{\gamma} + z_1 + \frac{v_1^2}{2g}$$

$$P_2 = P_1 + \left[(z_1 - z_2) + h_L\right]\gamma$$

$$= 140\,\text{kPa} + \left[(10\text{m} - 1.5\text{m}) + 37.86\,\text{m}\right](1.10)\left(9.81\frac{\text{kN}}{\text{m}^3}\right) = \underline{640\,\text{kPa}}$$

From Article 6.2 of the PE Civil Handbook: Pressure Drop for Laminar Flow, the equation for Q in terms of the pressure drop ΔP_f, is the Hagen-Poiseuille equation. This relation is valid only for flow in the laminar region. The equation is given below:

$$Q = \frac{\pi R^4 \Delta P_f}{8\mu L} = \frac{\pi D^4 \Delta P_f}{128\mu L}$$

From Article 6.2 of the PE Civil Handbook: For flow in Conduits (Circular or Noncircular), analysis of flow in conduits uses the hydraulic radius, $R_H = \dfrac{\text{Cross-sectional area}}{\text{Wetted perimeter}} = \dfrac{D_H}{4}$

The drag force F_D on objects immersed in a large body of flowing fluid or objects moving through a stagnant fluid is:

$$F_D = \frac{C_D \rho v^2 A}{2}$$

C_D = drag coefficient
v = velocity (m/s) of the flowing fluid or moving object

A = projected area (m2) of blunt objects such as spheres, ellipsoids, disks, and plates, cylinders, ellipses, and air foils with axes perpendicular to the flow

ρ = fluid density

For flat plates placed parallel with the flow:

$C_D = 1.33/Re^{0.5}$ ($10^4 < Re < 5 \times 10^5$)

$C_D = 0.031/Re^{1/7}$ ($10^6 < Re < 10^9$)

The characteristic length in the Reynolds Number (Re) is the length of the plate parallel with the flow. For blunt objects, the characteristic length is the largest linear dimension (diameter of cylinder, sphere, disk, etc.) that is perpendicular to the flow.

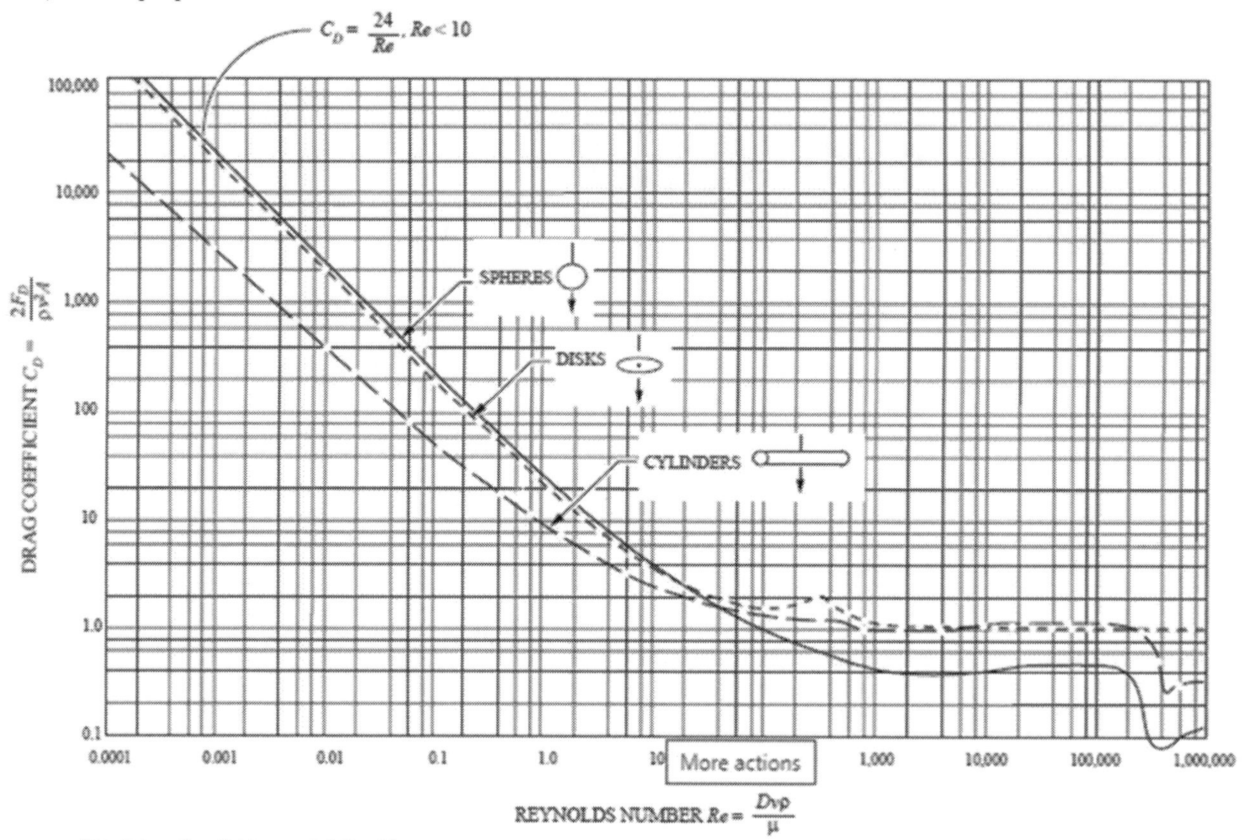

Drag coefficients for spheres, disks and cylinders

Example 5.35

A spherical object is placed inside a water flow with Re = 8 and velocity of 1 m/s. The projected area of the spherical object perpendicular to the flow is 0.01 m^2. The drag force exerted on the spherical body is most nearly:

Solution:

For $Re < 10$, from above $C_D = 24/Re$

So, $C_D = 24/8 = 24/8 = 3$

From the NCEES FE Ref. Handbook (Fluid Mechanics), the drag force, F_D on objects immersed in a large body of flowing fluid or object moving through a stagnant fluid is

$$F_D = \frac{C_D \rho v^2 A}{2} = \frac{3\left(1{,}000\ \frac{\text{kg}}{\text{m}^3}\right)\left(1\ \frac{\text{m}}{\text{s}}\right)^2\left(0.01\ \text{m}^2\right)}{2} = \underline{15\ \text{N}}$$

Chapter 6
Geometrics

This chapter is also primarily based on Chapter 5 of the PE Civil Handbook. Whatever areas you are familiar with transportation engineering especially the following items, please revise carefully.

6.1 Basic Circular Curve Elements

Horizontal curves are required at locations where the roadway needs to change its horizontal alignment to the left or right to accommodate some geographic conditions such as mountain or physical obstruction such as buildings. A simple curve is a circular arc that connects two tangents. Circular curve elements are shown below.

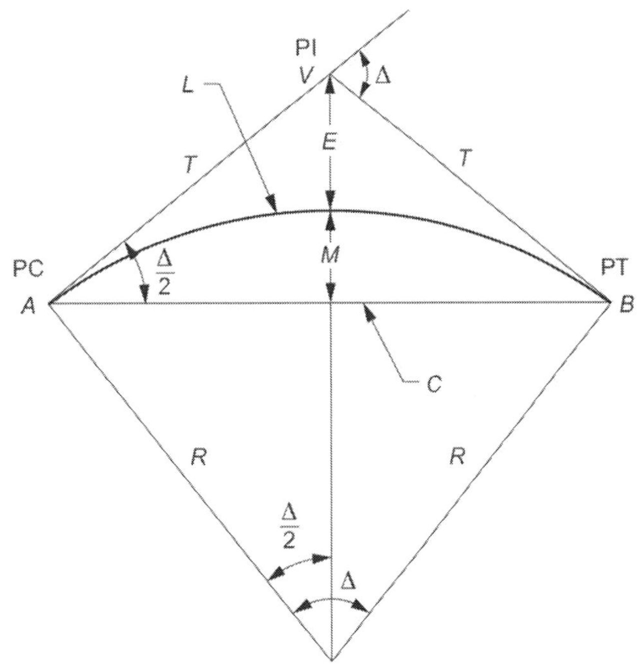

The beginning of the curve is the point of curvature *PC*, and the end of the curve is the point of tangency *PT*. Other expressions for these points are tangent to curve, *TC*, and curve to tangent, *CT*. The curve radius is R. Note that the radii at the PC and PT are perpendicular to the back tangent and forward tangent, respectively. The point of intersection PI, of the two tangents, is also called the vertex V. In stationing, the back tangent precedes the PI, the forward tangent follows it. The distance from PC to PI and from PI to PT is called the tangent distance, T. The line connecting the PC and PT is the long chord LC. The length of the curve, L, is the distance from PC to PT, measured along the curve for the arc definition, or by 100-ft chords for the chord definition.

There are two different designations for degree of curve, the arc definition and the chord definition, both of which are defined using the English system of units. By the arc definition, degree of curve is the central angle subtended by a circular arc of 100 ft (see Figure below). This definition is preferred for highway work. By the chord definition, degree of curve is the angle at the center of a circular arc subtended by a chord of 100 ft. This definition is convenient for very gentle curves and hence, is preferred for railroads.

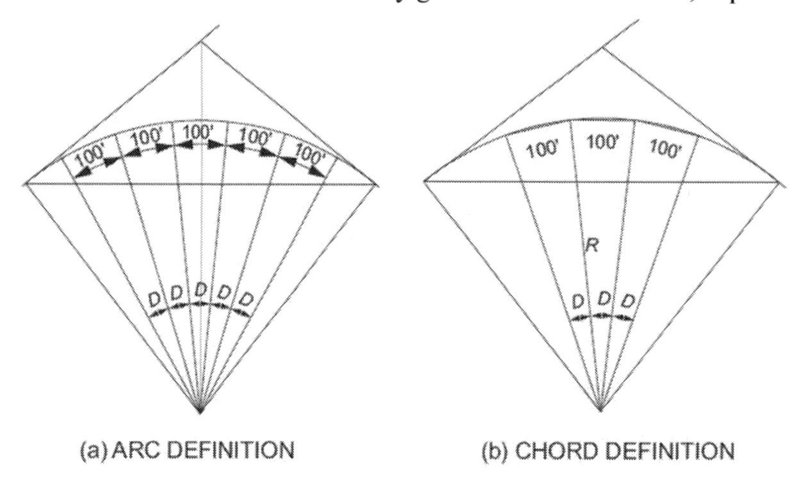

There are several methods of setting horizontal curve in field. Computing deflection angles and chords is one of them, and may be easiest to authors. Figure below shows the basics of computing deflection angles and chord. Let A is a point on the curve with PC being the point of curve. Also, let the curve length (arc) from PC to p is l_1, chord length be C_1, and the subtended angle be δ_1. Then, by geometry of the circle it can be shown that the deflection angle (angle between tangent and chord) is $\delta_1/2$.

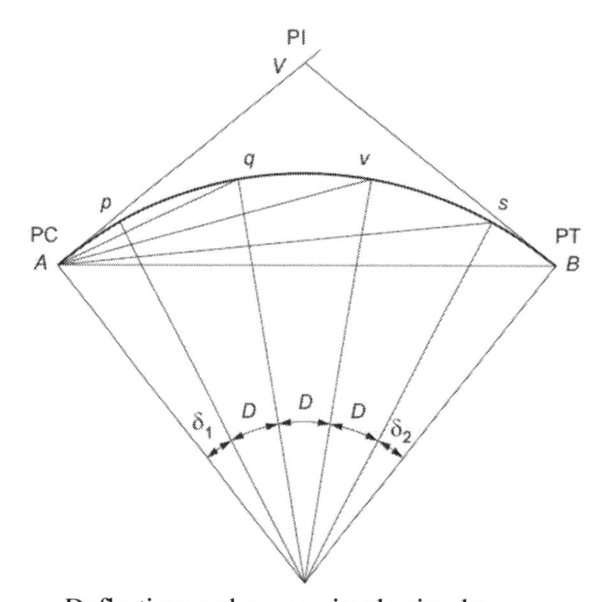

Deflection angles on a simple circular curve

By definition, and from inspection of figure below, following relationships can be derived:

Radius of curve by arc definition, $\frac{D}{360}=\frac{100}{2\pi R}$ or $R=\frac{5729.6}{D}$

$$D=\frac{100\left(\frac{180}{\pi}\right)}{R}=\frac{18,000}{\pi R}$$

Radius of curve by chord definition, $R=\frac{100}{2\sin\left(\frac{D}{2}\right)}=\frac{50}{\sin\left(\frac{D}{2}\right)}$

Tangent length, $T=R\tan\left(\frac{\Delta}{2}\right)$

Length of sub-chord, $C=2R\sin\frac{\Delta}{2}$

External distance, $E=R\sec\frac{\Delta}{2}-R=T\left(\tan\frac{\Delta}{4}\right)=R\left[\frac{1}{\cos\left(\frac{\Delta}{2}\right)}-1\right]$

Length of middle ordinate, $M=R-R\cos\frac{\Delta}{2}=R\left(1-\cos\frac{\Delta}{2}\right)$

Length of curve, from PC to PT, $L=\frac{R\Delta\pi}{180}$

Curve length for sub-chord, $l_1=\frac{R\pi}{180}\delta_1$ [The Civil PE Ref. Handbook Equation might be wrong unless NCEES revise it; there should be no Δ in this equation]

Where l_l = length of curve from PC to point, p subtended by central angle, δ_l

$C_1=2R\sin\frac{\delta_1}{2}$ = chord length from PC to any point p.

The below 2 equations are not listed in the PE Civil Ref but shown in the figure above.

$PC = PI - T$

$PT = PC + L$

Example 6.1

Given: Horizontal curve, PI = 11,500 + 66
Radius = 1,000 ft
Angle of deflection = 60°

The PT is located most nearly at:

Solution:

Tangent length, $T=R\tan\left(\frac{\Delta}{2}\right)=(1{,}000\,\text{ft})\tan\left(\frac{60}{2}\right)=577\,\text{ft}$

Length of curve, from PC to PT, $L=\frac{R\Delta\pi}{180}=\frac{(1{,}000\,\text{ft})(60)\pi}{180}=1{,}047\,\text{ft}$

$PC = PI - T$ = (11,500 + 66) – 577 ft = 10,989

$PT = PC + L$ = 10,989 + 1,047 ft = 12,036 = 12,000 + 36

Example 6.2
A horizontal curve has an external distance of 620 ft and a radius of 3,200 ft. The middle ordinate and the tangent length of the curve are most nearly:

Solution:

Middle Ordinate: $M = R\left[1-\cos\left(\frac{\Delta}{2}\right)\right]$

R = 3,200 ft; however, the $\Delta/2$ is unknown. Let us find $\Delta/2$ first.

Now, $E = R\left[\frac{1}{\cos\left(\frac{\Delta}{2}\right)}-1\right]$

$$620 = 3,200\left[\frac{1}{\cos\left(\frac{\Delta}{2}\right)}-1\right]$$

Therefore, $\Delta/2 = 33°$

$$M = 3,200\left[1-\cos 33\right] = \underline{516\,\text{ft}}$$

Tangent Length: $T = R\tan\left(\frac{\Delta}{2}\right)$ = (3,200 ft) tan(33) = <u>2,078 ft</u>

Example 6.3
A horizontal curve is to be designed with 1,500 ft radius and angle at intersection of 30°. The external distance and degree of curve by arc definition are most nearly:

Solution:

External distance, $E = R\left[\frac{1}{\cos\left(\frac{\Delta}{2}\right)}-1\right] = 1,500\left[\frac{1}{\cos 15}-1\right] = \underline{52.9\text{ ft}}$

Degree of curve by arc definition, $D = \frac{5729.58}{R} = \frac{5729.58}{1,500} = \underline{3.82^o}$

Example 6.4
A horizontal curve is to be designed with a tangent length of 250 ft and an intersection angle of 40°. What are most nearly the length of long chord and the curve length?

Solution:

Long Chord, $LC = 2T\cos\left(\frac{\Delta}{2}\right) = 2(250\,\text{ft})\cos 20 = \underline{470\,\text{ft}}$

Curve Length, $L = R\Delta\left(\frac{\pi}{180}\right)$

However, R is unknown. Let us find R first.

We know, $T = R\tan\left(\frac{\Delta}{2}\right)$

Therefore, $R = \frac{T}{\tan\left(\frac{\Delta}{2}\right)} = \frac{250 \text{ ft}}{\tan(20)} = 687 \text{ ft}$

Finally, $L = R\Delta\left(\frac{\pi}{180}\right) = 687(40)\left(\frac{\pi}{180}\right) = \underline{480 \text{ft}}$

Example 6.5

A simple-circular horizontal curve has the following features:

- Degree of curve = 15°
- Bearing on incoming (back) tangent is N 85°24'16" E
- Bearing on outgoing (forward) tangent is S 25°14'22" E
- Station of the PI = 178 + 33.87

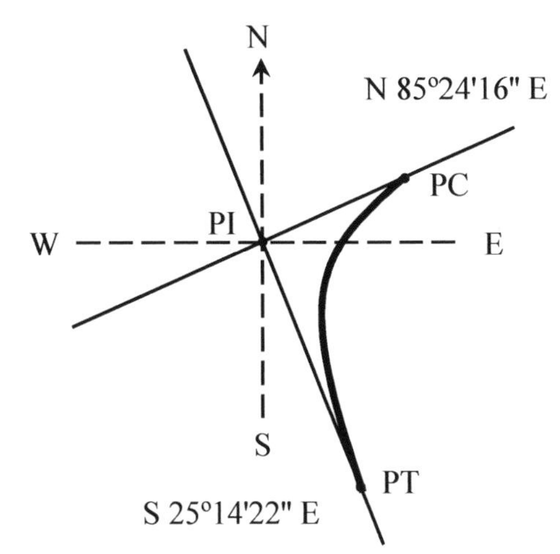

Determine the following:

(a) The intersection angle (Δ)
(b) The radius (R)
(c) The tangent (T)
(d) The external distance (E)
(e) The middle ordinate (M)
(f) The long chord (LC)
(g) The length of the curve (L)
(h) Station of the PC
(i) Station of the PT

Note: the NCEES exam will not ask you to solve for all of these at a time.

Solution:

(a) The intersection angle (Δ)

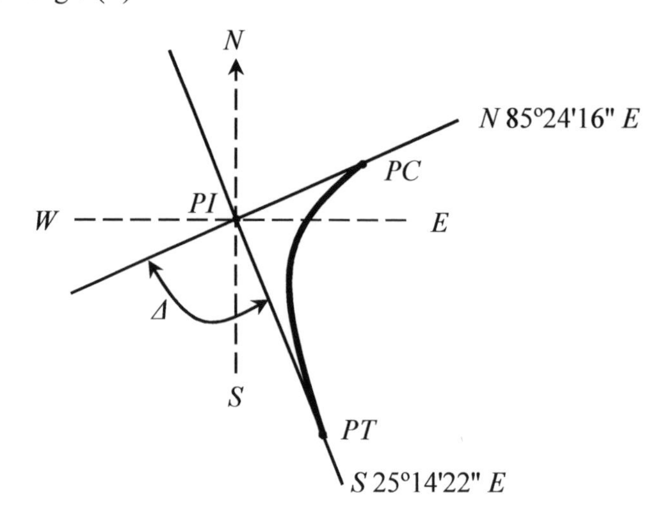

$\Delta = 85°24'16" + 25°14'22" = 110°38'38" = 110.6°$
$\Delta = 180° - 110.6° = 69.4°$

(b) The radius (R)

$$R = \frac{5,729.58}{D} = \frac{5,729.58}{15} = 382 \text{ ft}$$

(c) The tangent (T)

$T = R \tan(\Delta/2) = (382 \text{ ft}) \tan(69.4/2) = 265 \text{ ft}$

(d) The external distance (E)

$$E = R\left[\frac{1}{\cos\left(\frac{\Delta}{2}\right)} - 1\right] = (382 \text{ ft})\left[\frac{1}{\cos\left(\frac{69.4}{2}\right)} - 1\right] = 83 \text{ ft}$$

(e) The middle ordinate (M)

$$M = R\left[1 - \cos\left(\frac{\Delta}{2}\right)\right] = (382 \text{ ft})\left[1 - \cos\left(\frac{69.4}{2}\right)\right] = 68 \text{ ft}$$

(f) The long chord (LC)

$$LC = 2R\sin\left(\frac{\Delta}{2}\right) = 2(382 \text{ ft})\sin\left(\frac{69.4}{2}\right) = 436 \text{ ft}$$

(g) The length of the curve (L)

$$L = R\Delta\left(\frac{\pi}{180}\right) = (382 \text{ ft})(69.4)\left(\frac{\pi}{180}\right) = 464 \text{ ft}$$

(h) Station of the *PC*

$$PC = PI - T = (178 + 33.87) - (2 + 65.4) = 175 + 68.47$$

(i) Station of the PT

$$PT = PC + L = (178 + 33.87) + (4 + 63.93) = 182 + 97.8$$

Example 6.6

A horizontal curve is to be designed for a two-lane road in Colorado Spring. The following data are known:

Intersection angle: 40 degrees,
Tangent length = 450 ft
Station of PI: 3300 + 12.65

Deflection angle and chord length to the first full-station from the PC.

Solution:

Station of the $PC = PI - T = 3{,}300 + 12.65 - (4 + 50) = 3{,}295 + 62.65$

$$R = \frac{T}{\tan\left(\frac{\Delta}{2}\right)} = \frac{450\,\text{ft}}{\tan\left(\frac{40}{2}\right)} = 1{,}236\,\text{ft}$$

Reference point = $PC = 3{,}295 + 62.65$

First full-station is located at 3,296 + 00. The distance to the first full-station = (3,296 + 00) – (3,295 + 62.65) = 37.35 ft

Curve length for sub-chord, $l_1 = \dfrac{R\pi}{180}\delta_1$

$$\delta_1 = \frac{180 l_1}{\pi R} = \frac{180(37.35)}{\pi(1{,}236)} = \underline{1.731^o}$$

$$C_1 = 2R\sin\frac{\delta_1}{2} = 2(1{,}236)\sin\left(\frac{1.731}{2}\right) = \underline{37.34\,\text{ft}}$$

6.2 Basic Vertical Curve Elements

Article 5.3 Vertical Design of the PE Civil Handbook discusses this topic. Figure below shows a parabola that joins two intersecting tangents of a grade line. The parabola is essentially ideal except that the terms used are those commonly employed by surveyors and engineers. In the figure, *PVC* denotes the point of vertical curve, sometimes called the *BVC* (Beginning of vertical curve), or *VPC* (vertical point of curvature); *VPI* is the vertex, often called vertical point of intersection; and *PVT* is the Point of vertical tangency, interchangeably called the *VPT* (vertical point of tangency), or *EVC* (end of vertical curve). The percent grade of the back tangent (straight segment preceding PVI) is g_1, that of the forward tangent (straight segment following *PVI*) is g_2. The curve length *L* is the horizontal distance (in stations) from the *PVC* to the *PVT*. The curve of figure is called equal tangent because the horizontal distances from the *PVC* to *PVI* and from *PVI* to the *PVT* are equal, each being *L*/2. On the *xy* axis system, *x* values are horizontal distances measured from the *PVC*, and *y* values are elevations measured from the vertical datum of reference.

The general equation of parabola is $Y = c + bx + ax^2$

Now, let find out how this equation can be applied to vertical curve. First of all, when $x = 0$, $Y = c$. That means $c = Y_{PVC}$ (i.e., the elevation of the *PVC*) as x = 0 at the *PVC*. Now let us find out *b* and *a*. On differentiation of the above equation,

$$\frac{d(Y)}{dx} = \frac{d}{dx}\left(c + bx + ax^2\right)$$
$$\frac{dY}{dx} = 0 + b + 2ax = b + 2ax$$

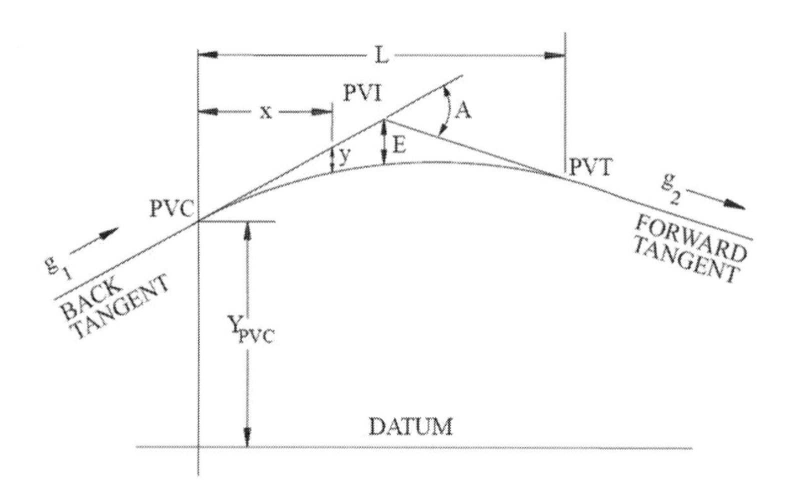

Now recall that $\frac{dY}{dx}$ means the slope of the curve at x. When $x = 0$, $\left.\frac{dY}{dx}\right|_{x=0} = b + 2a(0) = b$

That means, slope at $x = 0$ (at the *PVC*) is b, i.e., $b = g_1$.

Differentiating the equation one more time, $\frac{d}{dx}\frac{d(Y)}{dx} = \frac{d}{dx}(b + 2ax)$

Or, $\frac{d}{dx}\frac{dY}{dx} = 2a$

The above second-differentiation means the rate of change of slope $= 2a$

i.e., $\frac{Change\ in\ Slope}{L} = 2a$

or, $\frac{g_2 - g_1}{L} = 2a$

Therefore, $a = \frac{g_2 - g_1}{2L}$

Finally, the equation of the parabolic vertical curve (curve elevation) can be written as –

$$Y = Y_{PVC} + g_1 x + ax^2 = Y_{PVC} + g_1 x + \left[\frac{g_2 - g_1}{2L}\right]x^2$$

Some additional features can be derived as follows:

x_m = Horizontal distance to min./max. elevation on curve $= -\frac{g_1}{2a} = \frac{g_1 L}{g_1 - g_2}$

Tangent elevation $= Y_{PVC} + g_1 x$ and $= Y_{PVI} + g_2\left(x - \frac{L}{2}\right)$

$a = \frac{g_2 - g_1}{2L}$

$$E = a\left(\frac{L}{2}\right)^2$$

$$r = \frac{g_2 - g_1}{L}$$

$$K = \frac{L}{A}$$

Station of PVC = Station of $PVI - L/2$
Station of PVT = Station of $PVI + L/2$
Elevation of PVC = Elevation of $PVI - g_1 (L/2)$
Elevation of PVT = Elevation of $PVI + g_2 (L/2)$
where

PVC = point of vertical curvature, or beginning of curve
PVI = point of vertical intersection, or vertex
PVT = point of vertical tangency, or end of curve
A = algebraic difference in grades
a = parabola constant
E = tangent offset at PVI
g_1 = grade of back tangent
g_2 = grade of forward tangent
h_1 = height of driver's eyes above the roadway surface (ft)
h_2 = height of object above the roadway surface (ft)
K = rate of vertical curvature
L = length of curve
r = rate of change of grade
S = sight distance (ft)
x = horizontal distance from PVC to point on curve
x_m = horizontal distance to min/max elevation on curve
y = tangent offset
V = design speed (mph)

Example 6.7
Which of the following statements is not appropriate for horizontal and vertical curves in a highway?

A. Horizontal curves provide transitions between two tangents of a roadway
B. Vertical curve has the rate of change of slope not constant – it changes
C. Horizontal curve is preferred to be arc of a circle
D. Vertical curve form a parabolic shape

Solution:

All statements are true except – vertical curve has the constant rate of change of slope constant, which is presented as: $a = \frac{g_2 - g_1}{2L}$.

Example 6.8
A sag vertical curve connects –2.3% and +3% tangents, and has a curve length of 300 ft. The station of the PVC is 12 + 00. Determine the tangent slope at station 14 + 00.

Solution:

$$Y = Y_{PVC} + g_1 x + \left[\frac{g_2 - g_1}{2L}\right] x^2$$

$$\frac{d}{dx}(Y)=\frac{d}{dx}\left(Y_{PVC}+g_1x+\left[\frac{g_2-g_1}{2L}\right]x^2\right)$$

$$\frac{dY}{dx}=0+g_1+2\left(\frac{g_2-g_1}{2L}\right)x$$

$$\frac{dY}{dx}=g_1+\left(\frac{g_2-g_1}{L}\right)x$$

$$\left.\frac{dY}{dx}\right|_{x=200\text{ ft}}=-0.023+\left(\frac{0.03-(-0.023)}{300}\right)(200\text{ ft})=0.0123=\underline{1.23\%}$$

Example 6.9

A crest vertical curve joining 3.9% and -1.9% grade is to be designed for design speed of 65 mph. The elevation of the PVC is 1,722.45 ft located at station 0+00. Consider stopping sight distance criteria governs. K = 193 for speed for 55 mph, considering stopping sight distance criteria governs. The elevations of PVC and 100-ft from the PVC are most nearly:

Solution:

$$K=\frac{L}{A}$$

$L = KA = 193(3.9-(-1.9)) = 1{,}119$ ft

Elevation of PVC = 1,722.45 ft

Station of PVC = 0 + 00

$x =$ 100 ft from PVC

$$Y=Y_{PVC}+g_1x+\left[\frac{g_2-g_1}{2L}\right]x^2$$

$$\text{Elevation of PVC, } Y_0=1{,}722.45+(0.039)(0)+\left[\frac{-0.019-(0.039)}{2(1{,}119)}\right](0)^2=1{,}722.45\text{ft}$$

Elevation of 100-ft from the PVC,

$$Y_{100}=1{,}722.45+(0.039)(100)+\left[\frac{-0.019-(0.039)}{2(1{,}119)}\right](100)^2=\underline{1{,}726.09\text{ft}}$$

Example 6.10

A vertical 450 ft curve has the initial and the final grades of 2% and –3% respectfully. Determine the value of *K*, the parabola constant, *a,* and the tangent offset at PVI.

Solution:

$$K=\frac{L}{A}=\frac{450\,ft}{|-2-(-3)|}=\frac{450}{5}=\underline{90\text{ ft}}$$

$$a=\frac{g_2-g_1}{2L}=\frac{-3-2}{2(450)}=\underline{-0.0055}$$

$$E=\frac{AL}{800}=\frac{|2-(-3)|450\text{ ft}}{800}=\underline{2.81\text{ ft}}$$

Example 6.11
The point of vertical curve is located at 3,200 ft elevation. The uphill grade is 2%. Determine the tangent elevation at 500 ft from the PVC.

Solution: Tangent elevation= $Y_{PVC} + g_1 x = 3,200\,\text{ft} + (2\%)(500\,\text{ft}) = \underline{3,210\ \text{ft}}$

Example 6.12
A crest vertical curve connects a +3.33% grade and a –5.55% grade. The *PVI* is at station 121 + 22 at an elevation of 423.89 ft. The design speed is 60 mph. Use, K = 151 for economic design (passing sight distance criterion is rarely used). Determine the following:

(a) The length of the vertical curve using the AASHTO method ("K" factors)
(b) The station of the *PVC*
(c) The elevation of the *PVC*
(d) The station of the *PVT*
(e) The elevation of the *PVT*
(f) The station of the high point
(g) The elevation of the high point
(h) The elevation of station 123 + 50

Solution:

(a) The length of the vertical curve using the given K value
$L = KA = 151(3.33 - (-5.55)) = 1,340.88$ ft

(b) The station of the *PVC*
$PVC = PVI - L/2$
$L/2 = 1,340.88/2 = 670.44$ ft
$PVC = PVI - L/2 = (121 + 22) - (6 + 70.44) = 114 + 51.56$

(c) The elevation of the *PVC*
$PVC = PVI - g_1\,(L/2)$
$PVC = 423.89$ ft – (0.033) (670.44 ft) = 401.77 ft

(d) The station of the *PVT*
$PVT = PVI + L/2$
$PVT = PVI + L/2 = (121 + 22) + (6 + 70.44) = 127 + 92.44$

(e) The elevation of the *PVT*
$PVT = PVI + g_2\,(L/2)$
$PVT = 423.89$ ft + (–0.055) (670.44 ft) = 387.0 ft

(f) The station of the high point
Distance from the *PVC* to the maximum point of curve,

$$x_m = \frac{g_1 L}{g_1 - g_2} = \frac{0.033(1,340.88\,\text{ft})}{0.033 - (-0.055)} = 502.83\ \text{ft}$$

Station of x_m = PVC + x_m = (114 + 51.56) + (5 + 2.83) = 119 + 54.39

(g) The elevation of the high point

$$Y_{high} = Y_{PVC} + g_1 x_m + \left[\frac{g_2 - g_1}{2L}\right] x_m^2 = 401.77 + 0.033(502.83) +$$

$$\left(\frac{-0.055 - 0.033}{2(1,340.88)}\right)(502.83)^2$$

$$= 410.1 \text{ ft}$$

(h) The elevation of station 123 + 50

Distance from the PVC = (123 + 50) – (114 + 51.56) = 898.44 ft

$$Y = Y_{PVC} + g_1 x + \left[\frac{g_2 - g_1}{2L}\right] x^2 = 401.77 + 0.033(898.44) +$$

$$\left(\frac{-0.055 - 0.033}{2(1,340.88)}\right)(898.44)^2$$

$$= 404.93 \text{ ft}$$

Example 6.13

An equal-tangent crest vertical curve joining 3% and -2% grade is to be designed. If the tangents intersect at station (248+00) at an elevation of 2,250 ft, calculate the elevation at station 241+00 on the curve. Assume, rate of vertical curvature, $K = 300$.

Solution:

$$K = \frac{L}{A}$$

$L = KA = 300(3 - (-2) = 1500$ ft.

Elevation of PVC = 2,250 – 3% of 750 ft = 2,227.5 ft

Station of PVC = (248+00) – (15+00)/2 = 240+50

Station 241+00 is 50-ft away from the PVC

$$Y = Y_{PVC} + g_1 x + \left[\frac{g_2 - g_1}{2L}\right] x^2$$

$$Y_{50} = 2,227.5 + (0.03)(50) + \left[\frac{-0.02 - 0.03}{2(1500)}\right](50)^2 = \underline{2,228.96}$$

One of the learning from this problem is that the main aspect of setting vertical curve is to find out the length of curve. The rest of the part is following the calculation.

6.3 Traffic Volume

Article 5.1 Traffic Engineering of the PE Civil Handbook discusses this topic.

6.3.1 Traffic Flow, Density, Headway, and Speed Relationships

Traffic flow is the total number of vehicles passing a given point in a given time. Traffic flow in vehicles per unit time (q) is expressed as vehicles per hour as, $q = \frac{n}{t}$

Where n = number of vehicles passing some designated roadway point during time t

t = duration of time interval

Traffic flow is the equivalent hourly rate at which vehicles pass a point on a highway during a period less than 1 hour:

$$q = \frac{n(3{,}600)}{T}$$

n = number of vehicles passing a point in the roadway in T sec
q = equivalent hourly flow

Traffic density is defined as as the number of vehicles m that occupy a segment of a road of a length and expressed as $k = \frac{n}{l}$

where
k = traffic density in vehicles per unit distance
n = number of vehicles occupying some length of roadway at some specified time
l = length of roadway

6.3.2 Headway

The vehicle headway is defined as 'the time, in seconds, between two successive vehicles as they pass a point on the roadway, measured from the same common feature of both vehicles.

$$t = \sum_{i=1}^{n} h_i$$

t = duration of time interval
h_i = time headway of the i-th vehicle (time transpired between arrivals of vehicle i and $i - 1$)
n = number of measured vehicle time headways at some designated roadway point

$$q = \frac{n}{\sum_{i=1}^{n} h_i}$$

$$q = \frac{n}{\bar{h}}$$

where $\bar{h}$ = average time headway, $\frac{\sum h_i}{n}$ in unit time per vehicle

Example 6.14
Data obtained from aerial photography showed six (6) vehicles on a 210 m-long section of road. Traffic data collected at the same time indicated an average time headway of 3.7 sec. Calculate the traffic density and flow.

Solution

Now, density, $k = \frac{n}{l} = \frac{6\,\text{veh}}{210\,\text{m}} = 0.0286\,\frac{\text{veh}}{\text{m}} = 0.0286 \times 1{,}000\frac{\text{veh}}{\text{km}} = \underline{28.6\,\frac{\text{veh}}{\text{km}}}$

Flow, $q = \frac{n(3{,}600)}{T} = \frac{1(3{,}600)}{3.7\,\text{sec}} = \underline{973\frac{\text{veh}}{\text{h}}}$

6.3.3 Space Mean Speed

The space-mean speed is the average speed of vehicles traveling a given segment of roadway during a specified period of time and is calculated using the average travel time and length for the roadway segment.

$$u_s = \frac{q}{k} = \frac{flow}{density}$$

$$u_s = \frac{nL}{\sum_{i=1}^{n} t_i}$$

where

u_s = space mean speed (mph)
n = number of vehicles
L = length of section of highway (miles)
t_i = time it takes the i-th vehicle to travel across a section of highway
q = equivalent hourly flow (vph)
flow = density × space mean speed
$q = k \; x \; u_s$

6.3.4 Lane Occupancy Used in Freeway Surveillance

Lane occupancy is the ratio of vehicles to the distance between the vehicles on the highway per lane usually represented as a percentage. Here are some examples: A line of vehicles touching bumper to bumper would represent 100% occupancy. Vehicles separated equally by a single vehicle space would represent 50% occupancy.

$$\text{Lane occupancy, } R = \frac{\text{sum of length of vehicles}}{\text{length of roadway section}} = \frac{\sum L_i}{D}$$

where R can be divided by the average length of a vehicle to get an estimate of density k. This is an approximate estimate. To be more accurate, we should include the sensor length as well.

Example 6.15
Data from an inductive loop detector collected during a 30-second time period indicate that the mean speed of traffic is 80 km/h among the 16 vehicles counted. Assume an average vehicle length of 5.8 m. Determine the approximate lane occupancy used in freeway surveillance.

Solution:

$$\text{Mean speed, } u_s = \frac{q}{k} = \frac{flow}{density}$$

$$k = \frac{q}{u_s} = \frac{\frac{16\,\text{veh}}{30\,\text{sec}} \times 3{,}600 \frac{\text{sec}}{\text{h}}}{80 \frac{\text{km}}{\text{h}}} = 24 \frac{\text{veh}}{\text{km}}$$

R can be divided by the average length of a vehicle to get an estimate of density k.
Now, $k = R$ / Average Length
Therefore, $R = k$ x Average Length = 24 veh/km x (5.8/1,000 km) = 0.14 = 14%

6.3.5 Greenshields Maximum Flow Rate Relationship

Greenshield developed a model of uninterrupted traffic flow that predicts and explains the trends that are observed in real traffic flows. While Greenshield's model is not perfect, it is fairly accurate and relatively simple. According to this model,

Maximum flow rate for Greenshields relationship (vph), $q_{\max} = \dfrac{k_j u_f}{4}$

k_j = jam density (veh/mi)
u_f = mean free speed (mph)

6.3.6 Street Segment Interrupted Flow (e.g., Level of Service, Running Time, Speed)

Speed-Density Model, $u_s = u_f \left(1 - \dfrac{k}{k_j}\right)$

where

u_f = free-flow speed (mph)
k = density (veh/mi)
k_j = jam density (veh/mi)

Flow-Density Model, $q = ku_s = u_f \left(k - \dfrac{k^2}{k_j}\right)$

where $q_{cap} = u_{cap} \times k_{cap}$

$k_{cap} = \dfrac{k_j}{2}$

$u_{cap} = \dfrac{u_f}{2}$ and $q_{cap} = u_f \dfrac{k_j}{2}$

where q_{cap} = flow at capacity
k_{cap} = density at the capacity flow rate

Speed-Flow Model, $k = k_j \left(1 - \dfrac{u_s}{u_f}\right)$

Or, $q = k_j \left(u_s - \dfrac{u_s^2}{u_f}\right)$

Time Mean Speed is the arithmetic average speed of all vehicles for a specified period of time, $\bar{u}_t = \dfrac{\sum_i^t u_i}{n}$

where $\bar{u}_t$ = time mean speed in unit distance per unit time
u_i = spot speed of the i-th vehicle
n = number of measured vehicle spot speeds

Average Speed (Mean Speed), $\bar{x} = \dfrac{\sum n_i S_i}{N}$

where $\bar{x}$ = average or mean speed (mph)
n_i = frequency of observations in group i
S_i = middle speed of group i (mph)
N = total number of individual speed observations

Example 6.16
Results of traffic flow studies on a highway gives the following results.

Speed, u_s (km/h)	**Density, k (veh/km)**
50	18
45	25
40	41
34	58
22	71
13	88
12	99

The relationship between traffic density (k, veh/km) and mean vehicle speed (u, mile/hr) of the roadway can be presented as follows:

$$u_s = 58.984 - 0.4913k$$

Calculate:

(a) Free flow speed (km/hr)
(b) Density at maximum volume (veh/km)
(c) Maximum volume (veh/km)

Solution:

Speed-Density Model, $u_s = u_f\left(1 - \frac{k}{k_j}\right) = u_f - \frac{u_f}{k_j}k$

Flow-Density Model, $q = ku_s = u_f\left(k - \frac{k^2}{k_j}\right)$

(a) Free flow speed, u_f

Comparing $u_s = 58.984 - 0.4913k$ with $u_s = u_f - \frac{u_f}{k_j}k$

u_f = 58.984 km/h
$u_f / k_j = 0.4913$
k_j = 58.984 / 0.4913 = <u>120.06 km/h</u>

(b) Density at maximum volume

Flow, $q = ku_s = 58.984k - 0.4913k^2$

Differentiating, $\frac{dq}{dk} = 58.9 - 0.9826k$

For the maximum flow value, $\frac{dq}{dk} = 0$

or, $58.9 - 0.9826k = 0$
k = <u>60.00 veh/km</u> when $q = q_{max}$

(c) Maximum volume

$$q_{\max} = 58.984k - 0.4913k^2 = 58.984\left(60\frac{\text{veh}}{\text{km}}\right) - 0.4913\left(60\frac{\text{veh}}{\text{km}}\right)^2 = \underline{1{,}770\frac{\text{veh}}{\text{hr}}}$$

Example 6.17

In a freeway traffic stream, the capacity flow was observed to be 2,200 veh/h/ln, and the jam density at this location had been observed to be 125 veh/ln/km. If the traffic stream is modeled using Greenberg's model, determine the optimum speed and optimum density.

Solution:

Flow rate at capacity, $q_{cap} = u_f \dfrac{k_j}{4}$

$$u_f = \frac{4q_{cap}}{k_j}$$

$$u_f = \frac{4 \times 2{,}200 \dfrac{\text{veh}}{\text{hr.ln}}}{125 \dfrac{\text{veh}}{\text{ln.km}}} = 70.4 \frac{\text{km}}{\text{hr}}$$

For capacity flow, the optimum speed, $u_{cap} = \dfrac{u_f}{2} = \dfrac{70.4}{2}\dfrac{\text{km}}{\text{hr}} = 35.2 \dfrac{\text{km}}{\text{hr}}$

For capacity flow, the optimum density, $k_{cap} = \dfrac{k_j}{2} = \dfrac{125}{2} = 62.5 \dfrac{\text{veh}}{\text{ln.km}}$

Example 6.18

Travel time of eight vehicles for a 1000-ft segment are listed below. Calculate the Time Mean Speed (TMS) and Space Mean Speed (SMS).

Vehicle No.	Travel Time (sec)	Travel Distance (ft)	Travel Speed (ft/sec)	Travel Speed (mi/hr)
1	20.7	1,000	48.3	32.9
2	21.7	1,000	46.1	31.3
3	19.8	1,000	50.5	34.4
4	20.3	1,000	49.3	33.5
5	22.5	1,000	44.4	30.2
6	18.5	1,000	54.1	36.8
7	19.0	1,000	52.6	35.8
8	21.4	1,000	46.7	31.8
Total	163.8	-	392.0	266.7

Solution:

The TMS is computed as the arithmetic average of individual vehicle speeds. The SMS is a speed computed using the average travel time of the individual vehicles.

Time Mean Speed, $\bar{u}_t = \dfrac{\sum_i^t u_i}{n} = \dfrac{266.7\,\text{mph}}{8} = 33.3\text{ mph}$

Space mean speed, $u_s = \dfrac{nL}{\sum_{i=1}^{n} t_i} = \dfrac{8 \times 1{,}000\,\text{ft}}{163.8\,\text{sec}} = 48.8 \dfrac{\text{ft}}{\text{sec}} = \dfrac{48.8}{1.47}\text{ mph} = 33.2\text{ mph}$

6.3.7 Traffic Analysis (Volume, Peak Hour Factor, Speed Studies, Modal Split)

Average annual daily traffic (AADT), is the total volume of vehicle traffic of a highway or road for a year divided by 365 days, or the daily traffic multiplied by daily adjustment factor (Sunday and Monday is not the same) and monthly adjustment factor (snowy December and clear June is not the same).

$$\text{AADT} = V_{24ij} \times DF_i \times MF_j$$

where AADT = average annual daily traffic (vpd)
V_{24ij} = 24-hour volume for day i in month j (vehicles)
DF_i = daily adjustment factor for day i
MF_j = monthly adjustment factor for month j

$$DF = \frac{V_{avg}}{V_{day}}$$

where V_{avg} = average daily count for all days of the week (vehicles)
V_{day} = average daily count for each day of the week (vehicles)

$$MF_i = \frac{AADT}{ADT_i}$$

where MF_i = monthly adjustment factor for month i
AADT = average annual daily traffic (vehicles/day) (estimated as the average of 12 monthly ADTs)
ADT_i = average daily traffic for month i (vehicles/day)

Estimating Annual Vehicle-Miles Traveled, $VMT_{365} = AADT \times L \times 365$
where VMT_{365} = annual vehicle-miles traveled over the segment
AADT = vehicles per day for the segment
L = length of the segment

The AAWT is the total weekday volume divided by 260 days, or: $AAWT = \frac{total\ weekday\ traffic}{260}$

Make sure you know the difference between 'traffic' and 'truck traffic'. Traffic means all vehicles including motorbike. Truck traffic means more likely commercial vehicles excluding motorbike, passenger cars/trucks (Classes 4 to 13 by FHWA).

Example 6.19

A traffic engineer urgently needs to determine the AADT on a rural primary road that has the volume distribution characteristics shown in Tables below. She collected the data shown below on a Tuesday during the month of May.

7:00 –8:00 a.m.	400
8:00 –9:00 a.m.	535
9:00 –10:00 a.m.	650
10:00 –11:00 a.m.	710
11:00 –12 noon	650

Table. Hourly Expansion Factors to convert from hourly to daily traffic for a Rural Primary Road

Hour	Volume	HEF	Hour	Volume	HEF
6:00–7:00 a.m.	294	42.00	6:00–7:00 p.m.	743	16.62
7:00–8:00 a.m.	426	29.00	7:00–8:00 p.m.	706	17.49
8:00–9:00 a.m.	560	22.05	8:00–9:00 p.m.	606	20.38
9:00–10:00 a.m.	657	18.80	9:00–10:00 p.m.	489	25.26
10:00–11:00 a.m.	722	17.10	10:00–11:00 p.m.	396	31.19
11:00–12:00 p.m.	667	18.52	11:00–12:00 a.m.	360	34.31
12:00–1:00 p.m.	660	18.71	12:00–1:00 a.m.	241	51.24
1:00–2:00 p.m.	739	16.71	1:00–2:00 a.m.	150	82.33
2:00–3:00 p.m.	832	14.84	2:00–3:00 a.m.	100	123.50
3:00–4:00 p.m.	836	14.77	3:00–4:00 a.m.	90	137.22
4:00–5:00 p.m.	961	12.85	4:00–5:00 a.m.	86	143.60
5:00–6:00 p.m.	892	13.85	5:00–6:00 a.m.	137	90.14
Total daily volume = 12,350.					

Table. Daily Expansion Factors to convert from daily to weekly traffic for a Rural Primary Road

Day of Week	Volume	DEF
Sunday	7895	9.515
Monday	10,714	7.012
Tuesday	9722	7.727
Wednesday	11,413	6.582
Thursday	10,714	7.012
Friday	13,125	5.724
Saturday	11,539	6.510
Total weekly volume = 75,122.		

Table. Monthly adjustment Factors for a Rural Primary Road

Month	ADT	MEF
January	1350	1.756
February	1200	1.975
March	1450	1.635
April	1600	1.481
May	1700	1.394
June	2500	0.948
July	4100	0.578
August	4550	0.521
September	3750	0.632
October	2500	0.948
November	2000	1.185
December	1750	1.354
Total yearly volume = 28,450.		
Mean average daily volume = 2370.		

Determine the AADT of the road.

[Note that this example does not follow the equation exactly; however, the concept is the same.]

Solution:

Average annual daily traffic (AADT), $AADT = V_{24ij} \times DF_i \times MF_j$

Estimate the 24-hr volume for Tuesday:

$$\frac{(400\times 29.0)+(535\times 22.05)+(650\times 18.80)+(710\times 17.10)+(650\times 18.52)}{5}\approx 11{,}959$$

Therefore, $V_{24ij} = 11{,}959$

Adjust the 24-hr volume = Weekly volume ÷ 7 = V_{24ij} x Weekly Factor ÷ 7

= 11,959 x 7.727 ÷ 7 = 13,200

Monthly adjustment factor for May, $MF_j = 1.394$

AADT = 13,200 X 1.394 = 18,400

Example 6.20

An urban arterial street segment 0.2 mile long has an average annual daily traffic (AADT) of 15,400 veh/day. In a three-year period, there have been eight crashes resulting in death and/or injuries and 15 involving property damage only. Calculate the annual vehicle-miles traveled.

Solution:

Annual Vehicle-Miles Traveled, $VMT_{365} = AADT \times L \times 365$

= 15,400 veh/day × 0.2 mile × 365

= 1,124,200

Chapter 7
Materials

7.1 Soil Classification and Boring Log Interpretation

This section is primarily based on the Article 3.7 Soil Classification and Boring Log Interpretation of the PE Civil Handbook.

7.1.1 Subsurface Exploration and Planning

Article 3.7 of the PE Civil Handbook presented a table on guidelines for minimum number of exploration points and depth of exploration. A small part is shown below. Please go through the table. In fact, read any text given in the PE Civil Handbook, as about 50% of the questions are theory based or do not need any analytical calculation.

Application	Minimum Number of Exploration Points and Location of Exploration Points	Minimum Depth of Exploration
Retaining Walls	1. A minimum of one exploration point for each retaining wall. 2. For retaining walls more than 100 ft (30 m) in length, exploration points spaced every 100 to 200 ft (30 to 60 m) with locations alternating from in front of the wall to behind the wall. 3. For anchored walls, additional exploration points in the anchorage zone spaced at 100 to 200 ft (30 to 60 m). 4. For soil-nail walls, additional exploration points at a distance of 1.0 to 1.5 times the height	1. Investigate to a depth below bottom of wall between 1 and 2 times the wall height or a minimum of 10 ft (3 m) into bedrock. 2. Exploration depth should be great enough to fully penetrate soft highly compressible soils (e.g., peat, organic silt, soft fine-grained soils) into competent material of suitable bearing capacity (e.g., stiff to hard cohesive soil, compact dense cohesionless soil, or bedrock).

	of the wall behind the wall spaced at 100 to 200 ft (30 to 60 m).	
Embankment Foundations	1. A minimum of one exploration point every 200 ft (60 m) (erratic conditions) to 400 ft (120 m) (uniform conditions) of embankment length along the centerline of the embankment.	1. Exploration depth should be, at a minimum, equal to twice the embankment height unless a hard stratum is encountered above this depth.

7.1.2 Soil Classification

Soil can be classified in many ways as Unified Soil Classification System (USCS), American Association of State Highway and Transportation Officials (AASHTO) Soil Classification (AASHTO M 145), MIT Soil Classification, International Classification, etc. The following two criteria are found to be significant for soil classification after years of research and experience with wide-ranging soils, all over the world:

i. Particle size distribution of soils
ii. Liquid limit and the plasticity index

The soil in nature consists of a mixture of particles of different sizes rather than soil particles of single size. Thus, every soil consists of clay, silt, sand, and gravel in some proportion. Hence, to classify a given soil, it is necessary to determine its grain (or particle) size distribution. In addition to the grain size distribution, it is also necessary to consider the liquid limit and plasticity index of the soil for classifying the soil.

7.1.2.1 Gradation Tests

From Article 3.8 Material Test Methods of PE Civil Handbook, U.S. Standard Sieve Sizes and Corresponding Opening Dimension:

U.S. Standard Sieve No.	**Sieve Opening (in.)**	**Sieve Opening (mm)**	**Comment [Based on the Unified Soil Classification System (USCS)]**
3	0.2500	6.35	
4	0.1870	4.75	Breakpoint between fine gravels and coarse sands Soil passing this sieve is used for compaction test
6	0.1320	3.35	
8	0.0937	2.36	
10	0.0787	2.00	Breakpoint between coarse and medium sands
12	0.0661	1.70	
16	0.0469	1.18	
20	0.0331	0.850	
30	0.0234	0.600	
40	0.0165	0.425	Breakpoint between medium and fine sands Soil passing this sieve is used for Atterberg limits
50	0.0117	0.300	
60	0.0098	0.250	
70	0.0083	0.212	
100	0.0059	0.150	
140	0.0041	0.106	
200	0.0029	0.075	Breakpoint between fine sand and silt or clay
270	0.0021	0.053	
400	0.0015	0.038	

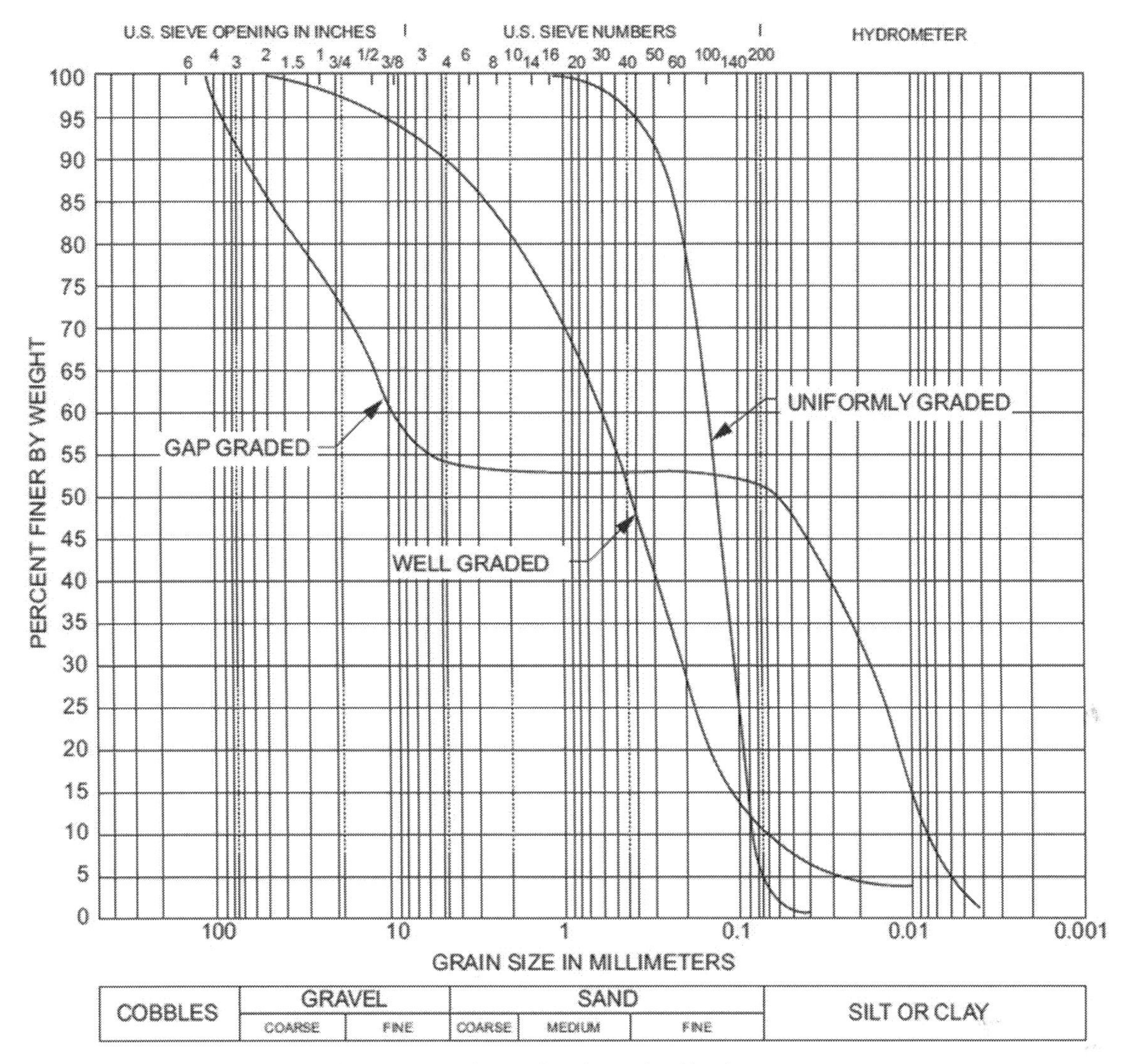

Figure. Sample Grain Size Distribution Curves

The particle size distribution, or gradation, of an aggregate is one of the most influential aggregate characteristics in determining how it will perform as a pavement material. In asphalt concrete, gradation helps determine almost every important property including stiffness, stability, durability, permeability, workability, fatigue resistance, frictional resistance and moisture susceptibility. In portland cement concrete, gradation helps determine durability, porosity, workability, cement and water requirements, strength, and shrinkage.

Typical sieve analysis involves a nested column of sieves with wire mesh cloth (screen). A representative weighed sample is poured into the top sieve which has the largest screen openings. The column is typically placed in a mechanical shaker. The shaker shakes the column for some fixed amount of time. After the shaking is complete the material on each sieve is weighed. The weight of the sample of each sieve is then divided by the total weight to give a percentage retained on each sieve. The size of the average particle on each sieve is then analyzed to get a cut-off point or specific size range, which is then captured on a screen. The results of this test are used to describe the properties of aggregate gradation. Results of this test are provided in graphical form to identify the type of gradation of the aggregate.

From the sieve analysis curve, two parameters, Coefficient of Curvature (C_c) and Coefficient of Uniformity (C_u) are determined as follows:

$$C_u = \frac{D_{60}}{D_{10}} \quad \text{and} \quad C_c = \frac{(D_{30})^2}{(D_{60})(D_{10})}$$

D_{60} = diameter at 60% passing
D_{30} = diameter at 30% passing
D_{10} = diameter at 10% passing

Another term, D_{50} which is the size corresponding to cumulative 10% passing by weight (or 10% finer) is known as the median size of the soil sample.

Table. Gradation Based on C_u and C_c Parameters

Gradation	Gravels	Sands
Well-graded	$C_u \geq 4$ and $1 < C_c < 3$	$C_u \geq 6$ and $1 < C_c < 3$
Poorly graded	$C_u < 4$ and $1 < C_c < 3$	$C_u < 6$ and $1 < C_c < 3$
Gap graded*	C_c not between 1 and 3	C_c not between 1 and 3

*Gap-graded soils may be well-graded or poorly graded. In addition to the C_c value, it is recommended that the shape of the GSD be the basis for definition of gap graded.

Example 7.1

The sieve analysis of an aggregate sample is presented below.

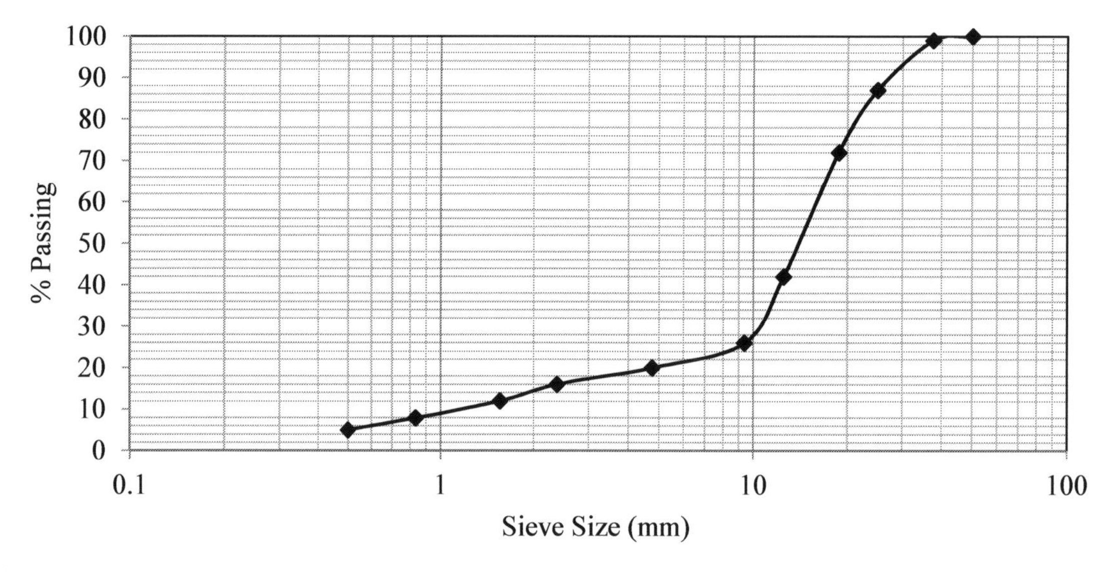

From this curve, determine Coefficient of Curvature (C_c) and Coefficient of Uniformity (C_u) of the aggregate sample.

Solution:

From the curve with best reading with naked eye:
D_{60} = diameter at 60% passing ≈ 17 mm
D_{30} = diameter at 30% passing ≈ 11 mm
D_{10} = diameter at 10% passing ≈ 1.4 mm

Coefficient of Uniformity $C_u = \frac{D_{60}}{D_{10}} = \frac{17\text{mm}}{1.4\text{mm}} = \underline{12.1}$

Coefficient of Curvature $C_c = \frac{(D_{30})^2}{(D_{60})(D_{10})} = \frac{(11\text{mm})^2}{(17\text{mm})(1.4\text{mm})} = \underline{5.1}$

For this type of problem, human error for curve reading should not a problem. The answer options will have a good gap.

7.1.2.2 Atterberg Limits

Soil consistence provides a means of describing the degree and kind of cohesion and adhesion between the soil particles as related to the resistance of the soil to deform or rupture. Since the consistence varies with moisture content, the consistence can be described as dry consistence, moist consistence, and wet consistence.

Atterberg limits are important to describe the consistency of fine-grained soils. A fine-grained soil usually exists with its particles surrounded by water. The amount of water in the soil determines its state or consistency. Four states are used to describe the soil consistency; solid, semi-solid, plastic and liquid. The knowledge of the soil consistency is important in defining or classifying a soil type or predicting soil performance when used a construction material. The soil consistency is a practical and an inexpensive way to distinguish between silts and clays. The Atterberg limits are the basic measure of the critical water contents of a fine-grained soil: its shrinkage limit, plastic limit, and liquid limit.

- Liquid Limit (LL) is defined as the moisture content at which soil begins to behave as a liquid material and begins to flow. Liquid limit of a fine-grained soil gives the moisture content at which the shear strength of the soil is approximately 2.5 kN/m^2. The lowest water content above which soil behaves like liquid, normally below 100.
- Plastic Limit (PL) is defined as the moisture content at which soil begins to behave plastic. The lowest water content at which soil behaves like a plastic material, normally below 40.
- Shrinkage Limit (SL) is defined as the moisture content at which no further volume change occurs with further reduction in moisture content. (SL represents the amount of water required to fully saturate the soil (100% saturation)). In summary, the water content below which soils do not decrease their volume anymore as they continue dry out.

Plasticity means the degree to which puddled or reworked soil can be permanently deformed without rupturing. To determine LL, First of all a grooved is made in the soil sample by using a standard grooving tool along the diameter through the center line of the cam follower so that a clean, sharp groove of proper dimension is formed, the cup shall be dropped by turning the crank at the rate of two revolutions per seconds and the number of blows counted until the two halves of the soil cake come into contact with the bottom of the groove along a distance of about 12 mm. A representative soul sample nearer the groove is taken for moisture content determination. The moisture content is reported along with number of blows required to close a groove. The operations specified above shall be repeated for at least three trails at different moisture content. A semi-log graph is plotted for moisture content (arithmetic scale) versus number of blows N (log scale) versus number of blows N (log scale). This will approximate a straight line. From the straight line, determine the moisture content w(%) corresponding to 25 blows. This is the liquid limit of the soil.

The basic steps of determining PL are mentioned below:

1) Take about 20 grams of soil passing #40 sieve
2) Thoroughly mix small amount of water and cure it for at least 16 minutes
3) Take 2 grams of wet soil
4) Roll by hand between palm and glass plate
5) If it breaks before reaching the thread diameter of 3.2 mm, mix more water and repeat steps up to (4).
6) If the diameter can be reached, break it into several pieces and reroll.

7) Repeat until the thread crumbles into several pieces when it reaches a diameter of 1/8-in. It is possible that a thread may crumble at a diameter larger than 1/8-in. during a given rolling process, whereas it did not crumble at the same diameter during the immediately previous rolling.
8) Collect the small crumble pieces in a can and determine the water content.

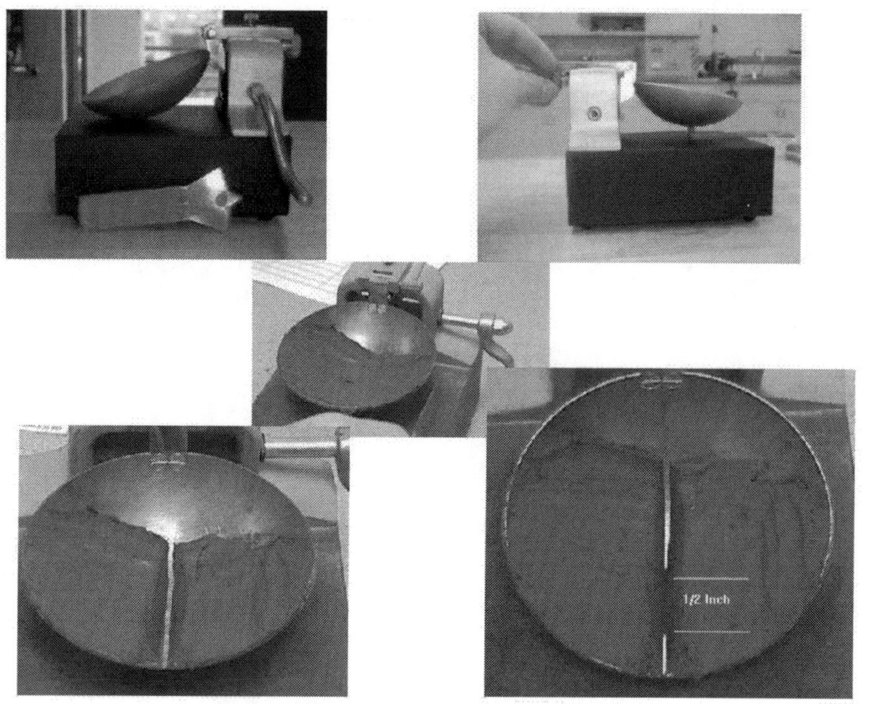

Figure. Determining Liquid Limit of soil
(Courtesy of Dr. Lanbo Liu, University of Connecticut)

The plasticity index, PI can be calculated using the following equation:

$$PI = LL - PL$$

7.1.2.3 Unified Soil Classification System (USCS)

The method is standardized in ASTM D 2487 as the Unified Soil Classification System (USCS). USCS is the most common soil classification system among geotechnical engineers. This system classifies soils into two broad categories:

1) Coarse-Grained Soils. If less than 50% of the material by weight passes through the No. 200 sieve. The group symbols start with a prefix of G or S. G stands for gravel or gravelly soil, and S for sand or sandy soil.
2) Fine-Grained Soils. If 50% or more of the material by weight passes through the No. 200 sieve. The group symbols start with prefixes of M, which stands for inorganic silt, C for inorganic clay, or O for organic silts and clays. The symbol Pt is used for peat, and other highly organic soils.

Some other symbols used are listed below:

H: High Plastic (LL>50)
L: Low Plastic (LL)
W: Well-graded
P: Poorly-graded

Table. Unified Soil Classification System

Criteria for Assigning Group Symbols and Group Names Using Laboratory Tests[a]			Soil Classification	
COARSE-GRAINED SOILS (Sands and Gravels): More than 50% retained in No. 200 (0.075 mm) sieve **FINE-GRAINED (Silts and Clays):** 50% or more passes the No. 200 (0.075 mm) sieve			**Group Symbol**	**Group Name[b]**
GRAVELS More than 50% of coarse fraction retained in No. 4 sieve	CLEAN GRAVELS < 5% fines	$C_u \geq 4$ and $1 \leq C_c \leq 3$[e]	GW	Well-graded gravel[f]
		$C_u < 4$ and/or $1 > C_c > 3$[e]	GP	Poorly graded gravel[f]
	GRAVELS WITH FINES > 12% of fines[c]	Fines classify as ML or MH	GM	Silty gravel[f, g, h]
		Fines classify as CL or CH	GC	Clayey gravel[f, g, h]
SANDS 50% or more of coarse fraction passes No. 4 sieve	CLEAN SANDS < 5% fines[d]	$C_u \geq 6$ and $1 \leq C_c \leq 3$[e]	SW	Well-graded sand[i]
		$C_u < 6$ and/or $1 > C_c > 3$[e]	SP	Poorly graded sand[i]
	SANDS WITH FINES > 12% fines[d]	Fines classify as ML or MH	SM	Silty sand[g, h, i]
		Fines classify as CL or CH	SC	Clayey sand[g, h, i]
SILTS AND CLAYS Liquid limit less than 50	Inorganic	$PI > 7$ and plots on or above "A" line[j]	CL	Lean clay[k, l, m]
		$PI < 4$ or plots below "A" line[j]	ML	Silt[k, l, m]
	Organic	$\frac{\text{Liquid limit} - \text{oven dried}}{\text{Liquid limit} - \text{not dried}} < 0.75$	OL	Organic clay[k, l, m, n]
				Organic silt[k, l, m, o]
SILTS AND CLAYS Liquid limit 50 or more	Inorganic	PI plots on or above "A" line	CH	Fat clay[k, l, m]
		PI plots below "A" line	MH	Elastic silt[k, l, m]
	Organic	$\frac{\text{Liquid limit} - \text{oven dried}}{\text{Liquid limit} - \text{not dried}} < 0.75$	OH	Organic clay[k, l, m, p]
				Organic silt[k, l, m, q]
Highly fibrous organic soils	Primary organic matter, dark in color, and organic odor		Pt	Peat

[a]Based on the material passing the 3-in. (75-mm) sieve.

[b]If field sample contained cobbles and/or boulders, add "with cobbles and/or boulders" to group name.

[c]Gravels with 5 to 12% fines require dual symbols:

GW-GM, well-graded gravel with silt
GW-GC, well-graded gravel with clay
GP-GM, poorly graded gravel with silt
GP-GC, poorly graded gravel with clay

[d]Sands with 5 to 12% fines require dual symbols:

SW-SM, well-graded sand with silt
SW-SC, well-graded sand with clay
SP-SM, poorly graded sand with silt
SP-SC, poorly graded sand with clay

[e] $C_u = \frac{D_{60}}{D_{10}}$ and $C_c = \frac{(D_{30})^2}{(D_{60})(D_{10})}$

[f] If soil contains $\geq$ 15% sand, add "with sand" to group name.

[g]If fines classify as CL-ML, use dual symbol GC-GM, SC-SM.

[h] If fines are organic, add "with organic fines" to group name.

[i]If soil contains $\geq$ 15% gravel, add "with gravel" to group name.

[j]If the liquid limit and plasticity index plot in hatched area on plasticity chart, soil is a CL-ML, silty clay.

[k]If soil contains 15 to 29% plus No. 200 (0.075 mm), add "with sand" or "with gravel, " whichever is predominant.

[l]If soil contains $\geq$ 30% plus No. 200 (0.075 mm), predominantly sand, add "sandy" to group name.

[m]If soil contains ≥ 30% plus No. 200 (0.075 mm), predominantly gravel, add "gravelly" to group name.
[n]$PI \geq 4$ and plots on or above "A" line.
[o]$PI < 4$ and plots below "A" line.
[p]PI plots on or above "A" line.
[q]PI plots below "A" line.

$$PI = LL - PL$$

$$LI = \frac{w - PL}{PI}$$

w = water content (%)
LL = Liquid Limit (%)
PL = Plastic Limit (%)
PI = Plasticity Index (%)
LI = Liquidity Index (%)

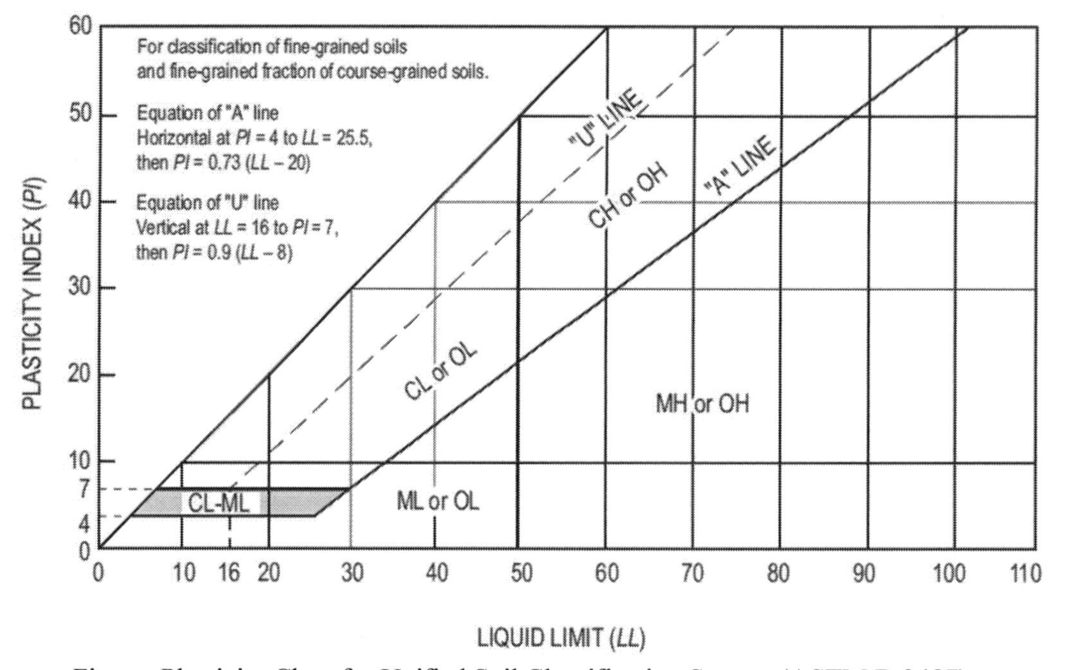

Figure. Plasticity Chart for Unified Soil Classification System (ASTM D 2487)

Flow chart to determine the group symbol and group name for coarse-grained soils and fine-grained soils respectively are presented below.

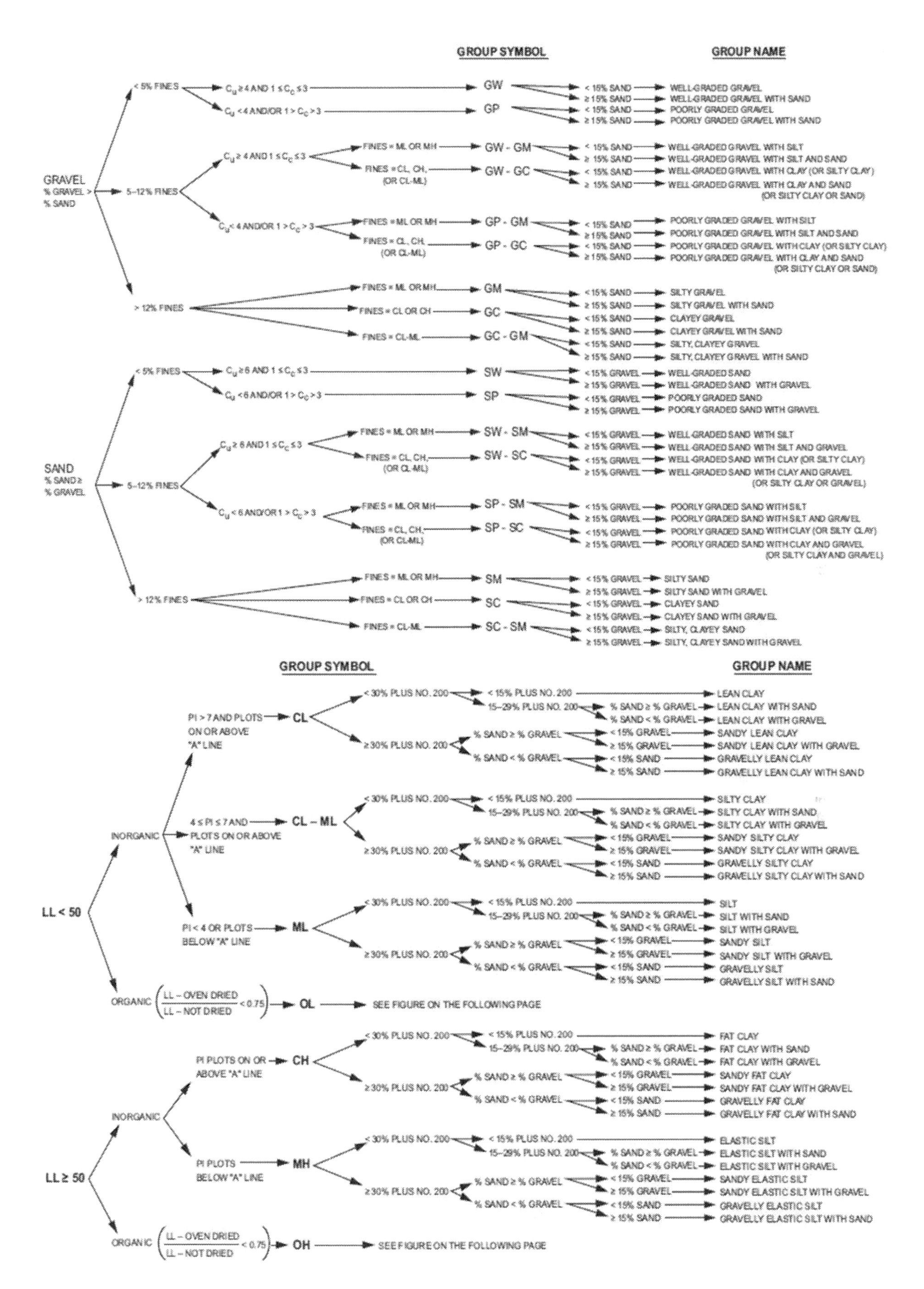
GROUP SYMBOL
GROUP NAME
GRAVEL
% GRAVEL > % SAND
< 5% FINES
Cu ≥ 4 AND 1 ≤ Cc ≤ 3
Cu < 4 AND/OR 1 > Cc > 3
GW
GP
< 15% SAND
≥ 15% SAND
WELL-GRADED GRAVEL
WELL-GRADED GRAVEL WITH SAND
POORLY GRADED GRAVEL
POORLY GRADED GRAVEL WITH SAND
5–12% FINES
FINES = ML OR MH
FINES = CL, CH, (OR CL-ML)
GW - GM
GW - GC
WELL-GRADED GRAVEL WITH SILT
WELL-GRADED GRAVEL WITH SILT AND SAND
WELL-GRADED GRAVEL WITH CLAY (OR SILTY CLAY)
WELL-GRADED GRAVEL WITH CLAY AND SAND (OR SILTY CLAY OR SAND)
GP - GM
GP - GC
POORLY GRADED GRAVEL WITH SILT
POORLY GRADED GRAVEL WITH SILT AND SAND
POORLY GRADED GRAVEL WITH CLAY (OR SILTY CLAY)
POORLY GRADED GRAVEL WITH CLAY AND SAND (OR SILTY CLAY OR SAND)
> 12% FINES
FINES = ML OR MH
FINES = CL OR CH
FINES = CL-ML
GM
GC
GC - GM
SILTY GRAVEL
SILTY GRAVEL WITH SAND
CLAYEY GRAVEL
CLAYEY GRAVEL WITH SAND
SILTY, CLAYEY GRAVEL
SILTY, CLAYEY GRAVEL WITH SAND
SAND
% SAND ≥ % GRAVEL
< 5% FINES
Cu ≥ 6 AND 1 ≤ Cc ≤ 3
Cu < 6 AND/OR 1 > Cc > 3
SW
SP
< 15% GRAVEL
≥ 15% GRAVEL
WELL-GRADED SAND
WELL-GRADED SAND WITH GRAVEL
POORLY GRADED SAND
POORLY GRADED SAND WITH GRAVEL
5–12% FINES
SW - SM
SW - SC
WELL-GRADED SAND WITH SILT
WELL-GRADED SAND WITH SILT AND GRAVEL
WELL-GRADED SAND WITH CLAY (OR SILTY CLAY)
WELL-GRADED SAND WITH CLAY AND GRAVEL (OR SILTY CLAY OR GRAVEL)
SP - SM
SP - SC
POORLY GRADED SAND WITH SILT
POORLY GRADED SAND WITH SILT AND GRAVEL
POORLY GRADED SAND WITH CLAY (OR SILTY CLAY)
POORLY GRADED SAND WITH CLAY AND GRAVEL (OR SILTY CLAY AND GRAVEL)
> 12% FINES
SM
SC
SC - SM
SILTY SAND
SILTY SAND WITH GRAVEL
CLAYEY SAND
CLAYEY SAND WITH GRAVEL
SILTY, CLAYEY SAND
SILTY, CLAYEY SAND WITH GRAVEL
GROUP SYMBOL
GROUP NAME
LL < 50
INORGANIC
PI > 7 AND PLOTS ON OR ABOVE "A" LINE
CL
< 30% PLUS NO. 200
< 15% PLUS NO. 200
15–29% PLUS NO. 200
% SAND ≥ % GRAVEL
% SAND < % GRAVEL
≥ 30% PLUS NO. 200
< 15% GRAVEL
≥ 15% GRAVEL
< 15% SAND
≥ 15% SAND
LEAN CLAY
LEAN CLAY WITH SAND
LEAN CLAY WITH GRAVEL
SANDY LEAN CLAY
SANDY LEAN CLAY WITH GRAVEL
GRAVELLY LEAN CLAY
GRAVELLY LEAN CLAY WITH SAND
4 ≤ PI ≤ 7 AND PLOTS ON OR ABOVE "A" LINE
CL – ML
SILTY CLAY
SILTY CLAY WITH SAND
SILTY CLAY WITH GRAVEL
SANDY SILTY CLAY
SANDY SILTY CLAY WITH GRAVEL
GRAVELLY SILTY CLAY
GRAVELLY SILTY CLAY WITH SAND
PI < 4 OR PLOTS BELOW "A" LINE
ML
SILT
SILT WITH SAND
SILT WITH GRAVEL
SANDY SILT
SANDY SILT WITH GRAVEL
GRAVELLY SILT
GRAVELLY SILT WITH SAND
ORGANIC
(LL – OVEN DRIED / LL – NOT DRIED) < 0.75
OL
SEE FIGURE ON THE FOLLOWING PAGE
LL ≥ 50
INORGANIC
PI PLOTS ON OR ABOVE "A" LINE
CH
FAT CLAY
FAT CLAY WITH SAND
FAT CLAY WITH GRAVEL
SANDY FAT CLAY
SANDY FAT CLAY WITH GRAVEL
GRAVELLY FAT CLAY
GRAVELLY FAT CLAY WITH SAND
PI PLOTS BELOW "A" LINE
MH
ELASTIC SILT
ELASTIC SILT WITH SAND
ELASTIC SILT WITH GRAVEL
SANDY ELASTIC SILT
SANDY ELASTIC SILT WITH GRAVEL
GRAVELLY ELASTIC SILT
GRAVELLY ELASTIC SILT WITH SAND
ORGANIC
(LL – OVEN DRIED / LL – NOT DRIED) < 0.75
OH
SEE FIGURE ON THE FOLLOWING PAGE

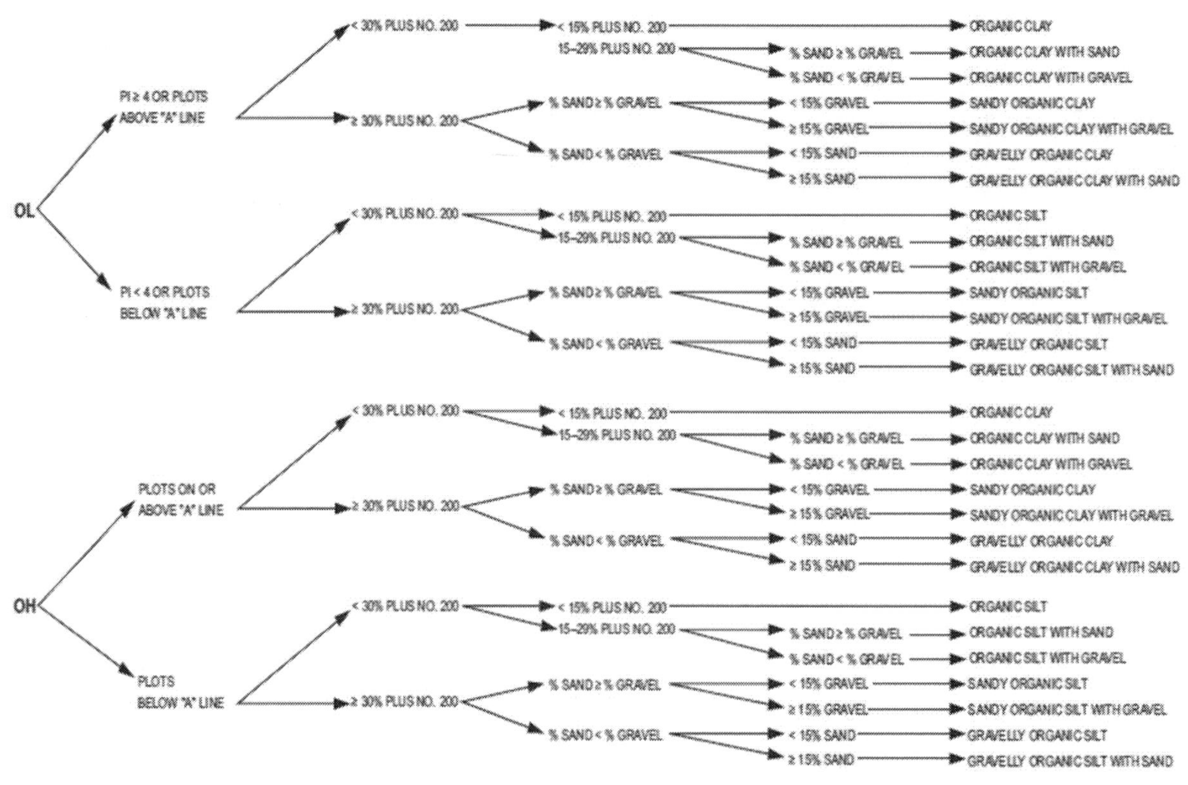

Figure. Flow Chart to Determine the Group Symbol and Group Name for Organic Soils (ASTM D 2487)

Table. Adjectives to Describe Water Content of Soils (ASTM D 2488)

Description	Conditions
Dry	No sign of water and soil dry to touch
Moist	Signs of water and soil is relatively dry to touch
Wet	Signs of water and soil definitely wet to touch; granular soil exhibits some free water when densified

Table. Particle Size Definition for Gravels and Sands (after ASTM D 2488)

Component	Grain Size	Determination
Boulders*	12"+ (300 mm+)	Measurable
Cobbles*	3"–12" (300 mm–75 mm)	Measurable
Gravel:		
Coarse	3/4"–3" (19 mm–75 mm)	Measurable
Fine	3/4"–#4 sieve (3/4"–0.187") (19 mm–4.75 mm)	Measurable
Sand:		
Coarse	#4–#10 sieve (0.19"–0.079") (4.75 mm–2.00 mm)	Measurable and visible to the eye
Medium	#10–#40 sieve (0.079"–0.017") (2.00 mm–0.425 mm)	Measurable and visible to the eye
Fine	#40–#200 sieve (0.017"–0.003") (0.425 mm–0.075 mm)	Measurable but barely discernible to the eye

*Boulders and cobbles are not considered soil or part of the soils classification or description, except under miscellaneous description, i.e., with cobbles at about 5 percent (volume).

Table. Adjectives for Describing Size Distribution for Sands and Gravels (after ASTM D 2488)

Particle-Size Adjective	Abbreviation	Size Requirement
Coarse	c.	< 30% m–f sand or < 12% f. gravel
Coarse to medium	c–m	< 12% f. sand
Medium to fine	m–f	< 12% c. sand and > 30% m. sand
Fine	f.	< 30% m. sand or < 12% c. gravel
Coarse to fine	c–f	> 12% of each size[1]

[1]12% and 30% criteria can be modified depending on fines content. The key is the shape of the particle-size distribution curve. If the curve is relatively straight or dished down, and coarse sand is present, use c-f; also use m-f sand if a moderate amount of m. sand is present. If one has any doubts, determine the above percentages base on the amount of sand or gravel present.

Table. Field Methods to Describe Plasticity (FHWA, 2002b)

Plasticity Range	Adjective	Dry Strength	Smear Test	Thread Smallest Diameter
0	Nonplastic	None—crumbles into powder with mere pressure	Gritty or rough	ball cracks
1–10	Low plasticity	Low—crumbles into powder with some finger pressure	Rough to smooth	1/4"–1/8" (6 mm–3 mm)
> 10–20	Medium plasticity	Medium—breaks into pieces or crumbles with considerable finger pressure	Smooth and dull	1/16" (1.5 mm)
> 20–40	High plasticity	High—cannot be broken with finger pressure; specimen will break into pieces between thumb and a hard surface	Shiny	0.03" (0.75 mm)
> 40	Very plastic	Very high—cannot be broken between thumb and a hard surface	Very shiny and waxy	0.02" (0.5 mm)

Table. Descriptive Terms for Layered Soils (NAVFAC, 1986a)

Type of Layer	Thickness	Occurrence
Parting	< 1/16" (< 1.5 mm)	
Seam	1/16"–1/2" (1.5 mm–12 mm)	
Layer	1/2"–12" (12 mm–300 mm)	
Stratum	> 12" (> 300 mm)	
Pocket		Small erratic deposit
Lens		Lenticular deposit
Varved (also Layered)		Alternating seams or layers of silt and/or clay and sometimes fine sand
Occasional		One or less per 12" (300 mm) of thickness or laboratory sample inspected
Frequent		More than one per 12" (300 mm) of thickness or laboratory sample inspected

Example 7.2
For a given soil, the following are known:

- Percentage passing No. 4 sieve = 70
- Percentage passing No. 200 sieve = 30
- Liquid limit = 33
- Plastic limit = 12

Classify the soil using the USCS mentioning group symbol and the group name.

Solution:

The percentage passing No. 200 sieve is 30%, which is less than 50%. So it is a coarse-grained soil. Thus,
Coarse fraction = 100 – 30 = 70%
Gravel fraction = percent retained on No. 4 sieve = 100 = 70 – 30% Hence, more than 50% of the coarse fraction is passing No. 4 sieve. Thus, it is a sandy soil.
Since more than 12% is passing No. 200 sieve, it is SM or SC.
For this soil, PI = 33 – 12 = 21 (which is greater than 7). With LL = 33 and PI = 21, it plots above the A-line. Thus, the group symbol is SC.
Since the percentage of gravel is more than 15%, it is clayey sand with gravel.

Example 7.3
For the data given below, classify the soils according to the USCS. For each soil, give both the letter symbol and the narrative description.

(a) 65% material retained on No. 4 sieve, 32% retained on No. 200 sieve. $C_u = 3$, $C_c = 1$.
(b) 100% material passed No. 4 sieve, 90% passed No. 200 sieve. $LL = 23$, $PL = 17$.
(c) 70% material retained on No. 4 sieve, 27% retained on No. 200 sieve. $C_u = 5$, $C_c = 1.5$.

Solution:

(a) GP – Poorly graded gravel with sand
(b) CL-ML – Silty clay
(c) GW – Well-graded gravel with sand

Example 7.4
A sample of soil was tested in the laboratory and the following grain size analysis results were obtained. Classify this soil according to the USCS, providing the group symbol for it.

Sieve	Sieve Opening (mm)	Percent Coarser by Weight	Percent Finer by Weight
1/2"	12.7	30	70
4	4.75	36	64
10	2.00	52	48
20	0.85	64	36
40	0.425	69	31
60	0.25	71	29
100	0.15	77	23
200	0.075	91	9

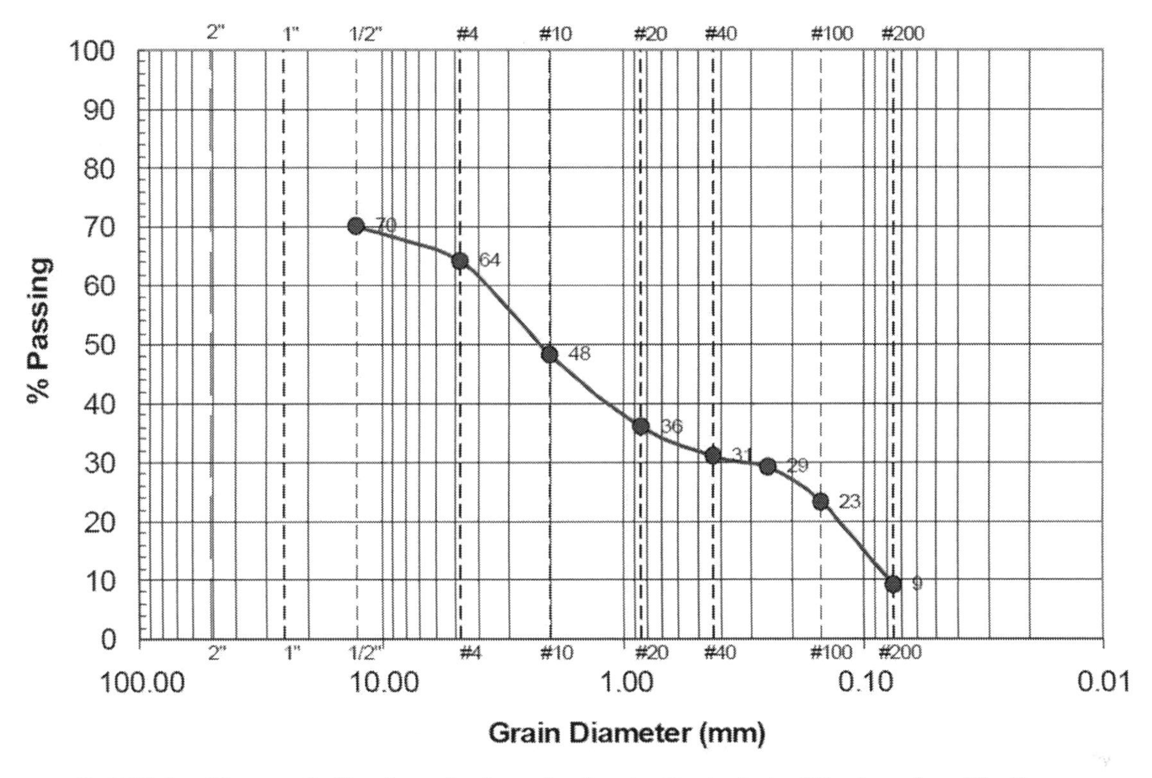

Ref. Holtz, Kovacs & Sheahan, An Introduction to Geotechnical Engineering, 2/e, Pearson.

Solution:

PI = LL – PL = 26 – 23 = 3

From the curve with best reading with naked eye:

$$C_u = \frac{D_{60}}{D_{10}} = \frac{3.9\,\text{mm}}{0.08\,\text{mm}} = 49$$

$$C_c = \frac{(D_{30})^2}{(D_{60})(D_{10})} = \frac{(0.4\text{ mm})^2}{3.9\text{ mm} \times 0.08\text{ mm}} = 0.51$$

SW-SM (Well-graded sand with silt)

7.1.2.4 AASHTO Soil Classification

AASHTO M 145 test standard describes the AASHTO Soil Classification system. For roads and highways, AASHTO Soil Classification system is commonly used. It classifies soil from A1 to A8 where A-1 is the best engineering soil, and A-8 is the worst engineering soil (organic soil). A8 soil is never recommended for engineering purpose although they have a good value in agriculture and gardening. With required test data available, proceed from left to right on chart; correct group will be found by process of elimination. The first group from left into which the test data will fit is the correct classification. At the beginning, the soil passing 0.075-mm sieve (No. 200 sieve) is looked at. If 35% of less passes through No. 200 sieve, then it is granular soil, either A-1, A-2, or A-3. If more than 35% passes through No. 200 sieve, then it is silt-clay materials, and falls under A-4 to A-7. As mentioned earlier, A-8 is the organic soil, and is excluded from the chart as unsuitable for engineering purpose. A-1 group consists of stone fragments, gravel, and sand with a maximum of 25% fines. A-3 group consists of fine sand with a maximum of 10% fines. Silty or clayey soil belongs to A-2, whereas pure silty soils with minimum 36% fines fall into A-4 and A-5 groups. A-6 and A-7 groups consist of clayey soils with minimum 36% fines. For A-1-a group, the percentages of soil passing through the 2-mm and 425-μm sieves are the additional criteria. For classifying into A-1-b and A-3 groups, the percentage passing through the 425-μm sieve is the additional criterion. For all other groups, liquid limit, and plasticity index of the soil are the additional criterion.

Table. AASHTO Soil Classification System

General Classification	Granular Materials [35 percent or less of total sample passing No. 200 sieve (0.075 mm)]							Silt-Clay Materials [More than 35 percent of total sample passing No. 200 sieve (0.075 mm)]			
Group Classification	A-1		A-3	A-2				A-4	A-5	A-6	A-7
	A-1-a	A-1-b		A-2-4	A-2-5	A-2-6	A-2-7				A-7-5, A-7-6
Sieve Analysis Percent Passing:											
No. 10 (2 mm)	50 max.										
No. 40 (0.425 mm)	30 max.	50 max.	51 min.								
No. 200 (0.075 mm)	15 max.	25 max.	10 max.	35 max.	35 max.	35 max.	35 max.	36 min.	36 min.	36 min.	36 min.
Characteristics of Fraction Passing No. 40 (0.425 mm):											
Liquid Limit				40 max.	41 min.	40 max.	41 min.	40 max.	41 min.	40 max.	41 min.
Plasticity Index	6 max.		NP	10 max.	10 max.	11 min.	11 min.	10 max.	10 max.	11 min.	11 min.*
Usual Significant Constituent Materials	Stone fragments, gravel and sand		Fine sand	Silty or clayey gravel and sand				Silty soils		Clayey soils	
Group Index**	0		0	0		4 max.		8 max.	12 max.	16 max.	20 max.

*Plasticity Index of A-7-5 subgroup is equal to less than *LL* minus 30. Plasticity Index of A-7-6 subgroup is greater than *LL* minus 30.

**See Group Index formula. Group Index should be shown in parentheses after Group Classification as A-2-4(0), A-5(11), etc.

Plasticity Index of A-7-5 subgroup is equal to less than *LL* minus 30. Plasticity Index of A-7-6 subgroup is greater than *LL* minus 30 (see AASHTO Plasticity Chart below).

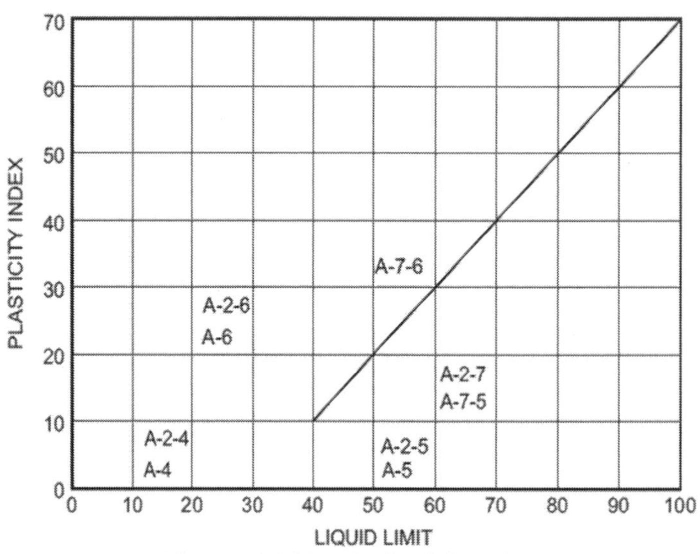

Figure. AASHTO Plasticity Chart

Group Index: To evaluate the quality of a soil as a highway subgrade material, a number called the *group index* (*GI*) is also incorporated along with the groups and subgroups of the soil. The group index is written in parenthesis after the group or subgroup designation. The group index is given by the following equation:

$$GI = (F - 35)\,[0.2 + 0.005\,(LL - 40)] + 0.01\,(F - 15)\,(PI - 10)$$

where:

GI = group index
F = percent passing the No. 200 sieve (0.075 mm)
LL = liquid limit (%)
PI = plasticity index (%)

The group index is rounded off to the nearest whole number and appended in parentheses. If the computed group index is either zero or negative, the number zero is used as the group index.

Example 7.5
The results of the particle-size analysis of a soil are as follows:

- Percent passing the No. 10 sieve = 100
- Percent passing the No. 40 sieve = 80
- Percent passing the No. 200 sieve = 58
- The liquid limit and plasticity index of the minus No. 40 fraction of the soil are 30 and 10, respectively.

Classify the soil by the AASHTO system.

Solution:

Using Table, since 58% of the soil is passing through the No. 200 sieve, it falls under silt-clay classifications, that is, it falls under group A-4, A-5, A-6, or A-7. Proceeding from left to right, it falls under group A-4.
$GI = (F - 35)[0.2 + 0.005(LL - 40)] + 0.01(F - 15)(PI - 10)$
$= (58 - 35)[0.2 + 0.005(30 - 40)] + (0.01)(58 - 15)(10 - 10)$
The soil will be classified as A-4(3).

Example 7.6
Ninety-five percent of a soil passes through the No. 200 sieve and has a liquid limit of 60 and plasticity index of 40. Classify the soil by the AASHTO system.

Solution:

According to Table, this soil falls under group A-7.
PI = 40 and LL = 60
Plasticity Index of A-7-5 subgroup is equal to less than *LL* minus 30. Plasticity Index of A-7-6 subgroup is greater than *LL* minus 30.
As, 40 > 60 – 30, this is an A-7-6 soil.

$GI = (F - 35)[0.2 + 0.005(LL - 40)] + 0.01(F - 15)(PI - 10)$
$= (95 - 35)[0.2 + 0.005(60 - 40)] + (0.01)(95 - 15)(40 - 10)$
$= 42$
For A-7-6 soil, GI is the maximum of 20. See the note (*) in the AASHTO Soil Classification System chart.

The classification is A-7-6(20).

7.1.3 Boring Log Interpretation

The exam may ask you some basics on soil identification based on boring log test. One example is given here.

Question 7.7

Figure below shows a standard penetration testing result on a 20-m deep soil. Three soil types are listed. Drag the soil type and place at the appropriate soil layer.

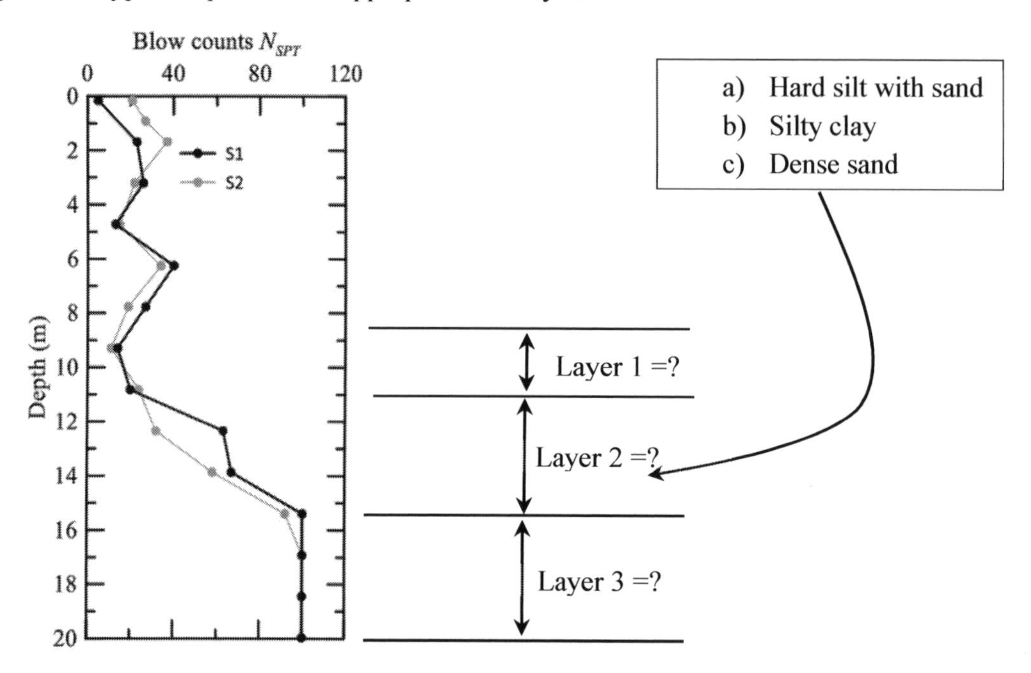

Solution: Clay soil requires less blow count being very soft – Layer 1 is silty clay.
Dense sand should be in between hard silt and clay – Layer 2 is dense sand.
Hard silt with sand requires high blow count being very stiff – Layer 3 is silty clay.

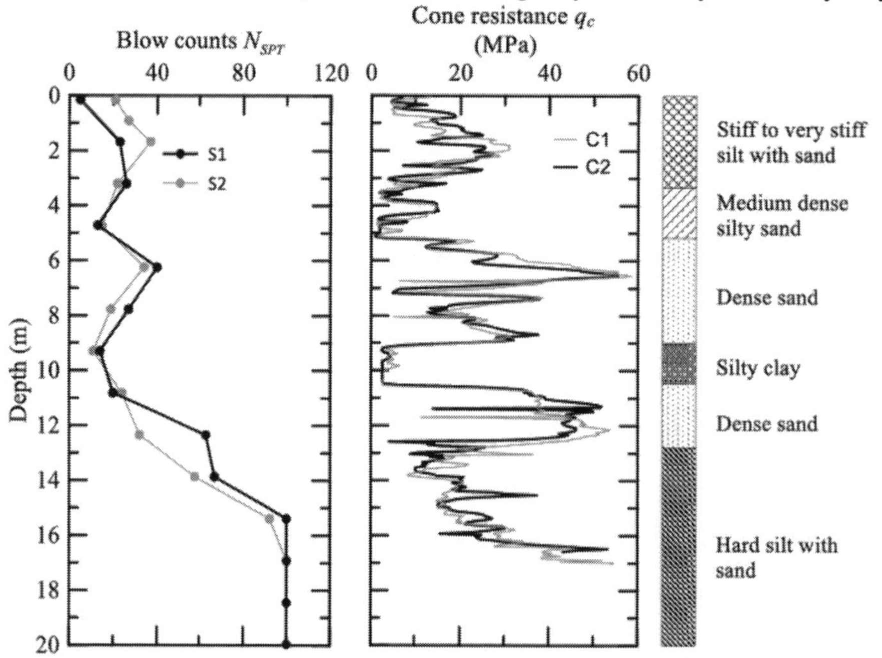

7.2 Soil Properties

7.2.1 Strength

This section is primarily based on the Article 3.3 Effective and Total Stresses of the PE Civil Handbook. Shear strength of soil refers to its ability to resist shear stresses. Shear stresses exist in a sloping hillside or result from filled land, weight of footings, and so on. If a given soil does not have sufficient shear strength to resist such shear stresses, failures in the forms of landslides and footing failures occur.

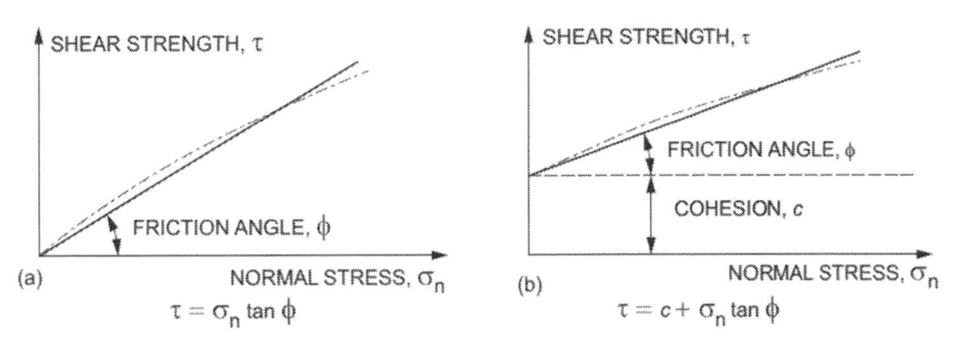

Figure. Shear Strength of (a) Cohesionless Soils and (b) Cohesive Soils

τ = shear strength
c = total cohesion
σ_n = normal stress
ϕ = friction angle

Shear Strength Effective Stress, $\tau' = c' + (\sigma_n - u)\tan\phi' = c' + \sigma_n' \tan\phi'$

τ' = effective shear strength
u = pore water pressure
c' = effective cohesion
σ'_n = effective normal stress
ϕ' = friction angle

During the exam, you may not need to draw in graph paper similar to below examples. However, understanding the solution may help you answer some questions.

Example 7.8
A sample of dry, cohesionless soil was subjected to a triaxial compression test that was carried out until the specimen failed at a deviator stress of 105.4 kN/m^2. A confining pressure of 48.0 kN/m^2 was used for the test. This soil's angle of internal friction is most nearly:

Solution:

Given data are plotted on a shear diagram (see Figure below). Point A is located along the abscissa at 48.0 kN/m^2 (the confining pressure, σ_3) and point B at 48.0 kN/m^2 + 105.4 kN/m^2 or 153.4 kN/m^2 (confining pressure plus deviator stress at failure, $\sigma_3+\Delta p$). The Mohr's circle is drawn with a center along the abscissa at 100.7 kN/m^2 [i.e., 48.0 kN/m^2 + ½ of 105.4 kN/m^2] and a radius of 52.7 kN/m^2. Because cohesion is virtually zero for dry, cohesionless soil, a line is drawn through the origin and tangent to the Mohr's circle. The angle between this line and the horizontal is measured to be 32°. Therefore, the soil's angle of internal friction (ϕ) is 32°.

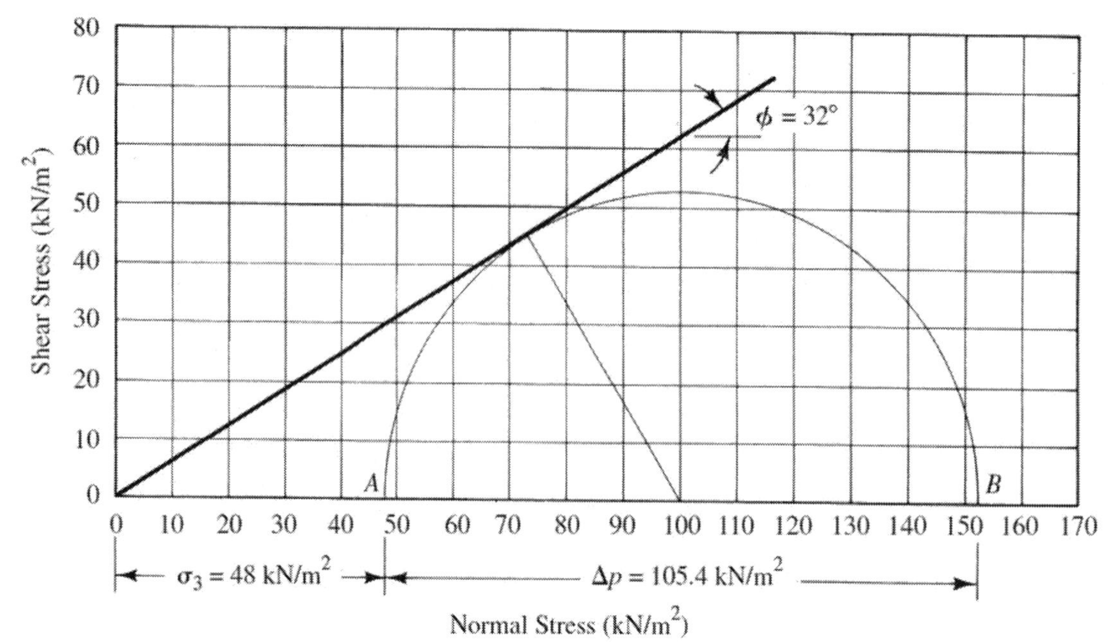

Reference: Liu and Evett, *Soils and Foundations*, Pearson.

Example 7.9
Drained shear box tests were carried out on a series of soil samples with the following results:

Test No	Total normal stress (kPa)	Total shear stress at failure (kPa)
1	100	98
2	200	139
3	300	180
4	400	222

Determine the effective cohesion and angle of shearing resistance.

Solution:

In this case, both the normal and the shear stresses at failure are known, so there is no need to draw stress circles and the four failure points may simply be plotted. These points must lie on the strength envelope and the best straight line through the points will establish it.

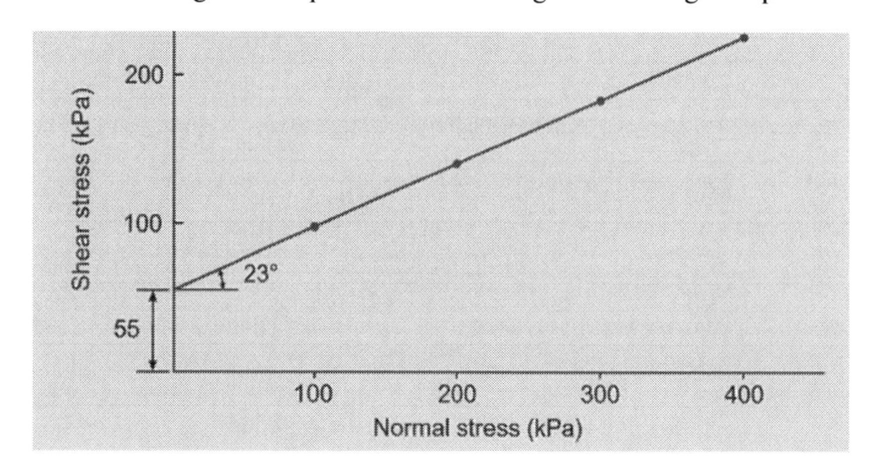

From the plot, c'=55 kPa; $\phi' = 23°$

Example 7.10
A granular soil is tested in direct shear under a normal stress of 350 kPa. The size of the specimen is 7.62 cm in diameter. If the soil to be tested is a dense sand with an angle of internal friction of 38°, determine the size (kPa) of the force transducer required to measure the shear force with a factor of safety of 2.

Solution:

The capacity of the transducer should be twice that required to shear the sand.

Shear stress, $\tau' = c' + \sigma_n' \tan\phi' = 0 + (350\text{ kPa})\tan 38 = 273.4\,\text{kPa}$

Transducer required = Shear Stress x Factor of Safety = 273.4 kPa x 2.0 = 546.9 kPa

7.2.2 Permeability

Permeability refers to the movement of water within soil. Actual water movement is through the voids, which might be thought of as small, interconnected, irregular conduits. Because the water moves through the voids, it follows that soils with large voids (such as sands) are generally more permeable than those with smaller voids (such as clays). Additionally, because soils with large voids generally have large void ratios, it may be generalized that permeability tends to increase as the void ratio increases. From Article 3.8 Material Test Methods of PE Civil Handbook: schematic of a constant head permeameter is shown below. It utilizes a device known as a *constant-head permeameter*, as depicted in Figure below. The general test procedure is to allow water to move through the soil specimen under a stable-head condition while the engineer determines and records the time required for a certain quantity of water to pass through the soil specimen. By measuring and recording the quantity (volume) of water discharged during a test (Q), length of the specimen (distance between manometer outlets) (L), cross-sectional area of the specimen (A), time required for the quantity of water Q to be discharged (t), and head (difference in manometer levels) (h), the engineer can derive the coefficient of permeability (k) as follows:

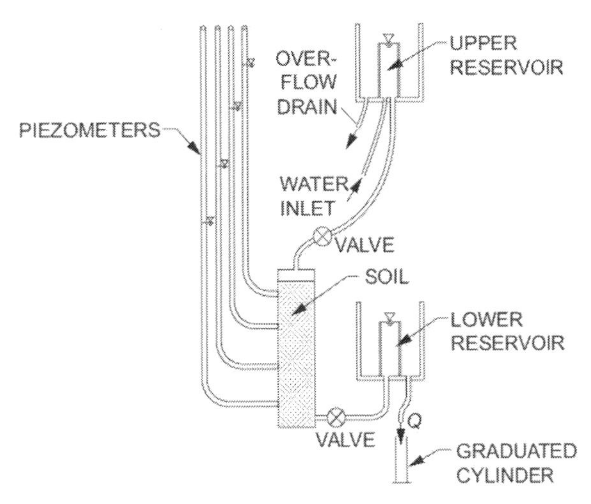

Coefficient of permeability $k = \dfrac{QL}{tAh}$

Q = volume of flow
L = length of sample
t = time of flow
A = cross-sectional area of sample
h = constant hydraulic head

Example 7.11

A constant-head permeability test gives these values:

- $L = 30$ cm
- A = area of the specimen = 177 cm^2
- Constant-head difference, $h = 50$ cm
- Water collected in a period of 5 min = 350 cm^3

Calculate the hydraulic conductivity in cm/sec.

Solution:

Given $Q = 350$ cm^3, $L = 30$ cm, $A = 177$ cm^2, $h = 50$ cm, and $t = 5$ min

$$k = \frac{QL}{tAh} = \frac{\left(350\text{cm}^3\right)\left(30\text{cm}\right)}{\left(5\times 60\text{sec}\right)\left(177\text{cm}^2\right)\left(50\text{cm}\right)} = 3.95\times 10^3 \frac{\text{cm}}{\text{sec}}$$

Example 7.12

In a constant head permeameter test the following results were obtained:

- Duration of test = 4.0 min
- Quantity of water collected = 300 ml
- Head difference in manometer = 50 mm
- Distance between manometer toppings = 100 mm
- Diameter of test sample = 100 mm

Determine the coefficient of permeability in m/s.

Solution:

Given, $Q = 300$ ml = 300,000 mm^3, $L = 100$ mm, $h = 50$ mm

Cross-sectional area of the sample, $A = \dfrac{\pi\left(100\text{mm}\right)^2}{4} = 7{,}854\,\text{mm}^2$

$$k = \frac{QL}{tAh} = \frac{\left(300{,}000\,\text{mm}^3\right)\left(100\text{mm}\right)}{\left(4\times 60\text{sec}\right)\left(7{,}854\,\text{mm}^2\right)\left(50\text{mm}\right)} = 0.32\frac{\text{mm}}{\text{sec}} = 3.2\times 10^{-4}\frac{\text{m}}{\text{sec}}$$

Schematic of a Falling Head Permeameter (Coduto, 1999) is shown below.

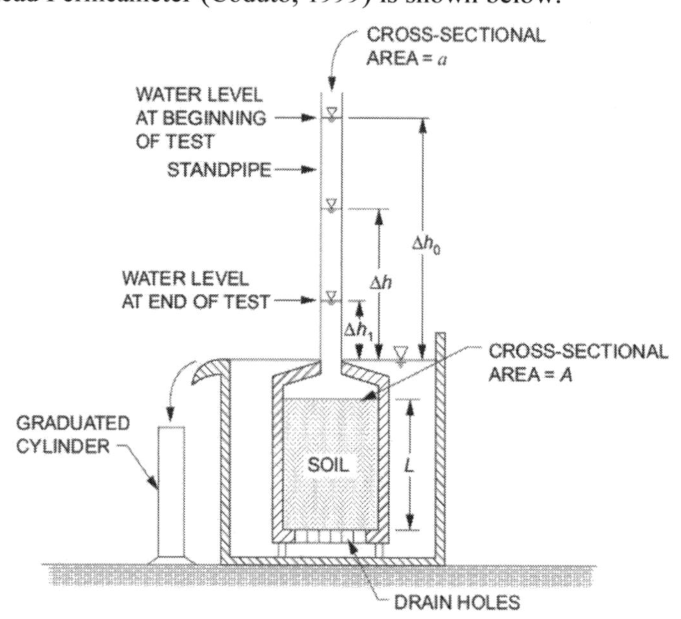

The specimen is first saturated with water. Water is then allowed to move through the soil specimen under a falling-head condition (rather than a stable-head condition) while the time required for a certain quantity of water to pass through the soil specimen is determined and recorded. If a is the cross-sectional area of the burette, and h_1 and h_2 are the hydraulic heads at the beginning and end of the test, respectively (Figure below), the coefficient of permeability can be derived as follows.

$$\text{Coefficient of permeability } k = \frac{aL}{A(t_1 - t_2)} \ln\left(\frac{h_1}{h_2}\right)$$

a = cross-sectional area of standpipe
L = length of sample
A = cross-sectional area of sample
t_1 = time at start of flow
t_2 = time at end of flow
h_1 = hydraulic head at t_1
h_2 = hydraulic head at t_2

Example 7.13
For a falling-head permeability test, the following values are given:

- Length of specimen = 8 in.
- Area of soil specimen = 1.6 in.^{2}
- Area of standpipe = 0.06 in.^{2}
- Head difference at time t_o = 20 in.
- Head difference at time $t_{180\ \text{sec}}$ = 12 in.

Determine the hydraulic conductivity of the soil in in./sec.

Solution:

Given $a = 0.06$ in.^{2}, $L = 8$ in., $A = 1.6$ in.^{2}, $t = 180$ sec, $h_1 = 20$ in., and $h_2 = 12$ in.

$$k = \frac{aL}{A(t_1 - t_2)} \ln\left(\frac{h_1}{h_2}\right) = \frac{(0.06\text{ in.}^2)(8.0\text{ in.})}{(1.6\text{ in.}^2)(180\text{sec})} \ln\left(\frac{20\text{in.}}{12\text{in.}}\right) = \underline{8.52 \times 10^{-4}\ \frac{\text{in.}}{\text{sec}}}$$

Example 7.14
An undisturbed soil sample was tested in a falling head permeameter. The results were:

- Initial head of water in stand pipe = 1,500 mm
- Final head of water in stand pipe = 605 mm
- Duration of test = 281 sec
- Sample length = 150 mm
- Sample diameter = 100 mm
- Stand-pipe diameter = 5 mm

Determine the permeability of the soil in mm/s.

Solution:

$$\text{Cross-sectional area of the stand-pipe, } a = \frac{\pi(5.0\text{mm})^2}{4} = 19.67\,\text{mm}^2$$

$$\text{Cross-sectional area of the sample, } A = \frac{\pi(100\text{mm})^2}{4} = 7{,}854\,\text{mm}^2$$

$$k=\frac{aL}{A(t_1-t_2)}\ln\left(\frac{h_1}{h_2}\right)=\frac{(19.67\ \text{mm}^2)(150\ \text{mm})}{(7854\ \text{mm}^2)(281\,\text{sec})}\ln\left(\frac{1{,}500\,\text{mm}}{605\,\text{mm}}\right)=1.2\times10^{-3}\ \frac{\text{mm}}{\text{sec}}$$

From Article 3.8 Material Test Methods of PE Civil Handbook: Hazen's Equation for Permeability, $k=C(D_{10})^2$

where

k = permeability (cm/s)
C = coefficient from 0.4 to 1.2 depending on sand size
D_{10} = effective grain size, in mm, passing at 10% by weight

Example 7.15

The sieve analysis curve of a soil is given below. The minimum permeability (cm/s) of the soil is most nearly:

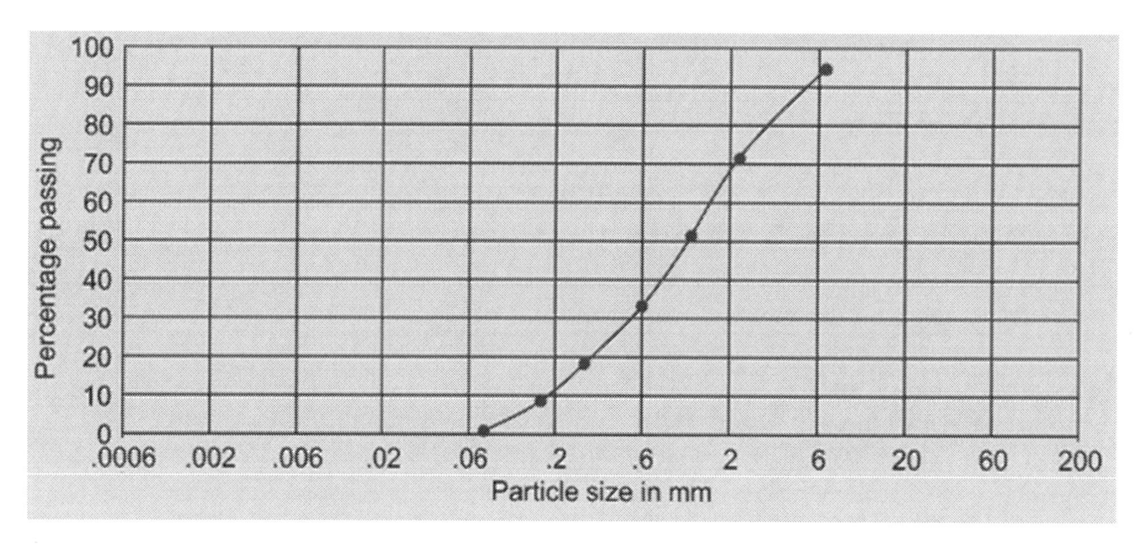

Solution:

From the curve, 10% passing by weight, $D_{10} \approx 0.17$ mm
C = 0.4 (the minimum value)

Minimum permeability, $k=C(D_{10})^2=0.4\times(0.17\,\text{mm})^2=0.01156\frac{\text{cm}}{\text{sec}}$

7.2.3 Compressibility

This topic has been covered in Chapter 3.

7.2.4 Phase Relationships

From Article 3.8 Material Test Methods of PE Civil Handbook, Weight-Volume Relationships, a number of important relationships exist among the components of soil in terms of both weight/mass and volume. For example, void ratio (e) is the ratio (expressed as a decimal fraction) of volume of voids to volume of solids. Porosity (n) is the ratio (expressed as a percentage) of volume of voids to total volume. Degree of saturation (S) is the ratio (expressed as a percentage) of volume of water to volume of voids. Water content

(w) is the ratio (expressed as a percentage) of weight of water to weight of solids or the ratio of mass of water to mass of solids. Unit weight (γ) is total weight (weight of solid plus weight of water) divided by total volume (volume of solid plus volume of water plus volume of air). Dry unit weight (γ_d) is weight of solids divided by total volume. Unit mass (ρ) is total mass divided by total volume. Dry unit density (γ_d) is mass of solids divided by total volume. Specific gravity of solids (G_s) is the ratio of unit weight of solids (weight of solids divided by volume of solids) to unit weight of water or of unit mass of solids (mass of solids divided by volume of solids) to unit mass of water.

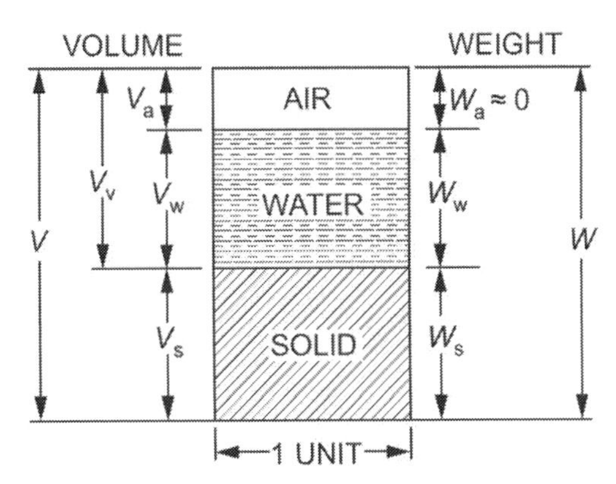

Figure. A Unit of Soil Mass and its Idealization

Based on the phase diagram, many equations can be derived. A list of from the PE Civil Handbook is given below. Please make sure you are familiar with all the symbols.

Table. Weight-Volume Relationships

Unit-Weight Relationship	Dry Unit Weight (No Water)	Saturated Unit Weight (No Air)
$\gamma_t = \dfrac{(1+w)G_s\gamma_w}{1+e}$	$\gamma_d = \dfrac{\gamma_t}{1+w}$	$\gamma_{sat} = \dfrac{(G_s+e)\gamma_w}{1+e}$
$\gamma_t = \dfrac{(G_s+Se)\gamma_w}{1+e}$	$\gamma_d = \dfrac{G_s\gamma_w}{1+e}$	$\gamma_{sat} = [(1-n)G_s+n]\gamma_w$
$\gamma_t = \dfrac{(1+w)G_s\gamma_w}{1+\dfrac{wG_s}{S}}$	$\gamma_d = G_s\gamma_w(1-n)$	$\gamma_{sat} = \left(\dfrac{1+w}{1+wG_s}\right)G_s\gamma_w$
$\gamma_t = G_s\gamma_w(1-n)(1+w)$	$\gamma_d = \dfrac{G_s\gamma_w}{1+\dfrac{wG_s}{S}}$	$\gamma_{sat} = \left(\dfrac{e}{w}\right)\left(\dfrac{1+w}{1+e}\right)\gamma_w$
	$\gamma_d = \dfrac{eS\gamma_w}{(1+e)w}$	$\gamma_{sat} = \gamma_d + n\gamma_w$
	$\gamma_d = \gamma_{sat} - n\gamma_w$	$\gamma_{sat} = \gamma_d + \left(\dfrac{e}{1+e}\right)\gamma_w$
	$\gamma_d = \gamma_{sat} - \left(\dfrac{e}{1+e}\right)\gamma_w$	

where

γ_t = total unit weight (or, wet unit weight)
γ_d = dry unit weight
γ_{sat} = saturated unit weight
γ_w = unit weight of water
G_s = specific gravity
e = void ratio
n = porosity
S = saturation (ratio)
w = water content (ratio)

Table. Volume and Weight Relationships

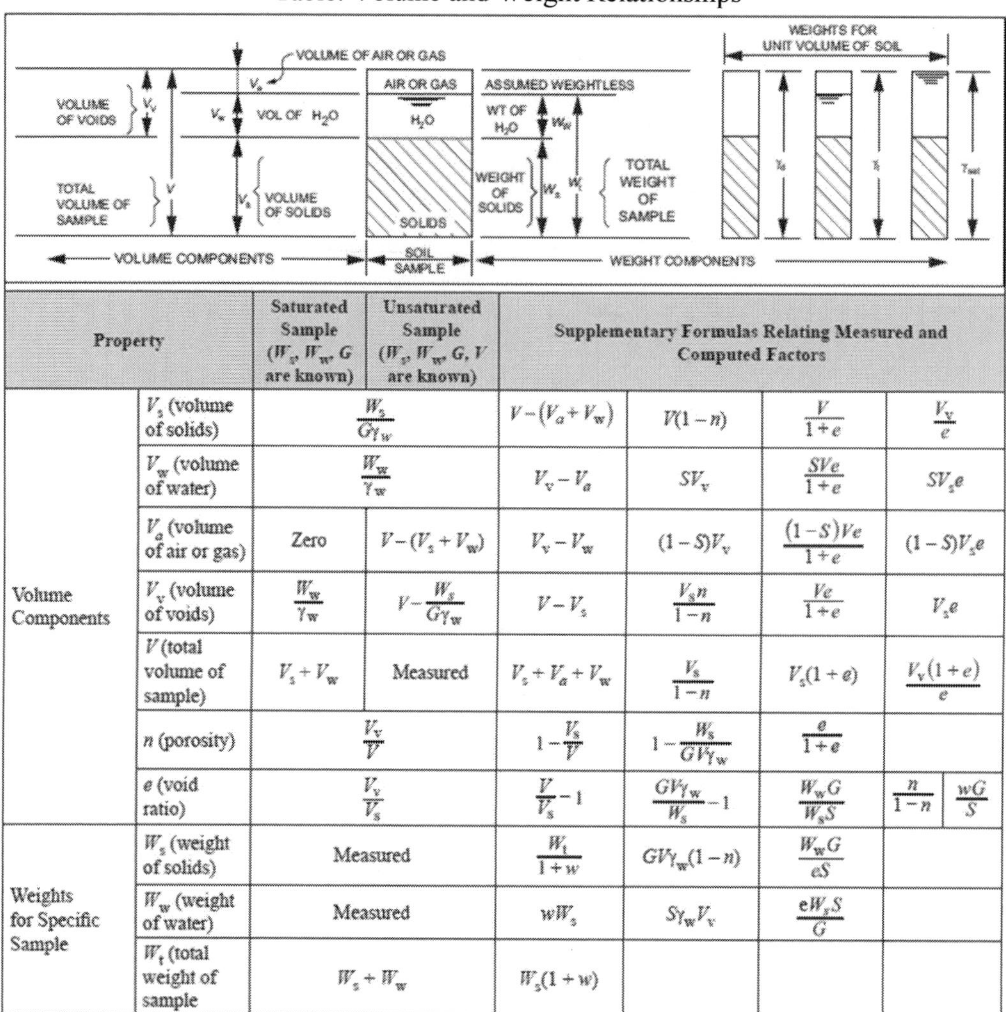

Property		Saturated Sample (W_s, W_w, G are known)	Unsaturated Sample (W_s, W_w, G, V are known)	Supplementary Formulas Relating Measured and Computed Factors			
Volume Components	V_s (volume of solids)	$\frac{W_s}{G\gamma_w}$		$V-(V_a+V_w)$	$V(1-n)$	$\frac{V}{1+e}$	$\frac{V_v}{e}$
	V_w (volume of water)	$\frac{W_w}{\gamma_w}$		V_v-V_a	SV_v	$\frac{SVe}{1+e}$	SV_se
	V_a (volume of air or gas)	Zero	$V-(V_s+V_w)$	V_v-V_w	$(1-S)V_v$	$\frac{(1-S)Ve}{1+e}$	$(1-S)V_se$
	V_v (volume of voids)	$\frac{W_w}{\gamma_w}$	$V-\frac{W_s}{G\gamma_w}$	$V-V_s$	$\frac{V_sn}{1-n}$	$\frac{Ve}{1+e}$	V_se
	V (total volume of sample)	V_s+V_w	Measured	$V_s+V_a+V_w$	$\frac{V_s}{1-n}$	$V_s(1+e)$	$\frac{V_v(1+e)}{e}$
	n (porosity)	$\frac{V_v}{V}$		$1-\frac{V_s}{V}$	$1-\frac{W_s}{GV\gamma_w}$	$\frac{e}{1+e}$	
	e (void ratio)	$\frac{V_v}{V_s}$		$\frac{V}{V_s}-1$	$\frac{GV\gamma_w}{W_s}-1$	$\frac{W_wG}{W_sS}$	$\frac{n}{1-n}$; $\frac{wG}{S}$
Weights for Specific Sample	W_s (weight of solids)	Measured		$\frac{W_t}{1+w}$	$GV\gamma_w(1-n)$	$\frac{W_wG}{eS}$	
	W_w (weight of water)	Measured		wW_s	$S\gamma_wV_v$	$\frac{eW_sS}{G}$	
	W_t (total weight of sample	W_s+W_w		$W_s(1+w)$			

Property		Saturated Sample (W_s, W_w, G are known)	Unsaturated Sample (W_s, W_w, G, V are known)	Supplementary Formulas Relating Measured and Computed Factors			
Weights for Sample of Unit Volume	γ_d (dry unit weight	$\frac{W_s}{V_s+V_w}$	$\frac{W_s}{V}$	$\frac{W_t}{V(1+w)}$	$\frac{G\gamma_w}{1+e}$	$\frac{G\gamma_w}{1+\frac{wG}{S}}$	
	γ_t (wet unit weight)	$\frac{W_s+W_w}{V_s+V_w}$	$\frac{W_s+W_w}{V}$	$\frac{W_t}{V}$	$\frac{(G+Se)\gamma_w}{1+e}$	$\frac{(1+w)\gamma_w}{\frac{w}{S}+\frac{1}{G}}$	
	γ_{sat} (saturated unit weight)	$\frac{W_s+W_w}{V_s+V_w}$	$\frac{W_s+V_v\gamma_w}{V}$	$\frac{W_s}{V}+\left(\frac{e}{1+e}\right)\gamma_w$	$\frac{(G+e)\gamma_w}{1+e}$	$\frac{(1+w)\gamma_w}{w+\frac{1}{G}}$	
	γ_{sub} [submerged (buoyant) unit weight]	$\gamma_{sat}-\gamma_w$		$\frac{W_s}{V}-\left(\frac{1}{1+e}\right)\gamma_w$	$\left(\frac{G+e}{1+e}-1\right)\gamma_w$	$\left(\frac{1-\frac{1}{G}}{w+\frac{1}{G}}\right)\gamma_w$	
Combined Relations	w (moisture content)	$\frac{W_w}{W_s}$		$\frac{W_t}{W_s}-1$	$\frac{Se}{G}$	$S\left(\frac{\gamma_w}{\gamma_d}-\frac{1}{G}\right)$	
	S (degree of saturation)	1.00	$\frac{V_w}{V_v}$	$\frac{W_w}{V_v\gamma_w}$	$\frac{wG}{e}$	$\frac{w}{\left(\frac{\gamma_w}{\gamma_d}-\frac{1}{G}\right)}$	
	G (specific gravity)	$\frac{W_s}{V_s\gamma_w}$		$\frac{Se}{w}$			

Example 7.16
For a moist soil sample, the following are given.

- Total volume: $V = 1.2\ \text{m}^3$
- Total mass: $M = 2{,}350$ kg
- Moisture content: $w = 8.6\%$
- Specific gravity of soil solids: $G_s = 2.71$

Determine the following.

a. Moist density
b. Dry density
c. Void ratio
d. Porosity
e. Degree of saturation

Solution:

a. Moist density, $\rho = \dfrac{M}{V} = \dfrac{2{,}350\,\text{kg}}{1.2\,\text{m}^3} = \underline{1{,}958.3\dfrac{\text{kg}}{\text{m}^3}}$

b. Dry density $\rho_d = \left(\dfrac{M_t}{V}\right)\dfrac{1}{1+w} = \dfrac{\rho_t}{1+w} = \left(\dfrac{1{,}958.3}{1+0.086}\right)\dfrac{\text{kg}}{\text{m}^3} = \underline{1{,}803.3\dfrac{\text{kg}}{\text{m}^3}}$

c. $\gamma_d = \dfrac{G\gamma_w}{1+e}$

$$\rho_d = \frac{G\rho_w}{1+e}$$

$$e = \frac{G\rho_w}{\rho_d} - 1 = \frac{2.71\left(1{,}000\dfrac{\text{kg}}{\text{m}^3}\right)}{1803.3\dfrac{\text{kg}}{\text{m}^3}} - 1 = \underline{0.503}$$

d. porosity, $n = \dfrac{e}{1+e} = \dfrac{0.503}{1+0.503} = \underline{0.335}$

e. Degree of saturation $S = \dfrac{wG}{e} = \dfrac{0.086(2.71)}{0.503} = 0.463 = \underline{46.3\%}$

7.3 Concrete

7.3.1 Non-reinforced Concrete

Concrete is a composite material composed of aggregate bonded together with a fluid cement which hardens over time. Most use of the term "concrete" refers to Portland cement concrete. In Portland cement, when the aggregate is mixed together with the dry cement and water, they form a fluid mass that is easily molded into shape. The cement reacts chemically with the water and other ingredients to form a hard matrix which binds all the materials together into a durable stone-like material that has many uses. Often, additives are included in the mixture to improve the physical properties of the wet mix or the finished material. Most concrete is poured with reinforcing materials (such as rebar) embedded to provide tensile strength, yielding reinforced concrete.

Cement
Portland cement is the most common type of cement in general usage. English masonry worker Joseph Aspdin patented Portland cement in 1824. It was named because of the similarity of its color to Portland limestone, quarried from the English Isle of Portland. It consists of a mixture of oxides of calcium, silicon, and aluminum. Portland cement and similar materials are made by heating limestone (a source of calcium) with clay and grinding this product with a source of sulfate (most commonly gypsum).

Water
Combining water with a cementitious material forms a cement paste by the process of hydration. The cement paste glues the aggregate together, fills voids within it, and makes it flow more freely. A lower water-to-cement ratio yields a stronger, more durable concrete, whereas more water gives a freer-flowing concrete with a higher slump. Hydration involves many different reactions, often occurring at the same time. As the reactions proceed, the products of the cement hydration process gradually bond together the individual sand and gravel particles and other components of the concrete to form a solid mass.

Aggregates
Fine and coarse aggregates make up the bulk of a concrete mixture. Sand, natural gravel, and crushed stone are used mainly for this purpose. Recycled aggregates (from construction, demolition, and excavation waste) are increasingly used as partial replacements of natural aggregates, while a number of manufactured aggregates, including air-cooled blast furnace slag and bottom ash are also permitted.

Reinforcement
Concrete is strong in compression, as the aggregate efficiently carries the compression load. However, it is weak in tension as the cement holding the aggregate in place can crack, allowing the structure to fail. Reinforced concrete adds either steel reinforcing bars, steel fibers, glass fibers, or plastic fibers to carry tensile loads.

Chemical Admixtures
Chemical admixtures are materials in the form of powder or fluids that are added to the concrete to give it certain characteristics not obtainable with plain mixes. In normal use, admixture dosages are less than 5% by mass of cement and are added to the concrete at the time of batching/mixing. Common types of admixtures:

- Accelerators speed up the hydration (hardening). Accelerating admixtures are especially useful for modifying the properties of concrete in cold weather.
- Retarders slow the hydration and are used in large or difficult pours where partial setting before the pour is complete is undesirable.
- Air entraining agents add and entrain tiny air bubbles which reduces damage during freeze-thaw cycles, increasing durability.
- Plasticizers increase the workability of plastic or “fresh” concrete, allowing it be placed more easily, with less consolidating effort.
- Pigments can be used to change the color for aesthetics.
- Corrosion inhibitors are used to minimize the corrosion of steel and steel bars in concrete.
- Bonding agents are used to create a bond between old and new concrete (typically a type of polymer) with wide temperature tolerance and corrosion resistance.
- Pumping aids improve pumpability, thicken the paste, and reduce separation and bleeding.

7.3.2 Reinforced Concrete

Article 4.3 Concrete Design of the PE Civil Handbook discusses this topic.

Table. ASTM Standard Reinforcing Bars

Bar Size	Diameter (in.)	Area (in.²)	Weight (lb/ft)
#3	0.375	0.11	0.376
#4	0.500	0.20	0.668
#5	0.625	0.31	1.043
#6	0.750	0.44	1.502
#7	0.875	0.60	2.044
#8	1.000	0.79	2.670
#9	1.128	1.00	3.400
#10	1.270	1.27	4.303
#11	1.410	1.56	5.313
#14	1.693	2.25	7.650
#18	2.257	4.00	13.60

Definitions

a = depth of equivalent rectangular stress block, in.

A_g = gross area of column, in.^{2}

A_s = area of reinforcement, in.^{2}

A_{st} = total area of longitudinal reinforcement, in.^{2}

A_v = area of shear reinforcement within a distance s, in.

b = width of compression face to member, in.

β_1 = ratio of depth rectangular stress block, a, to depth to neutral axis, c

$$= 0.85 \geq 0.85 - 0.05\left(\frac{f_c' - 4,000}{1,000}\right) \geq 0.65$$

c = distance from extreme compression fiber to neutral axis, in.

d = distance from extreme compression fiber to centroid of tension reinforcement

d_t = distance from extreme compression fiber to extreme tension steel, in.

E_c = modulus of elasticity $= 33 w_c^{1.5}\sqrt{f_c'}$ [w_c is in pcf and f_c' is in psi and E_c is in psi]

ε_t = net tensile strain in extreme tension steel at nominal strength.

f_c' = compressive strength of concrete, psi

f_y = yield strength of steel reinforcement, psi

M_n = nominal moment strength, in.lb

ϕM_n = design moment strength, in.lb

M_u = factored moment, in.lb

P_n = nominal axial load strength at given eccentricity, lb

ϕP_n = design axial load strength at given eccentricity, lb

P_u = factored axial force, lb

ρ_g = ratio of total reinforcement area to cross–sectional area of column $= \dfrac{A_{st}}{A_g}$

s = spacing of shear ties measured along longitudinal axis of member, in.

V_c = nominal shear strength provided by concrete, lb

V_n = nominal shear strength, lb
ϕV_n = design shear strength, lb
V_s = nominal shear strength provided by reinforcement, lb
V_u =factored shear force, lb

f_C' (psi)	β_1	
$2{,}500 \leq f_C' \leq 4{,}000$	0.85	(a)
$4{,}000 < f_C' < 8{,}000$	$0.85 - 0.05\left(\dfrac{f_C' - 4{,}000}{1{,}000}\right)$	(b)
$f_C' \geq 8{,}000$	0.65	(c)

The stress–strain diagrams due to applied moment in a doubly reinforced beam section is shown below. The section has both tensile and compressive reinforcements. Reinforced concrete section is assumed cracked in tension zone. So, the stress in concrete in tension zone is assumed zero. The compressive stress in concrete is assumed rectangular with uniform stress of $0.85 f_c'$. Note that, the stress distribution in concrete is not linear or uniform. The depth of the stress block is a, and the depth of the neutral axis is c. However, the strain distribution is linear as shown below.

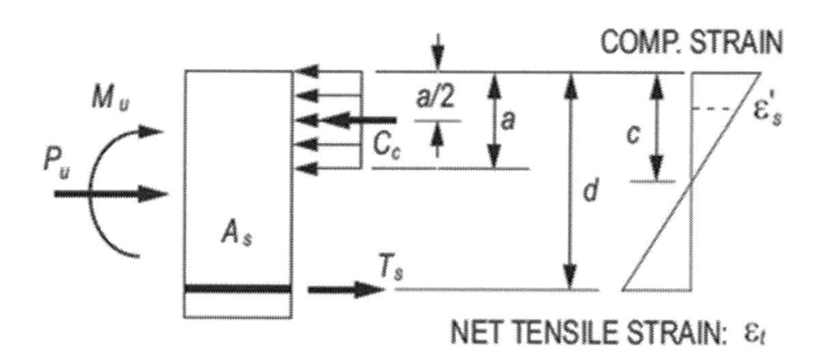

For a singly reinforced beam, equating the tensile force in tensile steel and the compressive force in concrete, the depth of the rectangular stress block can be determined as:

$$a = \frac{A_s f_y}{0.85 f_c' b}$$

Then, the nominal moment can be calculated as: $M_n = 0.85 f_C' ab\left(d - \frac{a}{2}\right) = A_s f_y\left(d - \frac{a}{2}\right)$

Steel ratio, $\rho = \dfrac{A}{bd}$

$$m = \frac{f_y}{0.85 f_c'}$$

$$R_n = \frac{M_u}{\phi b d^2}$$

$$\rho = \left(\frac{1}{m}\right)\left[1 - \sqrt{\left(1 - \frac{2mR_n}{f_y}\right)}\right]$$

Example 7.17

The elastic modulus (ksi) of a concrete with $f_c' = 4$ ksi and a unit weight = 150 pcf is most nearly:

Solution:

$$E_c = 33w_c^{1.5}\sqrt{f_c'} = 33(150\,\text{pcf})^{1.5}\sqrt{4{,}000\,\text{psi}} = 3{,}834{,}253 \text{ psi} = \underline{3{,}834 \text{ ksi}}$$

(Be careful about the units – units are not consistent in this equation)

Example 7.18

The nominal moment capacity, M_n of the following reinforced concrete beam section is most nearly: [$f_c' = 4$ ksi and $f_y = 60$ ksi]

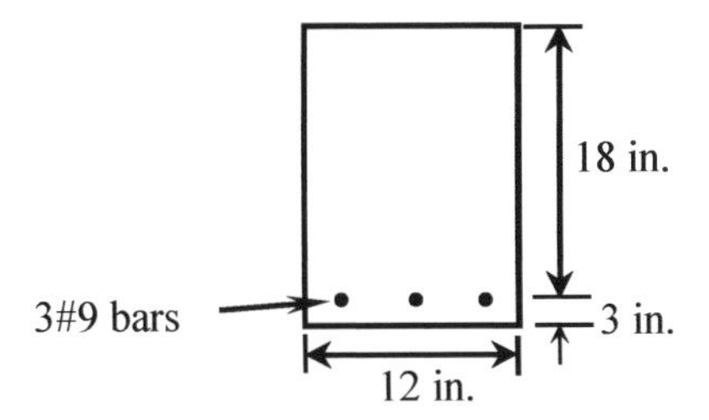

Solution:

$$A_s = (3)(1.0) = 3 \text{ in.}^2$$

$$a = \frac{A_s f_y}{0.85 f_c' b} = \frac{3 \text{ in.}^2 (60{,}000\,\text{psi})}{0.85(4{,}000\,\text{psi})(12 \text{ in.})} = 4.41 \text{ in.}$$

$$M_n = A_s f_y\left(d - \frac{a}{2}\right) = (3 \text{ in.}^2)(60\,\text{ksi})\left(18 \text{ in.} - \frac{4.41 \text{ in.}}{2}\right) = 2{,}843 \text{ kip.in.} = \underline{237 \text{ kip.ft}}$$

Example 7.19

A 22-ft simple span rectangular beam has the uniformly distributed factored load of 4.873 kip/ft. Assume the following:

- $\phi = 0.90$
- $b = 14$ in.
- $h = 27$ in. ($d = 24.5$ in.)
- 4,000 psi concrete
- 60,000 psi steel

The required steel ratio is most nearly:

Solution:

$$M_u = \frac{w_u L^2}{8} = \frac{\left(4.873\frac{\text{kip}}{\text{ft}}\right)(22\,\text{ft})^2}{8} = 294.8 \text{ kip.ft}$$

$$m = \frac{f_y}{0.85 f_c'} = \frac{60{,}000\,\text{psi}}{0.85(4{,}000\,\text{psi})} = 17.65$$

$$R_n = \frac{M_u}{\phi b d^2} = \frac{294.8 \times 1{,}000 \times 12\,\text{lb.in.}}{0.9(14\,\text{in.})(24.5\,\text{in.})^2} = 467.7$$

$$\rho = \left(\frac{1}{m}\right)\left[1-\sqrt{\left(1-\frac{2mR_n}{f_y}\right)}\right] = \left(\frac{1}{17.65}\right)\left[1-\sqrt{\left(1-\frac{2(17.65)(467.7)}{60,000}\right)}\right] = \underline{0.0084}$$

The flexural equations can be derived using the figure below for the stress of a singly-reinforced beam.

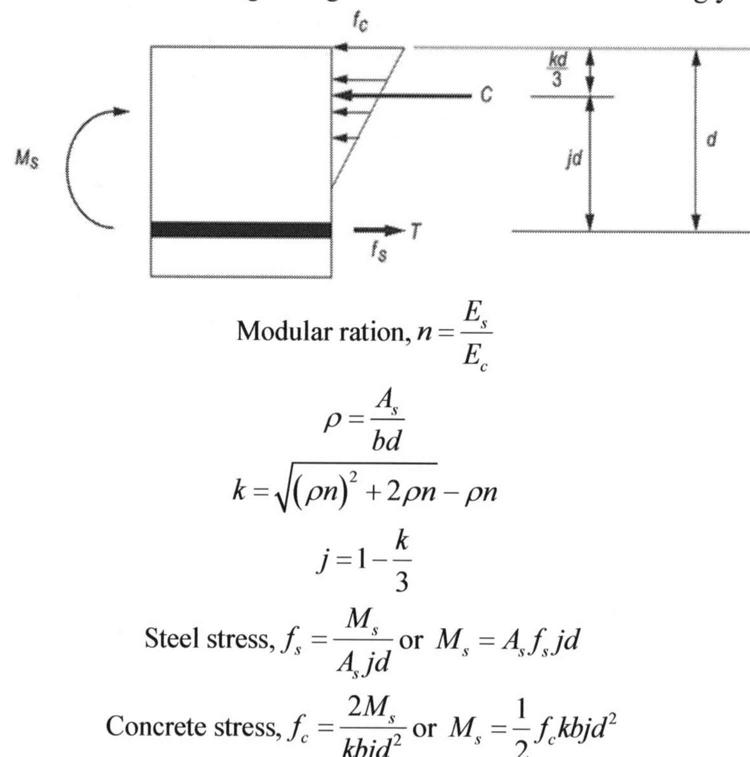

$$\text{Modular ration, } n = \frac{E_s}{E_c}$$

$$\rho = \frac{A_s}{bd}$$

$$k = \sqrt{(\rho n)^2 + 2\rho n} - \rho n$$

$$j = 1 - \frac{k}{3}$$

$$\text{Steel stress, } f_s = \frac{M_s}{A_s jd} \text{ or } M_s = A_s f_s jd$$

$$\text{Concrete stress, } f_c = \frac{2M_s}{kbjd^2} \text{ or } M_s = \frac{1}{2} f_c kbjd^2$$

Example 7.20

Compute the maximum resisting moment (kip.ft) for the given section below. The ultimate stress in concrete is 2,500 psi. Steel is of structural grade with a working stress of 18,000 psi. The ratio of modulus of steel and concrete is 10.

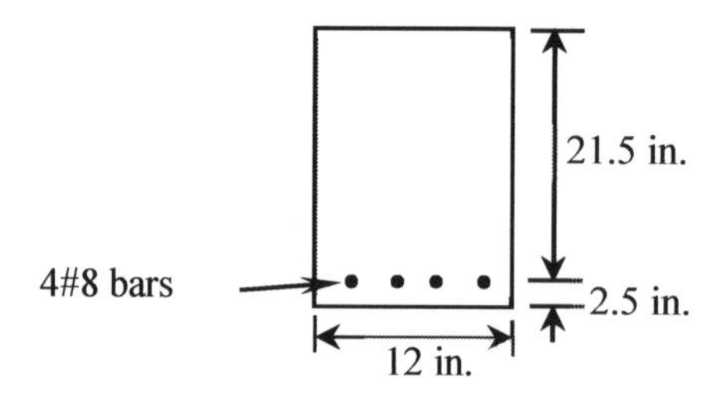

Solution:

Steel area, $A_s = 4 \text{ x } 0.79 \text{ in.}^2 = 3.16 \text{ in.}^2$

Effective depth, $d = 21.5$ in.

$$\text{Steel ratio, } \rho = \frac{A_s}{bd} = \frac{3.16 \text{ in.}^2}{(12 \text{ in.})(21.5 \text{in.})} = 0.0122$$

$$k = \sqrt{(\rho n)^2 + 2\rho n} - \rho n = \sqrt{(0.0122 \times 10)^2 + 2(0.0122)(10)} - (0.0122)(10) = 0.3868$$

$$j = 1 - \frac{k}{3} = 1 - \frac{0.3868}{3} = 0.871$$

Moment on the steel side, $M_s = A_s f_s jd = (3.16\text{in.}^2)(18\text{ksi})(0.871)(21.5\text{in.})$
$\approx 1{,}058\text{kip.in.}$

Moment on the concrete side,

$$M_s = \frac{1}{2} f_c kbjd^2 = \frac{1}{2}(2.500\text{ksi})(0.3868)(12\text{in.})(0.871)(21.5\text{in.})^2 \approx 1{,}054\text{kip.in.}$$

The lower value controls, i.e., M_s = 1,054 kip.in. = <u>87.8 kip.ft</u>

Example 7.21

A 6-in. thick concrete slab supported with effective depth of 5-in. spans between walls for 11 ft. #4 bars spaced at 5.5 in. on center are used for reinforcing the slab. The ratio of modulus of steel and concrete is 9. The working stresses in the concrete and steel are 1.350-ksi and 24-ksi respectively. Concrete weighs 150 pcf. Compute the uniform live load (lb/ft²) that the slab can carry.

#4 bars@5.5 in. o/c

5.0 in.

Solution:

Consider a 1-ft strip. Then, it became a beam of 12-in. width.
No of bars in a 1-ft strip = 12 in. / 5.5 in. = 2.182 bars/ft
Steel area, A_s = 2.182 x 0.20 in.² = 0.436 in.²
Effective depth, d = 5.0 in.

$$\text{Steel ratio, } \rho = \frac{A_s}{bd} = \frac{0.436\text{ in.}^2}{(12\text{ in.})(5.0\text{in.})} = 0.0073$$

$$k = \sqrt{(\rho n)^2 + 2\rho n} - \rho n = \sqrt{(0.0073 \times 9)^2 + 2(0.0073)(9)} - (0.0073)(9) = 0.434$$

$$j = 1 - \frac{k}{3} = 1 - \frac{0.434}{3} = 0.855$$

Moment on the steel side, $M_s = A_s f_s jd = (0.436\text{in.}^2)(24{,}000\text{psi})(0.855)(5.0\text{in.})$
$= 47{,}050\text{lb.in.}$

Moment on the concrete side, $M_s = \frac{1}{2} f_c kbjd^2$

$$= \frac{1}{2}(1{,}350\text{psi})(0.434)(12\text{in.})(0.855)(5.0\text{in.})^2 \approx 55{,}000\text{ lb.in.}$$

The lower value controls, i.e., M_s = 47,050 lb.in.

For a simply-supported beam/slab, $M = \frac{wL^2}{8}$

$$47{,}050\text{ lb.in.}\left(\frac{1}{12}\frac{\text{ft}}{\text{in.}}\right) = \frac{w(11\text{ft})^2}{8}$$

w = 259 lb/ft (in a 1-ft strip)
Total load = 259 lb/ft²
Dead load = (6/12 ft)(150 pcf) = 75 lb/ft²
Live load = 259 lb/ft² – 75 lb/ft² = <u>184 lb/ft²</u>

Example 7.22

A rectangular concrete beam is to resist a moment of 30 kip.ft. Use concrete working stress of 1,125 psi and steel working stress of 20 ksi. The ratio of modulus of steel and concrete is 10. The width (b) of the section is 9.0 in. The required amount of reinforcement (in.^{2}) is most nearly:

Solution:

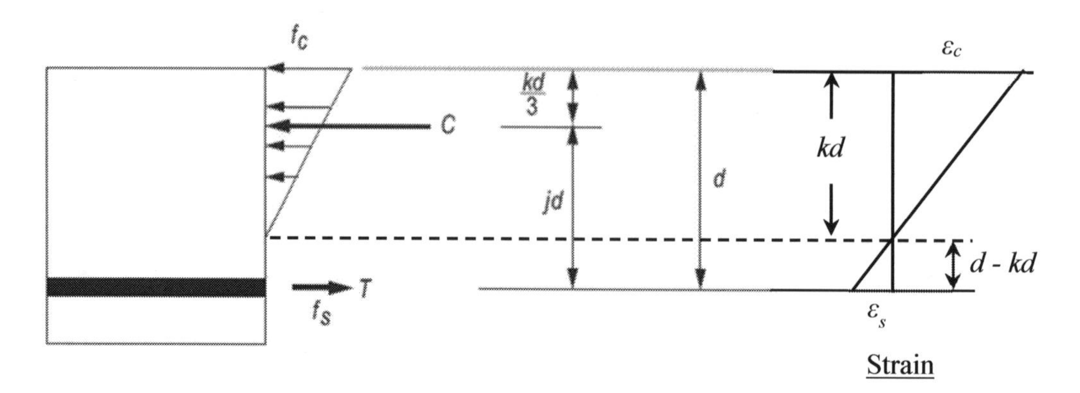

Using similar angled triangles rule in the strain diagram, $\frac{\varepsilon_c}{kd} = \frac{\varepsilon_s}{d - kd}$

$$\frac{f_c}{kd} = \frac{\frac{f_s}{n}}{d - kd}$$

$$\frac{1{,}125}{kd} = \frac{\frac{20{,}000}{10}}{d - kd}$$

$$\frac{1.125}{kd} = \frac{2}{d - kd}$$

$2kd = 1.125d - 1.125kd$

$3.125kd = 1.125d$

$k = 0.36$

Now, $j = 1 - \frac{k}{3} = 1 - \frac{0.36}{3} = 0.88$

Moment on the concrete side, $M_s = \frac{1}{2} f_c kbjd^2$

$$30 \times 12\,\text{kip.in.} = \frac{1}{2}(1{,}125\,\text{psi})(0.36)b(0.88)d^2$$

$bd^2 = 2{,}020$

$(9.0\text{ in.})\,d^2 = 2{,}020$

Therefore, $d \approx 15$ in.

Concrete stress, $f_s = \frac{M_s}{A_s jd}$

$$A_s = \frac{M_s}{f_s jd} = \frac{30 \times 12\,\text{kip.in.}}{20\,\text{ksi}(0.88)(15.0\,\text{in.})} = \underline{1.36\,\text{in.}^2}$$

7.4 Structural Steel

From the PE Civil Handbook, Article 1.6 Mechanics of Materials should be studied for structural steel or any other materials in civil engineering. For PE Civil Breadth (morning) exam, all topics in this article should be studied lightly. For PE Civil – Structural Depth exam only, this article should be studied rigorously. In a tension test, a specimen is clamped into a loading frame and then pulled gradually using a hydraulic loading system, as shown below. The deformation of the specimen is measured continuously with the application of loading. There are many devices used to measure the deformation, such as a gage, extensometer, or linear variable displacement transducer (LVDT). Stress is calculated by dividing the load by the cross-sectional area of the sample. Strain is calculated from the deformation divided by the initial dimension. Then, the stress-strain curve is plotted for the entire test until the failure occurs.

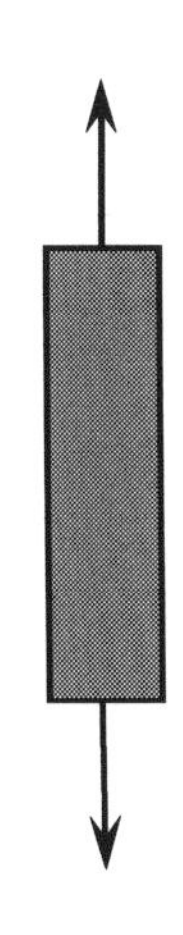

Let us consider a compressive force of P applied on a cylindrical sample of initial diameter, D_o, initial length, L_o, and initial cross-sectional area, A_o. After applying the tension, the body extends by ΔL ($\Delta L/2$ on both sides), and the diameter decreases by ΔD ($\Delta D/2$ on both sides), as shown below. The dashed area shows the initial shape and the solid area shows the final shape.

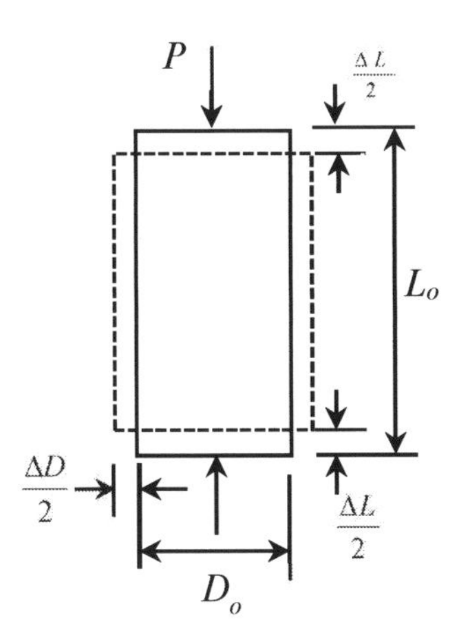

Engineering axial stress (σ_a), or simply *stress*, is defined as the reaction force over the initial area as:

$$\sigma_a = \frac{P}{A_o}$$

P = Axial force on the member
A_o = Initial cross-sectional area of the member

Engineering axial strain, commonly known as *strain* (ε_a), is defined as the change of length over the initial length, as:

$$\varepsilon_a = \frac{\Delta L}{L_o}$$

ΔL = Change in length of the member
L_o = Initial length of member; very often L_o is simply written as L

Transverse or *lateral strain* (ε_t) can be expressed as: $\varepsilon_t = \dfrac{\Delta D}{D_o}$

ΔD = Change in diameter of the member (final diameter minus the initial diameter)
D_o = Initial diameter of the member; very often D_o is simply written as D

Poisson's Ratio (υ) is defined as the ratio of the transverse strain (ε_t) and the axial strain (ε_a) as:

$$\upsilon = -\frac{\varepsilon_t}{\varepsilon_a} = -\frac{\dfrac{\Delta D}{D_o}}{\dfrac{\Delta L}{L_o}} = -\frac{Lateral\ Strain}{Axial\ Strain}$$

$$\%\ \text{elongation} = \left(\frac{\Delta L}{L_o}\right) x100$$

The % reduction in area from initial area, A_i, to final area, A_f, is: $\%\ RA = \left(\dfrac{A_i - A_f}{A_i}\right) x100$

The schematic stress-strain (σ-ε) curve of a ductile material is shown in figure below. The diagram begins with a straight line from the origin, *O*, to point *A*. In this region, the stress is proportional to the strain. The slope at this region is constant, and is called the *modulus of elasticity*, or *Young's modulus*. The linear relationship between the stress and the strain at the initial stage of loading is expressed as shown below:

$$\sigma \propto \varepsilon$$
$$\sigma = E\varepsilon$$

σ = Axial stress
ε = Axial strain
E = The modulus of elasticity or Young's modulus for the material

These equations are commonly referred to as *Hooke's law*. As the stress-strain is proportional up to the point *A*, the stress at *A* is called the *proportional limit*. Hooke's law is valid up to the proportional limit. The modulus of elasticity or Young's modulus of a material is a material property and does not change with the geometry of the materials.

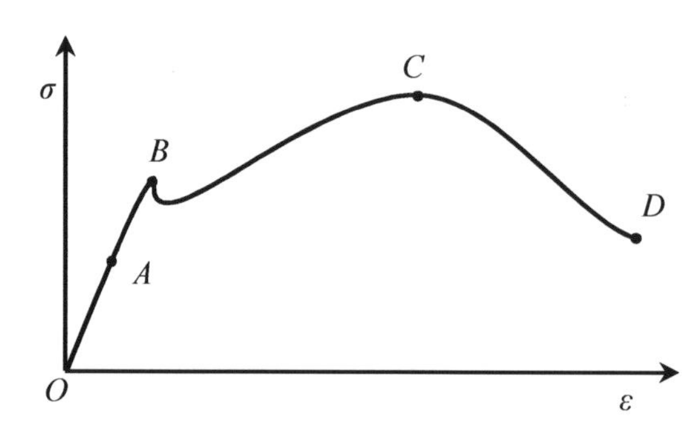

Figure. Stress-Strain Curve of a Ductile Material (i.e., mild steel)

Beyond point *A*, the stress-strain relationship is non-linear, but still in the elastic region. Being in the elastic region means that, if a load is removed, the material will return to the initial position, i.e., point, *O*. However, after reaching the point *B*, if the load is removed, the material will not return to its initial position. The starting point, *B*, of this behavior is called the *yield point*, or *yield stress*. After reaching the yield point, *strain hardening* occurs from the points *B* to *C*, which means the stress increases with the strain due to molecular level displacement inside the material. Eventually, the stress reaches the peak point, *C*, which is called the *ultimate stress*. After reaching the ultimate stress, a significant decrease in the cross-section occurs, stress goes down, and failure occurs by *necking*. This decrease in strain from the ultimate stress point, *C*, to the failure point, *D*, is called *strain softening*. A few definitions can be made from this curve:

- *Modulus of Elasticity*: The slope of the stress-strain diagram up to the proportional limit (*A*). The slope of the linear portion of the curve equals the modulus of elasticity.
- *Proportional Limit*: The linear portion of the stress-strain diagram (*O* to *A* region).
- *Elastic Limit*: The stress level up to which no plastic strain occurs (*B*).
- *Yield Point*: The stress level above which plastic strain occurs (*B*). Yield point is also known as the *Yield Stress* or *Yield Strength.*
- *Ultimate Stress*: The maximum stress a ductile material sustains before failing (*C*).
- *Fracture Stress*: The stress at which a material fails (*D*).
- *Modulus of Resilience or Strain Energy*: Area under stress-strain curve up to the elastic limit.
- *Modulus of Toughness*: Area under the stress-strain curve up to the failure.
- *Strain Hardening*: For ductile material, after yielding, an increase in load can be supported until it reaches the maximum stress (ultimate stress). This rise in the stress after the yield point is called the strain hardening (region *B* to *C*).
- *Necking*: Upon applying tensile stress, the cross-sectional area of ductile material decreases, forming a neck before the failure. This contraction of area before the failure is called necking.
- *Strain Softening*: After the ultimate stress and before the failure point, the stress capacity keeps on decreasing with the continuous development of plastic strain due to significant molecular displacement in the material. This region is called the strain softening (region *C* to *D*).
- *Elastic* or *Recovery Strain*: The strain that is recovered upon removal of the applied loading.
- *Permanent or Plastic Strain*: The strain that cannot be recovered in any amount upon removal of the applied loading.

From Article1.6 of the PE Civil Handbook, if the yield point on the σ-ε curve is not distinct, then a straight line parallel to the initial line is drawn at the 0.2% strain point, as shown in figure below. The intersection of the straight line and the original σ-ε curve is considered the yield point (σ_y).

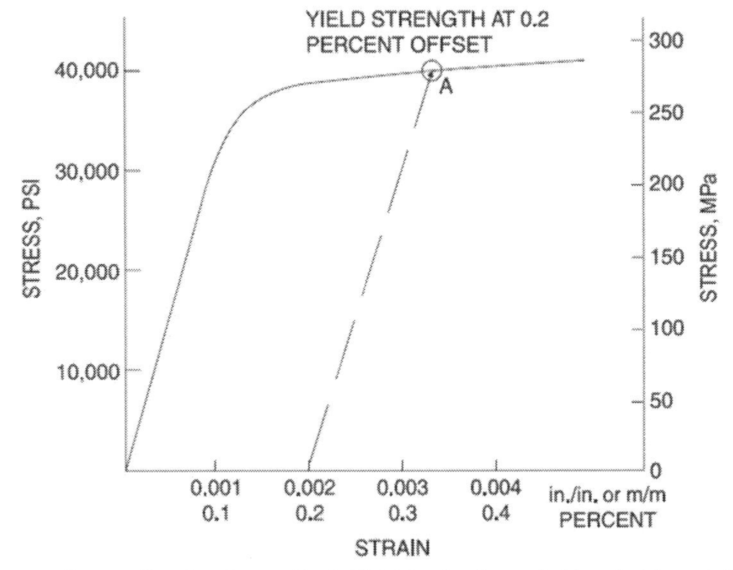

Figure. Stress-Strain Curve for Mild Steel when yield point is not distinct

Shear modulus or *modulus of rigidity* (G) is defined as the ratio of the shear stress and the shear strain. Consider the initial shape of a block is rectangular, as shown in figure below by the dashed line. Upon applying a force, P, at the left-top corner, let the lateral displacement be Δ. Then, the change of angle is calculated as shown below.

$$\frac{\Delta}{L} = \tan\gamma \approx \gamma$$

Figure. Shear Stress-Shear Strain Behavior under Shear Loading

Shear stress, $\tau = P/A$

Shear strain, γ = Change in angle, which was initially $\pi/2$.

$$G = \frac{\tau}{\gamma}$$

If the Poisson's ratio (υ) of the material is known, the shear modulus and the modulus of elasticity can be correlated as shown below.

$$G = \frac{E}{2(1+\upsilon)}$$

From Article1.6 of the PE Civil Handbook, Bulk (volume) modulus of elasticity: $K = \dfrac{E}{3(1-2\upsilon)}$

K = bulk modulus
E = modulus of elasticity
ν = Poisson's ratio

Example 7.23

Consider a carefully conducted experiment in which an aluminum bar of 2-1/4 in. diameter is stressed in a testing machine as in the Figure below. At a certain instant the applied force P is 32 kip while the measured elongation of the rod is 0.00938 in. in a 12–in. gage length and the dimension of the diameter is decreased by 0.000585 in. Calculate the:

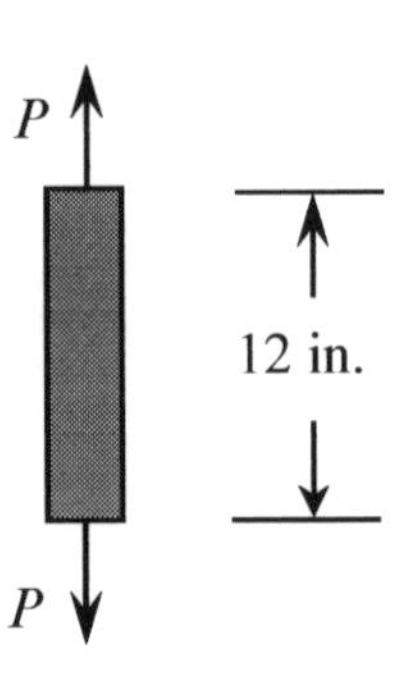

a) Poisson's ratio
b) modulus of elasticity
c) Bulk (volume) modulus of elasticity

Solution:

Part a.

$$\text{Transverse or lateral strain, } \varepsilon_t = \frac{\Delta D}{D_o} = \frac{-0.000585 \text{ in.}}{2.25 \text{in.}} = -0.00026$$

$$\text{Axial strain, } \varepsilon_a = \frac{\Delta L}{L_o} = \frac{0.00938 \text{ in.}}{12 \text{in.}} = 0.000782$$

$$\text{Poisson's Ratio, } \upsilon = -\frac{\varepsilon_t}{\varepsilon_a} = \frac{-0.00026}{0.000782} = \underline{0.333}$$

Part b.

$$\text{Cross-sectional area, } A = \frac{\pi D^2}{4} = \frac{\pi (2.25 \text{in.})^2}{4} = 3.976 \text{ in.}^2$$

$$\text{Axial stress, } \sigma = \frac{P}{A} = \frac{32 \text{ kip}}{3.976 \text{in.}^2} = 8.048 \text{ ksi} = 8{,}048 \text{ psi}$$

$$E = \frac{\sigma_a}{\varepsilon_a} = \frac{8{,}048 \text{ psi}}{0.000782} = \underline{10.3 \times 10^6 \text{ psi}}$$

Part c.

$$\text{Bulk modulus of elasticity: } K = \frac{E}{3(1-2\upsilon)} = \frac{10.3 \times 10^6 \text{ psi}}{3(1-2(0.333))} \approx \underline{10.3 \times 10^6 \text{ psi}}$$

Example 7.24

A steel bar has a length of 2.5 m and cross-section of 200-mm x 100-mm. The modulus of elasticity of this material is 210 GPa and Poisson's Ratio is 0.3. The change in width after applying a tensile force of 150 kN is most nearly:

Solution:

$$\text{Axial stress, } \sigma = \frac{P}{A} = \frac{150 \text{ kN}}{(0.2)(0.1)} = 7500 \text{ kPa}$$

$$\text{Axial strain, } \varepsilon = \frac{\sigma}{E} = \frac{7500{,}000 \text{ Pa}}{210{,}000{,}000{,}000 \text{ Pa}} = 0.0000357$$

$$\text{Lateral strain, } \varepsilon_t = -v\varepsilon = -0.3(0.0000357) = -0.0000107$$

$$\text{Change in width, } \Delta w = -\varepsilon_t w = -0.0000107(200 \text{ mm}) = \underline{-0.0021 \text{ mm}}$$

7.5 Material Test Methods and Specification Conformance

It is not well defined that which test methods and specifications should be studied. PE Civil Breadth (morning) is common for all PE Civil disciplines. However, only one common reference is available which is PE Civil Reference Handbook. Therefore, whatever test methods is mentioned in the PE Civil Handbook should be studied. No external data/information is required to be memorized. For example, in the next section (Compaction) two test methods are mentioned, ASTM D 698 or AASHTO T99 and ASTM D 1557 or AASHTO T180. Similarly, ASTM D 2487 for Unified Soil Classification System (USCS) soil classification, AASHTO M 145 (or ASTM D 3282) for AASHTO Soil Classification System.

7.6 Compaction

Article 3.9 Compaction discusses this topic. Soil compaction is the process in which a stress applied to a soil causes densification as air is displaced from the pores between the soil grains. When stress is applied that causes densification due to water (or other liquid) being displaced from between the soil grains then consolidation, not compaction, has occurred. The primary reasons for soil compaction are:

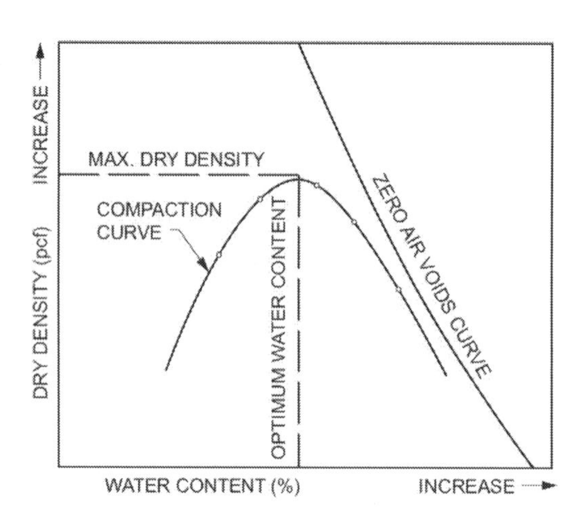

- Increase load-bearing capacity
- Prevent Soil Settlement and Frost Damage
- Provide stability
- Reduce water seepage, swelling and contraction
- Reduce settling of soil

Table. Characteristics of Laboratory Compaction Tests

Common Name	ASTM (AASHTO) Designations	Mold Dimensions			Hammer		No. of Layers	Blows/ Layer	Energy (ft-lb/ft³)
		Diam. (in.)	Height (in.)	Vol. (ft³)	Wt. (lb)	Drop Ht. (in.)			
Standard Proctor	D 698 (T 99)	4	4.5	1/30	5.5	12	3	25	12,375
Modified Proctor	D 1557 (T 180)	4	4.5	1/30	10	18	5	25	56,250

Note: Both tests are performed on minus No. 4 (4.75 mm) fraction of the soil.

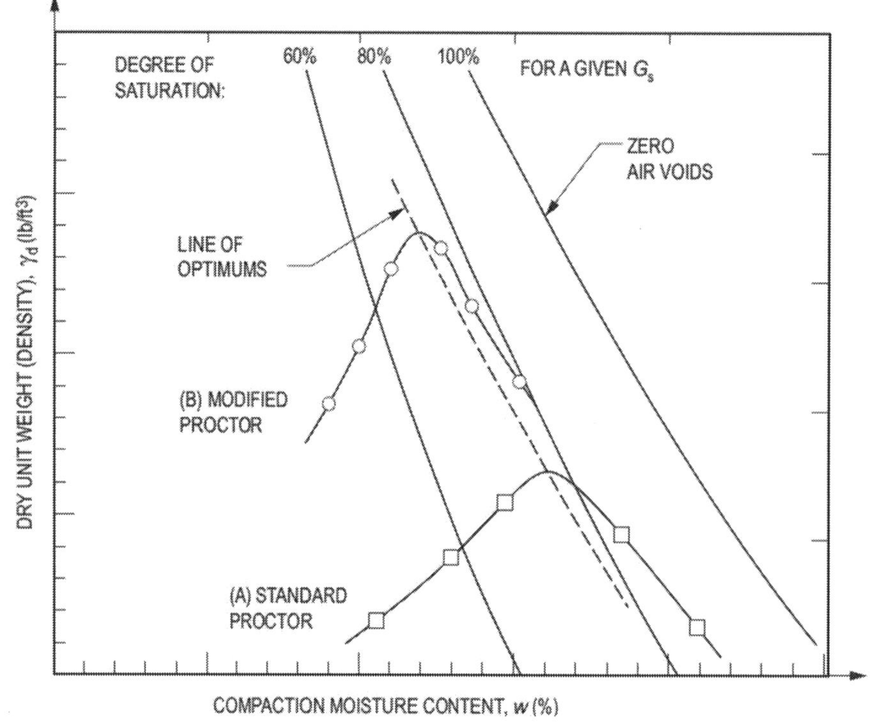

Figure. Compaction Curves

Moisture content and dry density relationship:

$$\gamma_d = \frac{\gamma_t}{(1+w)}$$

The zero Air Void line is obtained when there is no presence of the air in the pores of a soil mass and totally filled with the water (with a 100% degree of saturation) and soil mass get saturated. It is determined by the compaction test of a soil. Draw the graph between Dry Density vs. water content, calculate the dry density from the compaction test results, and Zero Air void line is drawn on the graph.

Zero air voids (100% saturation) can be calculated as, $\gamma_d = \dfrac{G_s \gamma_w}{(1+e)}$

γ_t = total unit weight
γ_d = dry unit weight
γ_w = unit weight of water
w = water content
G_s = specific gravity
e = void ratio

Example 7.25
During construction of a soil embankment, a sand-cone in-place unit weight test was performed in the field. The following data were obtained:

- Weight of sand used in test hole = 1.20 lb
- Unit weight of sand used in test hole = 98.0 pcf
- Mass of wet soil collected from the test hole = 1.65 lb
- Moisture content of soil collected from test hole = 13.7%

Calculate the dry unit weight of the compacted soil.

Solution:

Weight of sand used in test hole = 1.20 lb

Volume of test hole, $V = \dfrac{W}{\gamma} = \dfrac{1.20 \text{ lb}}{98.0 \dfrac{\text{lb}}{\text{ft}^3}} = 0.01224 \text{ ft}^3$

Wet unit weight of soil in-place, $\gamma = \dfrac{W}{V} = \dfrac{1.65 \text{ lb}}{0.01224 \text{ ft}^3} = 134.8 \dfrac{\text{lb}}{\text{ft}^3}$

Dry unit weight of soil in-place, $\gamma_d = \dfrac{\gamma_t}{(1+w)} = \dfrac{134.8 \dfrac{\text{lb}}{\text{ft}^3}}{1+0.137} = \underline{118.6 \dfrac{\text{lb}}{\text{ft}^3}}$

Relative compaction is the ratio of in-place wet density to test the maximum wet density of the same soil:

$$RC = \frac{\gamma_{d,field}}{\gamma_{d,\max}} \times 100$$

RC = relative compaction (%)
$\gamma_{d\ field}$ = dry unit weight from field density test
$\gamma_{d\ max}$ = maximum dry unit weight from laboratory test (standard or modified Proctor)

Example 7.26

A Proctor test was performed on a soil which has a specific gravity of solids of 2.71. For the water content and total unit weight data below:

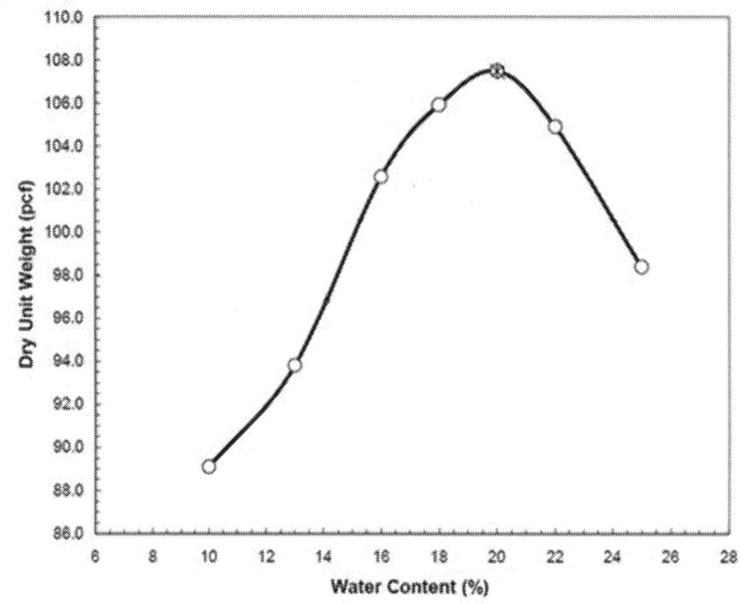

Ref. Holtz, Kovacs & Sheahan, An Introduction to Geotechnical Engineering, 2/e, Pearson.

a) Find the maximum dry density and optimum moisture content.
b) Determine the moisture range permitted if a contractor must achieve 90% relative compaction.
c) What volume of water, in ft^3, must be added to obtain 1 yd^3 of soil at the maximum dry density if the soil is originally at 10% water content?

Solution: (a) From the curve below: Maximum dry density, $\gamma_{d\,max}$ = <u>107.5 pcf</u>
Optimum moisture content, w = <u>20%</u>

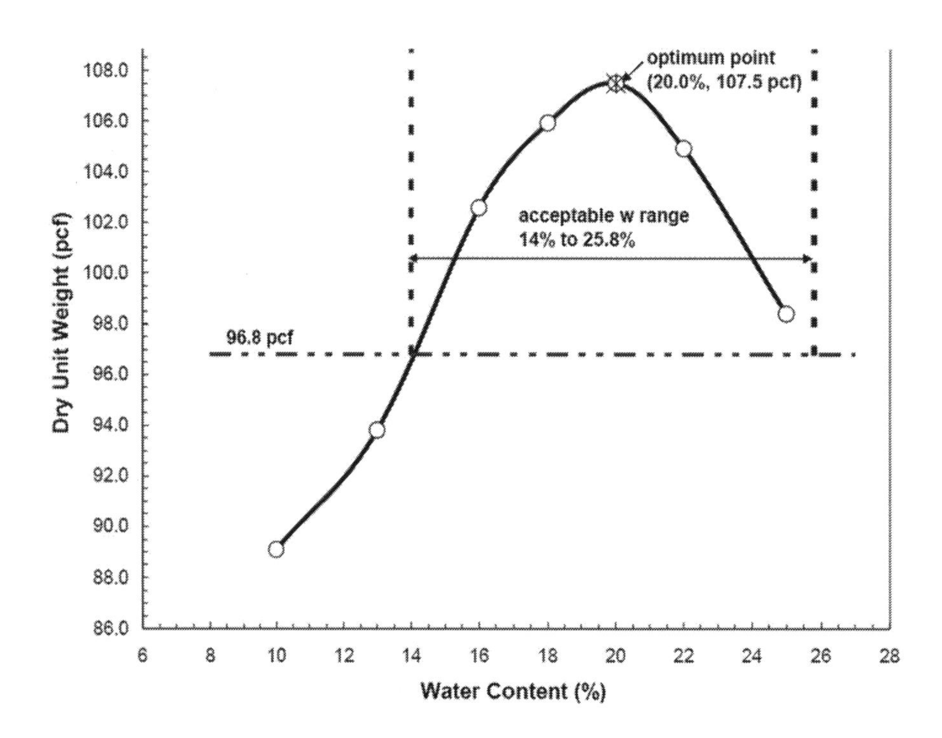

b) Relative compaction, $RC = \dfrac{\gamma_{d,field}}{\gamma_{d,\max}} \times 100$

Or, $\gamma_{d\ field}$ = RC x $\gamma_{d\ max}$ = 0.90 x 107.5 pcf = 96.8 pcf
From the curve, acceptable range of water content = 14% to 25.8%

c) Dry-weight or solid's weight never changes.
Volume, V = 1 yd^3 = 27 ft^3
Dry-weight of the soil, W_s = V x γ_d = 27 ft^3 x 107.5 pcf = 2,903 lb
Initial weight of water, $w_{10\%}$ = 10% of 2,903 lb = 290.3 lb
Final weight of water, $w_{20\%}$ = 20% of 2,903 lb = 580.6 lb
Weight of water to be added = 580.6 lb – 290.3 lb = 290.3 lb
Volume of water to be added = 290.3 lb / 62.4 pcf = 4.65 ft^3

Example 7.27

The specification for compaction states that the field-compacted soil must be at least 95% of the maximum control density and within 2% of the optimum moisture for the control curve. You dig a hole 1/30 ft^3 in the compacted layer and extract a sample that weighs 3.8 lb wet and 3.1 lb after over-drying.

a) Find the maximum dry density and optimum moisture content.
b) Calculate the compacted dry density.
c) Calculate the compaction water content
d) Calculate the percent of compaction.
e) Does the sample meet the specifications?

Water Content (%)	Dry Unit Weight (pcf)
14	104
16	105.5
18	106
20	105
22	103.5
24	101

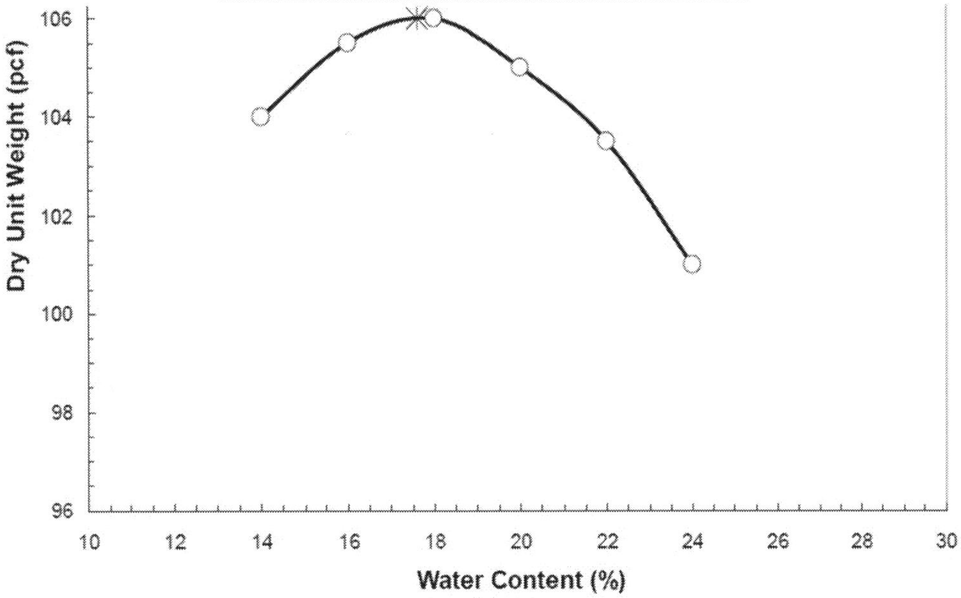

Ref. Holtz, Kovacs & Sheahan, An Introduction to Geotechnical Engineering, 2/e, Pearson.

Solution:

a) From the curve below:

Maximum dry density, $\gamma_{d\,max} = \underline{106\text{ pcf}}$

Optimum moisture content, $w = \underline{17.6\%}$

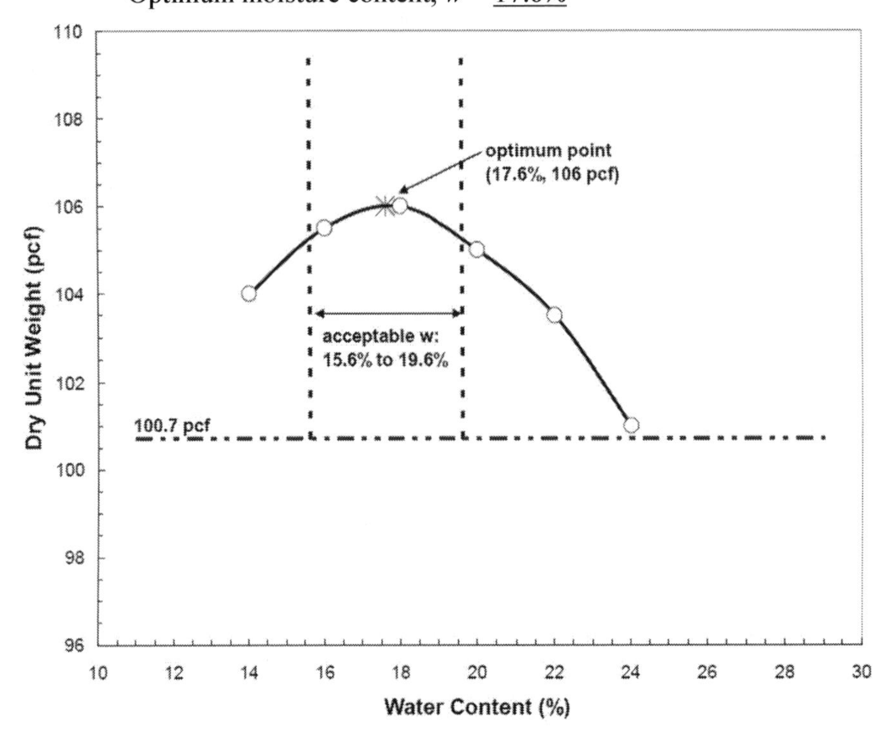

In the curve, within 2% of the optimum moisture, the moisture content varies from 15.6% to 19.6%

b) Compacted dry unit weight, $\gamma_d = \dfrac{W_s}{V_t} = \dfrac{3.1\text{ lb}}{\frac{1}{30}\text{ ft}^3} = \underline{93\text{pcf}}$

c) Compacted moisture content, $w = \dfrac{W_w}{W_s} \times 100 = \dfrac{3.8\text{ lb} - 3.1\text{ lb}}{3.1\text{ lb}} \times 100 = \underline{22.6\%} \gg 19.6\%$

d) Compacted wet unit weight, $\gamma_t = \dfrac{W_t}{V_t} = \dfrac{3.8\text{ lb}}{\frac{1}{30}\text{ ft}^3} = \underline{114\text{pcf}}$

Relative compaction, $RC = \dfrac{\gamma_{d,field}}{\gamma_{d,\max}} \times 100 = \dfrac{93\text{ pcf}}{106\text{ pcf}} \times 100 = \underline{87.7\%} \ll 95\%$

e) The field-compacted soil is 87.7% (should be at least 95%) of the maximum control density. The water content is out of 2% (15.6% to 19.6%) of the optimum moisture. Therefore, the soil does not meet any of the 2 specifications.

Chapter 8
Site Development

This chapter is primarily based on Chapter 2 and some part from Chapter 3 of the PE Civil Handbook.

8.1 Excavation and Embankment

Excavation is the process of removing rock and soil from a site. The removed rock and soil is either not required so is therefore being hauled away or placed on a construction site to fill voids or change contours of embankment. Embankment is the placement and compaction of layers of earth or rock to form a roadbed of the planned shape, density, and profile grade. Various sections of a roadway design require bringing in earth. Other sections may require earth to be removed. Earth that is brought in is considered Fill while earth that is removed is considered Cut. Generally, designers generate drawings called Cut and Fill Diagrams, which illustrate the cut or fill present at any given site. This drawing is quite standard, being no more than a graph with site location on the X-axis and fill being the positive range of the Y-axis while cut is the negative range of the Y-axis. A few equation from PE Civil Handbook, Article 2.1 Earthwork Construction and Layout:

$$V_L = \left(1 + \frac{S_w}{100}\right) V_B$$

$$V_C = \left(1 - \frac{S_h}{100}\right) V_B$$

$$V_B = \left(\frac{\gamma_F}{\gamma_B} \times V_F\right) + \frac{W_L}{\gamma_B}$$

$$\gamma_L = \frac{\gamma_B}{1 + \frac{S_W}{100}}$$

$$\gamma_C = \frac{\gamma_B}{1 - \frac{S_h}{100}}$$

Relative compaction (%), $RC = \frac{\gamma_{d,field}}{\gamma_{d,\max}} \times 100$

$$\text{Shrinkage factor} = \frac{\dfrac{Weight}{V_B}}{\dfrac{Weight}{V_C}} = \frac{compacted\ dry\ unit\ weight}{bank\ dry\ unit\ weight}$$

$$\text{Shrinkage (\%)},\ S_h = \frac{compacted\ dry\ unit\ weight - bank\ unit\ weight}{compacted\ unit\ weight} \times 100$$

$$\text{Swell factor} = \frac{loose\ dry\ unit\ weight}{bank\ dry\ unit\ weight}$$

$$\text{Swell (\%)},\ S_w = \left(\frac{\dfrac{Weight}{V_B}}{\dfrac{Weight}{V_L}} - 1 \right) \times 100$$

where

V_B = volume of undisturbed soil (bank measure)
V_F = volume of fill soil
V_L = volume of loose soil
V_C = volume of compacted soil
W_L = weight lost in stripping, waste, and transportation
$\gamma_{d,\text{field}}$ = dry unit weight of soil in the field
$\gamma_{d,\max}$ = maximum dry density of soil measured in the laboratory
γ_B = unit weight of undistributed soil (bank measure)
γ_F = unit weight of fill soil
γ_L = unit weight of loose soil
γ_C = unit weight of compacted soil
Optimum soil moisture content for compaction: Well-graded granular soils: 7 to 12% Fine-grained soils: 12 to 25%

Amount of water to be added or removed from soil to achieve desired soil moisture content:

$$\text{Gallons of water} = \text{desired dry density, lb/ft}^3 \times \frac{(\text{desired \% of water content}) - (\text{\% of water content of borrow})}{100} \times \frac{\text{compacted volume of soil, ft}^3}{8.33\ \text{lb/gal}}$$

Available soil compaction techniques can be classified as:

1. Static Pressure – A large stress is slowly applied to the soil and then released.
2. Impact – A stress is applied by dropping a large mass onto the surface of the soil.
3. Vibrating – A stress is applied repeatedly and rapidly via a mechanically driven plate or hammer.
4. Kneading – Shear is applied by alternating movement in adjacent positions.

Method of Compaction Categorized by Soil Type

Soil Type	Impact	Pressure	Vibrating	Kneading
Gravel	Poor	No	Good	Very Good
Sand	Poor	No	Excellent	Good
Silt	Good	Good	Poor	Excellent
Clay	Excellent	Very Good	No	Good

Example 8.1

Find the shrinkage of a soil that weighs 2800 lb/cu yd in its natural state and 3500 lb/cu yd after compaction.

Solution:

$$\text{Shrinkage (\%)},\ S_h = \frac{\textit{compacted dry unit weight} - \textit{bank unit weight}}{\textit{compacted unit weight}} \times 100$$

$$= \frac{3{,}500 - 2{,}800}{3{,}500} \times 100$$

$$= \underline{20\%}$$

Example 8.2

A contractor is excavating a trench of 5 ft deep and 3 ft wide. The soil has an approximate swell factor of 15% and a shrinkage factor of 12%. The contractor is placing an 8-in. outer-diameter water pipe in the trench and then, backfilling with the soil that was removed. The given dimensions are on centerline. The amount of soil (LCY), the contractor requires to borrow is most nearly:

[Note: A bank cubic yard (BCY) is 1.0 yd^3 of material as it lies in its natural/undisturbed state. A loose cubic yard (LCY) is 1.0 $yd^3$of material after it has been disturbed by an excavation process.]

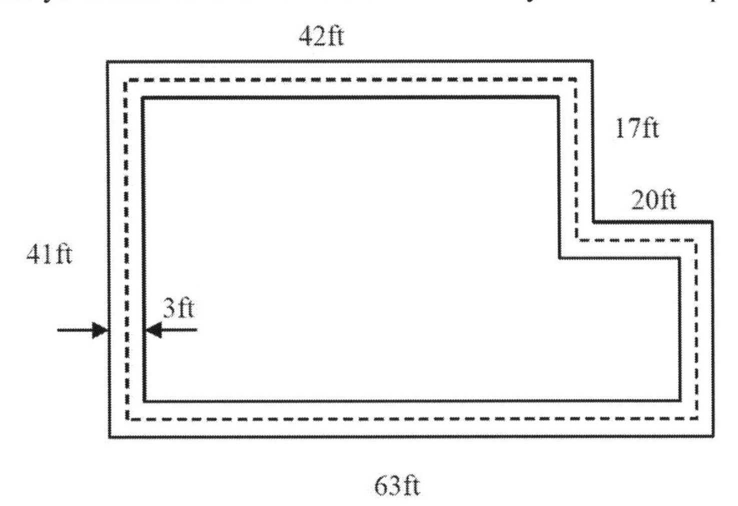

(Ref: EngineeringDesignResources)

Solution:

Trench perimeter = 42 ft+17 ft+20 ft+24 ft+63 ft+41 ft = 207 ft

Volume of the soil in the trench = 5 ft x 3ft x 207 ft = 3105 ft^3

Volume after compaction = (3105 ft^3)(1 – 0.12) = (3105 ft^3)(0.88) = 2732.4 ft^3

Volume of the soil needed = Volume of Trench – Volume of Pipe

$$3105\ ft^3 - \pi(d^2/4)(207\ ft) = \pi((8/12)^2/4)(207\ ft)$$

$$3105\ ft^3 - 72.25\ ft^3 = 3032.75\ ft^3$$

Find out if you need more soil = Vol. of compacted soil need – Vol. of compacted soil available

= 3032.75 ft^3 – 2732.4 ft^3

= 300.35 ft^3 (positive, meaning the contractor needs to bring in more soil)

Volume of compacted soil = (1 – Shrinkage factor) x BCF

or, 300.35 = 0.88 x BCF

or, BCF = 341

Therefore, LCF = BCF x 1.15 = 392/27 = <u>14.5 LCY</u>

Example 8.3
A soil weighs 1960 lb/LCY, 2800 lb/BCY, and 3500 lb/CCY.

(a) Find the shrinkage factor and swell for the soil.
(b) How many bank cubic yards (BCY) and compacted cubic yards (CCY) or are contained in 1 million loose cubic yards of this soil?

Solution:

Part a.

$$\text{Shrinkage factor} = \frac{\dfrac{Weight}{V_B}}{\dfrac{Weight}{V_C}} = \frac{compacted\ dry\ unit\ weight}{bank\ dry\ unit\ weight} = \frac{2,800}{3,500} = 0.8$$

$$\text{Swell factor} = \frac{loose\ dry\ unit\ weight}{bank\ dry\ unit\ weight} = \frac{1,960}{2,800} = 0.70$$

Part b.

Bank volume = 1,000,000 x 0.70 = 700,000 BCY
Compacted volume = 700,000 x 0.80 = 560,000 CCY

From PE Civil Handbook, Article 2.1, the average end-area method for earthwork calculates volume V between two consecutive cross sections as the average of their areas multiplied by the distance between them, where fill is positive and cut is negative:

$$V = L\left(\frac{A_1 + A_2}{2}\right)$$

V = volume
A_1, A_2 = end areas of cross sections 1 and 2
L = distance between cross sections

The prismoidal formula for earthwork calculates volume V between two consecutive cross sections, taking the area of the midsection into account:

$$V = L\left(\frac{A_1 + 4A_m + A_2}{6}\right)$$

V = volume
A_1, A_2 = end areas of cross sections 1 and 2
A_m = area of midsection
L = distance between cross sections

With the grid formula, the volume of material excavated from a borrow pit may be estimated by taking grade-rod readings at grid points before and after excavation. For differential elevations a, b, c, and d at the corners of a grid square:

Volume of material in one grid square = ¼ $(a + b + c + d)$ × (area of grid square)

Example 8.4
Calculate the total net cut (yd^3) for the following cross-section using the average end area method:

- Station 1: 1+00 is 112 ft^2
- Station 2: 3+15 is 700 ft^2

Solution:

Using the Average End Area Method, $V = L\left(\frac{A_1 + A_2}{2}\right)$

L (the distance between the two stations) = 315 ft – 100 ft = 215 ft

Volume (V) = 215 ft [(700 ft^2 + 112 ft^2)/2]
= 87,290 ft^3
= 87,290 / 27 [1 yd^3= 27 ft^3]
= 3,232 yd^3

Example 8.5
Calculate the total net fill (yd^3) for the following cross-section using the prismoidal method:

- Station 1: 1+00 is 112 ft^2
- Station 2: 2+07 is 25 ft^2
- Station 3: 3+15 is 700 ft^2

Solution:

Using the Prismoidal Method, $V = L\left(\frac{A_1 + 4A_m + A_2}{6}\right)$

L (the distance between the two stations) = 315 ft – 100 ft = 215 ft
Volume = 215 ft x [(700 ft^2 + 4(25 ft^2) + 112 ft^2)/6] = 32,680 ft^3
= 32,680 / 27 = 1,210 yd^3

The coordinate method calculates area,

$$A = \frac{1}{2}\left[X_A\left(Y_B - Y_N\right) + X_B\left(Y_C - Y_A\right) + X_C\left(Y_D - Y_B\right) + \ldots + X_N\left(Y_A - Y_{N-1}\right)\right]$$

The trapezoidal rule calculates area, $A = w\left[\frac{1}{2}\left(h_1 + h_n\right) + h_2 + h_3 + h_4 + \ldots + h_{n-1}\right]$

where w = length of the common interval

For partial grid squares at edges of an excavation, the amount of material V may be estimated using standard volume formulas for three-dimensional shapes, such as the following:

Wedge (triangular prism), $V = \frac{1}{2}\left(b \times h \times l\right)$

Quarter of right circular cone, $V = \frac{1}{12}\left(\pi \times r^2 \times h\right)$

Sample layout for use of the grid formula:

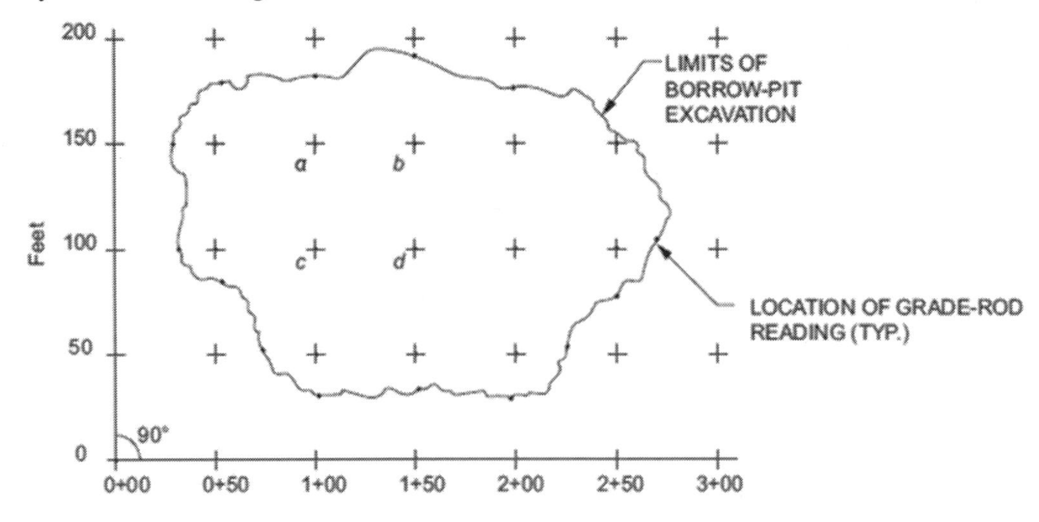

Simpson's Rule calculates area, A for a section of earthwork as follows, given the elevation values of cut and fill at equal intervals (e.g., stations) along a baseline:

$$A = \frac{1}{3}\left[first\ value + last\ value + \left(4 \times sum\ of\ odd\text{-}numbered\ values\right) + \left(2 \times sum\ of\ even\text{-}numbered\ values\right)\right] \times length\ of\ interval$$

To use Simpson's Rule, there must be an even number of intervals. The sum of odd-numbered values (e.g., 3rd, 5th, and 7th terms) and even-numbered values (e.g., 2nd, 4th, and 6th terms) does not include the first and last terms along the baseline.

8.2 Construction Site Layout and Control

PE Civil Handbook, Article 2.1:

Benchmark (BM) = permanent point of known elevation
Turning point (TP) = point temporarily used to transfer an elevation
Backsight (BS) = rod reading taken on a point of known elevation to establish elevation of instrument's line of sight
Foresight (FS) = rod reading taken on a benchmark or turning point to determine its elevation
Height of instrument (HI) = elevation of line of sight through the level

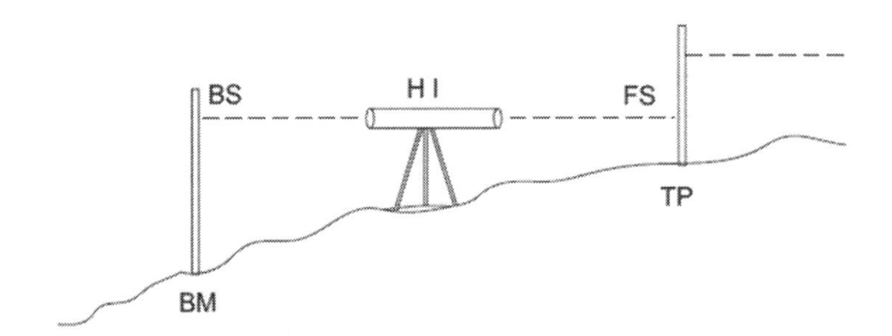

With reference to the diagram:

Height of Instrument (HI) = Known Elevation (BM) + Backsight (BS)

Turning Point (TP) = Height of Instrument (HI) – Foresight (FS)

Example 8.6
For the following site, calculate the elevation at Point B.

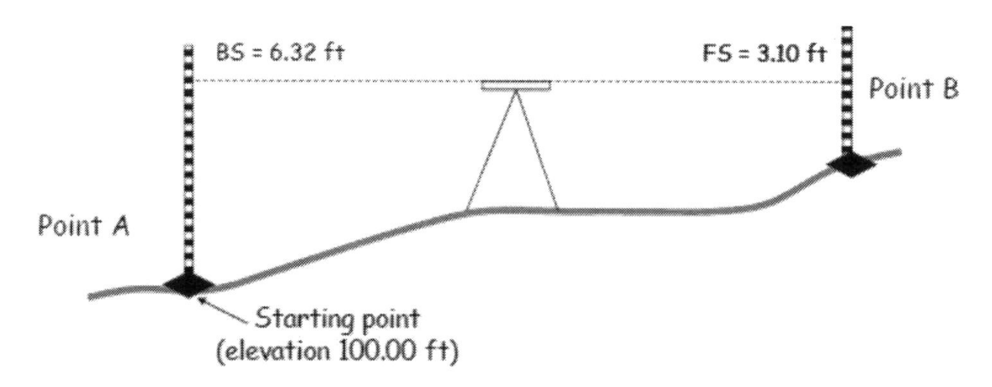

Solution:

Height of Instrument (HI) = Known elevation + Back sight (BS)
HI = 100 ft + 6.32 ft = 106.32 ft
Turning Point (TP) = Height of Instruction (HI) – Foresight (FS)
Point B = 106.32 ft – 3.10 = <u>103.22 ft</u>

Example 8.7
The known benchmark elevation is known to be 86.3 ft. When surveying you find the rod reading at Point A is 4.56 ft and the rod reading at the benchmark is 8.5 ft. What is the elevation at Point A?

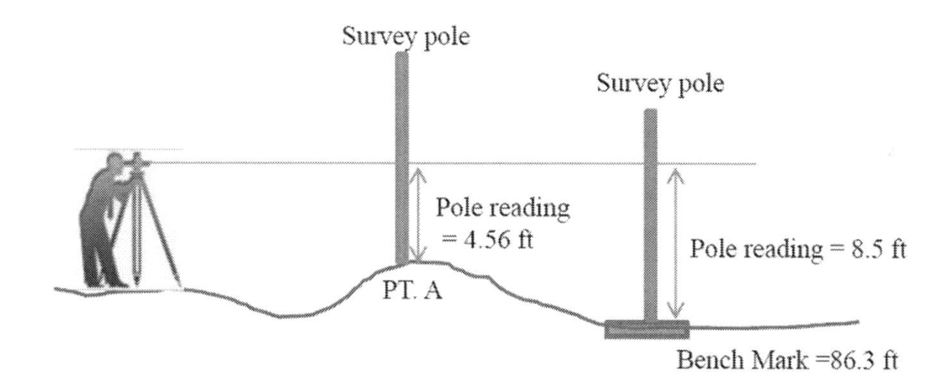

Solution:

Elevation of Line of Sight = 86.3 ft + 8.5 ft = 94.8 ft
Elevation at Point A = 94.8 ft –4.56 ft = 90.24 ft

Example 8.8
For the following site, determine the elevation at the bottom of the ditch shown.

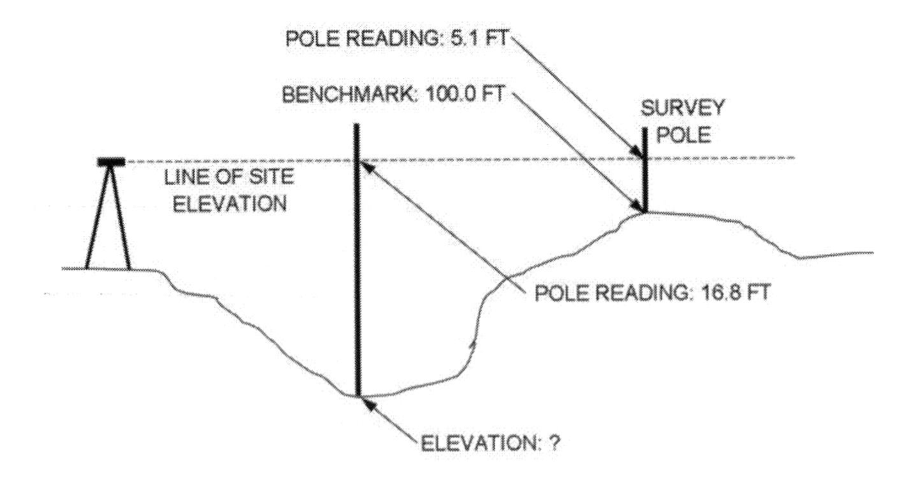

Solution:

Line of Site Elevation = Benchmark + Survey Pole Reading = 100 ft + 5.1 ft = 105.1 ft
Elevation at the bottom of the ditch = Line of Site Elevation – Survey Pole Reading
Elevation at the bottom of the ditch = 105.1 ft – 16.8 ft = 88.3 ft

8.3 Temporary and Permanent Soil Erosion and Sediment Control

There are two main section for Storm Water Management:

a) Erosion Control
b) Sediment Control

Erosion Control is any control practice that protects the soil surface and prevents soil particles from being detached by rainfall, flowing water, or wind. Erosion control method includes the following:

- Preservation of existing vegetation is the careful planned clearing and grubbing plans can protect soil from erosion
- Hydraulic mulch consists of applying a mixture of shredded wood fiber and a stabilizing emulsion with hydro-mulching equipment.
- Hydroseeding consists of applying a mixture of wood fiber, seed, fertilizer and a stabilizing emulsion with hydro-mulching equipment.
- Soil binders consists of applying and maintaining a soil stabilizer to exposed soil surfaces.
- Straw mulch consists of placing a uniform layer of straw and incorporating it into the soil with a studded roller or anchoring it with a tackifier stabilizing emulsion.
- Geotextiles and mats are the mattings of natural materials are used to cover the soil surface. Mattings may be used to stabilize soils until vegetation is established.
- Wood mulching consists of applying a mixture of shredded wood mulch, bark or compost to disturbed soils.
- Earth dikes and drainage swales is an earth dike is a temporary berm of compacted soil used to divert runoff or channel water to a desired location. A drainage swale is a shaped and sloped depression in the soil used to convey runoff to a desired location.
- Velocity dissipation devices is a physical device composed of rock, riprap, or concrete rubble.
- Slope drains: a pipe used to intercept and direct surface runoff into a stabilized area. They are usually used with earth dikes and drainage ditches in order to direct the surface flow.
- Streambank stabilization may require numerous measures to prevent any increase in sediment load to the stream.

- Polyacrylamide is a chemical that can be applied to disturbed soils at construction sites to reduce erosion and improve settling of suspended sediment.

Sediment Control is any practice that traps soil particles after they have been detached and moved by rain, flowing water, or wind. Sediment control practices can consist of installing linear sediment barriers (such as silt fence, sandbag barrier, and straw bale barrier); providing fiber rolls, gravel bag berms, or check dams to break up slope length or flow; or constructing a sediment trap or sediment basin. Sediment control method includes the following:

- Silt fence is made of a filter fabric that has been entrenched, attached to supporting poles
- Sediment basin: temporary basin formed by excavation or by constructing an embankment.
- Sediment trap is a containment area where sediment-laden runoff is temporarily detained. Sediment traps are formed by excavating or constructing an earthen embankment across a waterway or low drainage area.
- Check dams is a small barrier constructed of rock, gravel bags, sandbags, fiber rolls, or reusable products. Check dams reduce the effective slope of the channel, thereby reducing the velocity of flowing water, allowing sediment to settle and reducing erosion.
- Fiber rolls consists of straw, flax, or similar materials bound into a tight tubular roll.
- Gravel bag berms is a series of gravel-filled bags placed on a level contour to intercept sheet flows.
- Sandbag barrier is a series of sand-filled bags placed on a level contour to intercept sheet flows.
- Straw bale barrier: is a series of straw bales placed on a level contour to intercept sheet flows.

8.4 Impact of Construction on Adjacent Facilities

PE Civil Handbook, Chap 3 Geotechnical, Article 3.10 Trench and Construction Safety can be studied. OSHA categorizes soil and rock deposits into four types, A through D:

A. Stable Rock is natural solid mineral matter than can be excavated with vertical sides and remain intact while exposed. It is usually identified by a rock name such as granite or sandstone. Determining whether a deposit is of this type may be difficult unless it is known whether cracks exist and whether the cracks run into or away from the excavation.

B. Type A Soils are cohesive soils with an unconfined compressive strength of 1.5 tons per square foot (tsf) (144 kPa) or greater. Examples of Type A cohesive soils are often: clay, silty clay, sandy clay, clay loam, and, in some cases, silty clay loam and sandy clay loam. (No soil is Type A if it is fissured, is subject to vibration of any type, has previously been disturbed, is part of a sloped, layered system where the layers dip into the excavation on a slope of 4 horizontal to 1 vertical (4H:1V) or greater, or has seeping water.

C. Type B Soils are cohesive soils with an unconfined compressive strength greater than 0.5 tsf (48 kPa) but less than 1.5 tsf (144 kPa). Examples of other Type B soils are: angular gravel, silt, silt loam, previously disturbed soils unless otherwise classified as Type C, soils that meet the unconfined compressive strength or cementation requirements of Type A soils but are fissured or subject to vibration, dry unstable rock, and layered systems sloping into the trench at a slope less than 4H:1V (only if the material would be classified as a Type B soil).

D. Type C Soils are cohesive soils with an unconfined compressive strength of 0.5 tsf (48 kPa) or less. Other Type C soils include granular soils such as gravel, sand and loamy sand, submerged soil, soil from which water is freely seeping, and submerged rock that is not stable. Also included in this classification is material in a sloped, layered system where the layers dip into the excavation or have a slope of four horizontal to one vertical (4H:1V) or greater.

E. Layered Geological Strata. Where soils are configured in layers, i.e., where a layered geological structure exists, the soil must be classified on the basis of the soil classification of the weakest soil layer. Each layer may be classified individually if a more stable layer lies below a less stable layer, i.e., where a Type C soil rests on top of stable rock.

Article 3.10 presented the OSHA Slope and Shield Configurations as follows:

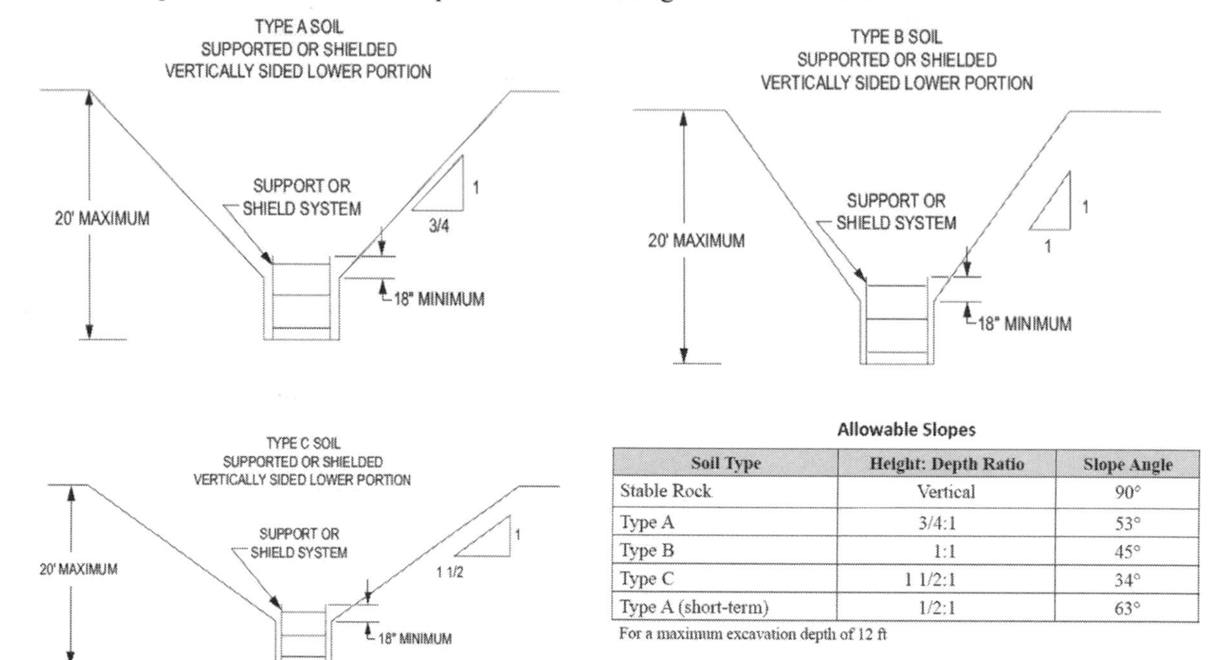

Allowable Slopes

Soil Type	Height: Depth Ratio	Slope Angle
Stable Rock	Vertical	90°
Type A	3/4:1	53°
Type B	1:1	45°
Type C	1 1/2:1	34°
Type A (short-term)	1/2:1	63°

For a maximum excavation depth of 12 ft

Read other articles in PE Civil Handbook as well as follows:

- Article 3.10.3 Slope Configurations: Excavations in Layered Soils
- Article 3.10.4 Excavations Made in Type A Soil
- Article 3.10.5 Excavations Made in Type B Soil

Example 8.9
Based on the soil classification system found in the federal OSHA regulation Part 1926, Subpart P, the soil adjacent to an existing building may be classified as Type A, B or C. The excavation depth is 15 ft deep. The undisturbed perimeter strip (X) along the face of the building is most nearly:
[select all that apply]

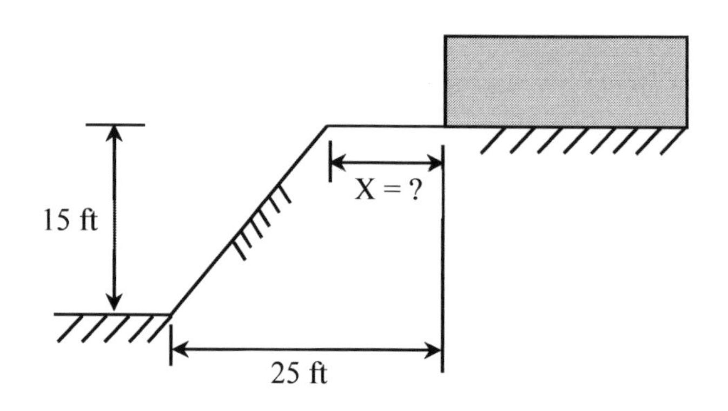

A. X = 13.75 ft for Type A soil
B. X = 10 ft for Type B soil
C. X = 2.5 ft for Type C soil
D. X = 7.5 ft for Type B soil

Solution:

PE Civil Handbook: Chap 3 Geotechnical (Section: Trench and Construction Safety)
(OSHA regulation Part 1926, Subpart P, Appendix B)

For Class A soil, all simple slope excavation 20 feet or less in depth shall have a maximum allowable slope of ¾:1. This means the horizontal distance of the slope will be ¾ x 15 ft = 11.25 ft. Therefore, X = 25 – 11.25 ft = 13.75 ft.
For Class B soil, all simple slope excavations 20 feet or less in depth shall have a maximum allowable slope of 1:1. This means the horizontal distance of the slope will be 1 x15 ft = 15 ft. Therefore, X = 25 – 15 ft = 10 ft.
For Class C soil, all simple slope excavations 20 feet or less in depth shall have a maximum allowable slope of 1½:1. This means the horizontal distance of the slope will be 1½ x 15 ft = 22.5 ft. Therefore, X = 25 – 22.5 ft = 2.5 ft.
The correct answers are A, B, and C.

Example 8.10
A twelve-story apartment is being constructed adjacent to a large residential areas. The soil testing shows the top 12-ft of soil is poor in strength. However, a thick rock layer exists below this 12-ft poor soil. The foundation type most suited for this site is most nearly:

A. Shallow spread footing
B. Driven piles
C. Mat foundation
D. Drilled piles

Solution:

Shallow spread footing – not suitable as the top 12-ft of soil is poor in strength.
Driven piles – not suitable for the adjacent residential areas.
Mat foundation – not suitable as the top 12-ft of soil is poor in strength.
Drilled piles – suitable as there is a rock layer below the poor soil and it needs minimal vibration.
The correct answer is D.

8.5 Safety

This topic is pretty undefined in the exam specification. OSHA document is not expected to be used in the Breadth (morning) exam. Therefore, study or practice general safety issues on construction safety. Construction, Structural and Geotechnical depth exams candidates may access the OSHA 1926 in the morning.

Example 8.11
Assume you are a quality control representative for a contractor on a project. During your visit to the site, you discover a potentially unsafe condition at the project site, the initial action you should take is to:

A. Make a general report of the condition to OSHA
B. Notify the contractor on the potential accident
C. Notify the condition to the owner or the architect
D. Issue a stop order of the construction immediately and fix the unsafe condition

Solution:

Taking care of unsafe condition is the contractor's responsibility. Reporting to the contractor is the first step. If he does not pay attention then OSHA may be reached out.
The correct answer is B.

- *Please make sure you study another PE Civil Review Manual from another author.*
- *After finishing the review manuals, it is the time to practice 2-3 full tests before the real exam.*
- *Again, if you fail the exam, you will lose the exam fees only - nothing else! Don't panic!*